Managing the Lost Person Incident

Second Edition

Kenneth Hill
Editor and Senior Author,
First Edition

Contributing Authors
To The First Edition:
Rick Gale
Hatch Graham
Chuck Kimball
Greg McDonald
Bill Wade

Daniel O'Connor
Editor, Second Edition

Contributors To The
Second Edition:
Dave Clark
J. R. Frost
Jim Greenway
David Lovelock
Mike McDonald
Valerie Mokides
Michael Murray
Dave Perkins
George Rice
Pete Roberts
Richard Toman
Chris Young

3rd Printing

Preface to the Second Edition

Someone once remarked that the way to develop a reputation for wisdom was to state the obvious, but to do it solemnly. In that vein, it can be said that there would be no Second Edition of this book without the First Edition. The Second Edition of Managing The Lost Person Incident rests squarely on the foundation of the First. Editing the second edition was like touching up the paint on a solid edifice, far less demanding than building an entire structure from scratch. The document assembled by Ken Hill and company nearly a decade ago was a remarkable achievement, synthesizing and presenting essential search management concepts for the first time in a single comprehensive text.

This edition includes a somewhat modified layout, an update of the crucially important Incident Command System, integration of search theory concepts from the field of Operations Research and the addition of some new statistical tools for defining the search area and empowering organizations to take the lead in analyzing their own lost person data.

Special thanks go to David Lovelock for his close proof-reading of the pre-review drafts and problem sets. David's assistance was so invaluable that I consider him my co-editor. Mike McDonald and Chris Young also deserve singular recognition for their extensive insights, as well as Katherina Condon for her help in preparing the text for printing.

Thanks too, to all the contributors, past and present, listed on the opening page and second edition reviewers in alphabetical order: Paul Burke, Ben Ermini, Chris Long, Mike McDonald, Dan Pontbriand, George Rice, Matthew Scharper, Randy Servis, Jim Stumpf, Richard Toman and Chris Young. The assistance of all these folks is a reminder that assembling a teaching manual of this breadth and complexity is a team effort, beyond the reach and expertise of a single individual.

In a world still reeling from the tragic events of September 11th, 2001 where suicide bombers lurk in the shadows of every news cycle, it is worth thinking about why we do the things we do. Unlike the geopolitical thugs who wantonly kill unknown innocents, volunteers and professionals engaged in Search and Rescue routinely risk their own health and lives for someone they have never met.

While this book is a manual of best practices for incident management, the best laid plans are useless without those selfless individuals who bushwhack through forests, rappel off cliffs, traverse avalanche prone slopes, dive into icy waters and otherwise put themselves on the line for complete strangers. To those great souls, often unacknowledged and under-appreciated, who go into the field and implement the incident management plans hatched in the command post, this Second Edition is dedicated.

Dan O'Connor
Ware, Massachusetts
March, 2007

Preface to the First Edition

Someone once observed that the Chinese character for crisis and opportunity are the same. Less optimistically, I would propose that the acronym we know as "SAR" has come to refer not only to an emergency incident, but to a monumental learning "opportunity" as well. Too often, the realization that good management is critical to the success of the search incident comes only after a prolonged and disorganized search which has ended tragically for the lost person.

As someone who has participated in several highly mismanaged searches, including the one described in Chapter Two, I can assure the reader that they are learning opportunities to be avoided at all costs. The intent behind this book is to provide the information you need to get it right without having to attend this particular school of "hard knocks."

A brief history of this book is in order. Originally, it was intended to be an updated version of the NASAR text entitled, "Managing the Search Function." Soon after we began the "update," it became apparent that a major overhaul was necessary, as there have been many important developments in search theory and methods during the ten years since MSF was published.

The most obvious changes pertain to the application of technology to SAR, search theory, stress management, and research on lost person behavior, but readers familiar with the older book will notice many subtler changes throughout. Indeed, about 75% of the text is new.

The most significant change, in my view, is that the book is more focused. It is addressed specifically to the first responding search manager during the initial operational period of the lost person incident. And, more than ever, the emphasis is on search *management,* defined broadly as the process of "controlling all of the events that can affect the outcome of the incident." Readers looking for an encyclopedic discussion of search tactics will have to search elsewhere. Although modern tactics are discussed, this book is less about "how to search" than how to manage the process.

Many people have contributed ideas and suggestion in response to previous drafts of this text. I especially want to thank the following reviewers, listed alphabetically: Kim Aufhauser, Don Bower, Steve Foster, Jude Moore, and Jim Stumpf. For me, this has been strictly a labor of love, and I dedicate my contribution to those prospective search managers who have the foresight to adopt good management principles without first having to experience a "monumental learning opportunity" of their own.
Good hunting!

Ken Hill
Halifax
August, 1997

Table of Contents

Part I: The Principles of Search Management..1
Chapter 1   Introduction 2
Chapter 2   A Cautionary Tale: The Search For Andy Warburton...7
Chapter 3   Managing and Leading..13
Chapter 4   The Incident Command System...24
Chapter 5   The Operational Preplan..43
Chapter 6   Search and Rescue Resources..53
Part II: Introduction to Search Planning...65
Chapter 7   Clues...66
Chapter 8   Initiating The Search..75
Chapter 9   Planning the Search..88
Chapter 10   Gathering Information...105
Chapter 11   Predicting Lost Person Behavior 132
Chapter 12   Establishing the Search Area..152
Chapter 13   Setting Priorities: The Probability Of Area (POA) 175
Part III: Managing Plans & Operations..187
Chapter 14   Allocating Resources (Search Tactics)...188
Chapter 15   Measuring Search Coverage: Estimating The Probability Of Detection (POD) 210
Chapter 16   Changing Search Priorities: Shifting the Probability of Area (POA)................230
Chapter 17   Briefing and Debriefing 238
Chapter 18   Documentation..247
Chapter 19   Suspending The Incident 254
Chapter 20   Demobilization 260
Part IV: Other Management Considerations 264
Chapter 21   Managing Incident Facilities 265
Chapter 22   Managing Searcher Stress...273
Chapter 23   Managing External Influences 279
Chapter 24   Search Management Technology 299
Chapter 25   Post-Incident Considerations 308
Chapter 26   The Agency Administrator 312
Glossary & SAR Acronyms...316
Photo Credits...332
Index 333
Bibliography and Suggested Readings..337
Appendix A: Map of the Andy Warburton Search Area 342
Appendix B: The K9 Resource for SAR – A Compilation 343
Appendix C: SAR Debriefing Form 350

Part I: The Principles of Search Management

CHAPTER 1

INTRODUCTION

Reduced to its essentials, search management is a **coordinated effort to control all of the events, within reason, that can affect the outcome of the search for a lost person**. The nature of those events, and the means whereby you can reasonably expect to control them, is the subject of this manual.

CHAPTER OBJECTIVES:

When you finish studying this chapter, you should be able to:

1. Define a "lost person incident."
2. Describe common management errors made during lost person incidents.

What is a "Lost Person Incident" and why Does it Need to be "Managed"?

As applied to search and rescue, the word "lost" is much more complex than suggested by its dictionary meaning, that is, "having wandered from the way." Most subjects of land searches are people who, during some sort of recreational activity in a forested or wilderness area, have become **spatially disoriented**. Thus, they are **unable to identify their present location with respect to known locations, and have no effective means or methods of reorienting themselves.**

Some common examples include:

- A hunter who is "turned around" and walks 20 miles on a dirt road, in the wrong direction.
- A hiker who becomes separated from the group and takes the wrong turn at an intersection of trails.
- A small child who follows an animal into a densely forested area.

However, some subjects of searches are not "lost" in the sense of being spatially disoriented. For example:

- A depressed individual who walks into a wooded area, contemplating suicide.
- An elderly Alzheimer's patient who wanders away from a nursing home.
- A lone skier on a remote hill who breaks his leg and cannot move.

These examples make it clear that we cannot define "lost" simply in terms of the mental state of the missing subject, because no single definition applies to all cases. Some subjects may know precisely where they are but may be unable or unwilling to return to safety. Others, such as the Alzheimer's patient, may vividly imagine that they are in some familiar place that only existed years in the past.

What is critical for Search and Rescue (SAR) responders is not so much how the person became missing (although this information may become important for search planning purposes), but rather that the person needs to be located as soon as possible.

From the perspective of searchers, then, **a lost person is a known individual in an unknown location, whose safety may be threatened by conditions related to the environment, the weather, or to the age or health factors of concern to family members or caregivers**.

The search for such an individual becomes an "incident" when a missing persons report is made to a jurisdictional authority, such as a policeman, a county sheriff's office, or a park warden. In turn, the jurisdictional authority will treat the subject of the report as a "lost person" rather than a "missing person" (1) when there is a perceived urgency for a prompt response, and (2) a specific locale has been identified for searching, such as a park, a wilderness area, or a suburban neighborhood. It is at this point that SAR activities may be initiated. The distinction between "lost" and "missing" is critical as in the possible case of an abducted child.

Once a search begins attempts are usually made to coordinate the efforts of individual searchers and support personnel toward reaching a common objective—to locate the missing subject. This is called **management**. Too frequently search coordinators have underestimated the difficulty of efficient search management. Instead they have used an informal, semi-structured "system" that has seemed to work well enough in the past.

One such system is the old "Search Boss" approach, where one individual takes on the responsibility of deciding where to search for the lost person and then directs available searchers to go to those locations. Such decisions about where to look next are not usually made until sufficient searchers are available to form a team. The Search Boss may suggest tactics to searchers, such as a "grid" or "sweep" pattern, where searchers walk abreast through an area while maintaining some designated spacing between them.

If the Search Boss happens to have access to VHF or FRS radios, then he or she may personally handle field communications, or appoint someone available to do so. Similar appointments of support personnel, such as people to feed searchers, or to drive them to their assigned locations, are usually made on an ad hoc basis; alternatively, some resourceful individuals may perform these functions on their own initiative. Typically, the Search Boss remained in command until either the missing subject is found, or the search is suspended.

This approach to search management may be familiar to many readers of this manual. Most of the time, especially for SAR responders who are used to working together, the system seems to function well. However, as the search for 9-year-old Andy Warburton illustrates (Chapter 2), the Search Boss management system is a formula for disaster. It is only a matter of time before the system breaks down.

A Compendium of Errors

A review of unsuccessful lost person incidents in the past reveals that many of the following nine errors have been made:

1) The agency responsible for conducting the search had been unprepared, or poorly prepared, for the problems encountered during the incident. Often these problems were related to difficulties in managing large, multi-agency incidents extending over several or more days, the arrival of large numbers of spontaneous volunteers, or the requirements of specialized resources. This error can also result from the infrequency of lost person events in the agency's jurisdiction.

2) There was ambiguity of authority during the incident. Personnel, including the search managers themselves, were uncertain as to who was in charge. There was no visible

chain of command. People involved in search coordination were unsure about their respective duties.

3) There was no system for relieving fatigued search managers. The Search Boss continued to coordinate activities despite exhaustion and lack of sleep.

4) The investigation concerning the missing person was incomplete or terminated too early. Vital pieces of information were missed. Important witnesses were not interviewed, or were asked the wrong questions. Often the investigation was terminated once the search was underway.

5) There was a lack of a coherent search plan or strategy to find the missing subject. High probability areas were not identified and given search priority. Often, the "plan" was simply to expand the search area away from the place where the subject was last seen.

6) Ineffective search tactics were employed. No attempt was made to confine the subject to a searchable area. Grid searching was conducted too early in the incident. Resources were wasted by re-searching the same areas repeatedly. Generally, search resources were not utilized efficiently.

7) Search coverage was not accurately recorded. It was not clear which areas had been searched, nor how thoroughly they had been covered. When search managers were relieved, their replacements were not adequately briefed regarding search progress. Consequently there was duplication in effort as well as gaps in coverage. Continuous, full documentation of all facts and decisions was neglected, particularly in the early phases of the search.

8) There was no effective system for dealing with clues. Searchers were not sensitized to the importance of clue detection. Important clues were missed, destroyed, or misinterpreted. Clues were not documented in terms of the time and the place where they were discovered.

9) Search managers lost control of external influences. Poor media relations led to unfavorable coverage while the incident was still in progress. External influences interfered with the conduct of the search. Members of the missing subject's family were allowed to pester the search coordinators for information, to negatively affect the morale of searchers, or to proceed into the woods to conduct their own search, possibly destroying clues. People claiming para-psychological abilities, such as psychics and astrologers, were given too much free reign, taking too much of the search coordinators' time or diverting their attention from more practical tasks that would increase the likelihood of finding the lost person.

The Focus of this Manual

The focus of this manual will generally be on two response phases: the initial or "hasty" phase into the first operational period followed by a second phase of increasing operational and logistic complexity that continues until the subject is found or the search is suspended. An approach to search management will be developed to help avoid all nine critical errors outlined previously. The emphasis will be on the principles of search strategy and tactics that are most likely to bring the search to an early and successful conclusion. Although we will have much to say about managing "large" lost person incidents, it is important to remember that the best way to handle a large search is to prevent one: find the missing subject before the incident has a chance to grow into an unmanageable event. Also, as this text is designed to be an overview of essential search management functions, it does not explicitly address Rescue techniques, the "R" in SAR.

Summary

A "lost person" is **a known individual in an unknown location, whose safety may be threatened by conditions related to the environment, the weather, or to the age or health factors of concern to family members or caregivers**. The search for such a person (or group of persons) is considered to be an **emergency**. Managing a lost person incident is an attempt to **control all the events that can affect the outcome of the search for the lost person.** Too often, agencies or organizations assigned the responsibility of conducting lost person incidents have underestimated or misunderstood the requirement for effective search management. A review of unsuccessful lost person incidents reveals nine critical errors. These errors are associated with an agency's lack of preparation for the incident, the absence of an effective management system, an improper investigation, little or no record keeping, or errors related to search strategy and tactics.

In the next chapter we will describe a large and unsuccessful search in which all these critical errors were made. In subsequent chapters we will discuss ways to avoid the nine errors through the development of appropriate SAR skills, training and preparation.

**Questions for Discussion:**

1. What problems have you encountered or seen in previous searches in your own area?

2. Who is in charge of searches in your jurisdiction?

3. Who is in charge of searches, skill development and training conducted by your SAR team?

CHAPTER 2

A CAUTIONARY TALE:
THE SEARCH FOR ANDY WARBURTON

With over 5000 searchers involved over an 8-day period, this tragic 1986 search in Beaverbank, Nova Scotia, is **one of the largest lost person incidents on record**.

CHAPTER OBJECTIVES:
When you finish studying this chapter, you should be able to:

1. Identify critical errors made during an unsuccessful lost person incident.
2. Describe some of the indicators that a search incident is not being well managed.

Day One: Sometime between 2 and 4 p.m. on a warm summer day, 9-year-old Andy Warburton set out from a rural home to travel the 110 yards (100 meters) to nearby Tucker Lake, to join his older brother, Gary. He wore only a bathing suit, sneakers, and a t-shirt. At 4:30, Gary returned and reported that Andy had not arrived at the lake. At 5:45, after a cursory search by family and neighbors, the Royal Canadian Mounted Police (RCMP) were notified. When an RCMP member arrived on the scene, she began to interview neighbors about possible sightings of Andy. She found one 12-year-old boy who claimed to have seen Andy crossing a stream, heading north, at about 2 p.m. (Note that Tucker Lake was east of the home, and did not require crossing the stream in order to be reached.) Although there was some doubt about the accuracy of the boy's report, the officer accepted the stream as the "place last seen," and north of the residence, into a densely forested region, as the "direction of travel."[1]

At 7:30 p.m., as requested by the RCMP, the local volunteer search team arrived on the scene. Without further investigation, the search director for the team went directly to the police officer for instructions, and was directed to the spot where Andy had allegedly crossed the stream. The first search team entered the woods shortly after 8:00 p.m., conducting a grid search in the vicinity of the place last seen. By approximately 8:30, there were 44 searchers in the woods, using grid patterns of about 10–20 feet (3–6 meters) between searchers, focusing on the area just north of the stream, within about 220–330 yards (200–300 meters) of the place last seen. The search continued in this fashion until 3:30

---

[1] Appendix A shows a map of the area.

a.m., when the search was postponed until daylight. During the night, the temperature dropped to 46°F (8°C).

Day Two: The search resumed at 5:30 a.m. Ground searchers re-entered the woods near the same locations that had been searched the previous night. That morning a government helicopter arrived on the scene and began conducting sweeps above the search area. Divers and boat crews began searching nearby lakes and shorelines. Radio and television news reports about the missing boy brought hundreds of volunteer searchers from nearby metropolitan areas. By 6:00 p.m. that evening, 400 people were in the woods, including firefighters, housewives, children, teenagers, elderly people, self-styled outdoorsmen wearing camouflage fatigues, and numerous local residents of varying descriptions and abilities.

The search base consisted of an area adjacent to the local volunteer SAR team's bus, which had been outfitted for relatively small search operations. The bus, parked near the boy's residence, was used for both search coordination and logistical purposes (searchers rested and ate on the bus, while the search director briefed team leaders). The onslaught of well-meaning volunteers greatly taxed the search team's resources. Because there were insufficient trained team leaders to lead the untrained searchers, several dozen of the volunteers were turned away. Those turned away for lack of leaders and many

curious onlookers milled around the area while their parked automobiles clogged the narrow, dead-end road leading to the search base.

At this point the search was being managed by three people: the search director, a hastily appointed assistant who went around "putting out fires," and a member of the amateur radio club, who took care of communications.

Search tactics continued to emphasize the sweep pattern, gradually expanding away from the place last seen. No promising clues were reported, although two newspaper carriers reported seeing a boy matching Andy's description. However, they said, when they called out to the boy, he ran into the woods. During mid-afternoon a light drizzle started, which turned to rain. The rain continued steadily for eight hours.

Day Three: Based on questionable sightings that occurred in the same vicinity as the news carriers had reported, all search activities in the prime search area were suspended and relocated to an area about 4.5 miles (7 kilometers) away from the place last seen. Many teams had to interrupt their search assignments to make the transition. At mid-day, requests were made to several adjoining volunteer search teams for assistance. The leaders of these teams later complained that they were not briefed about the boy's description or the nature of possible clues, apart from what they had heard in news reports. Several teams arrived at the scene only to be told that the base had been moved to a local school, about 0.3 mile (0.5 km) away.

The search coordinators now consisted of the search director (who had been on the scene since day one), several additional members of the team's executive board, a member of the local detachment of the RCMP (who had jurisdictional authority over the search), and a government official from the provincial emergency management office (who had little land search experience but had administrative responsibility for the volunteer search teams).

There was no coherent system for coordinating their efforts and each of these individuals began to make search assignments on their own accord. Minor disputes began to appear concerning who was in charge.

About 6:00 p.m. Andy's mother was taken to the new search area. Search coordinators began to suspect that the boy might be evading searchers, so she was asked to make direct requests to Andy over a loudspeaker to come out of the woods. She complied, pleading for her son to come home, and to trust the searchers. She received no response.

Most search activities were suspended around 8:00 p.m. About 200 trained searchers bivouacked at the school on cots and sleeping bags, while the untrained volunteers were told to return in the morning. Unfortunately, some

volunteers were apparently missing because they had not "signed out" after completing the day's assignments. Some searchers went into the woods to look for them.

About a dozen men, called "sleepers," were placed strategically in the woods with sensitive, parabolic microphones. Their instructions were to try to pick up any sounds the boy might be making, such as walking or crying. Their efforts were unsuccessful.

Searchers began to complain openly about the way the search was being conducted. They did not agree with the search tactics. They did not believe the right places were being covered. The search was not being expanded far enough. They said they spent far too much time waiting to go into the woods, and many did not go in at all. They did not know who was in charge because several people seemed to be giving contradictory orders. The atmosphere in the waiting area was described as "near riot-like."

Andy's father requested that the military be brought into the search. The emergency management official, for reasons that were not understood by the family, turned down the request.

The search was now national news. Dozens of reporters were on scene, interviewing anyone who would talk to them. Searchers now had an opportunity to air their complaints, and vehemently criticized the search coordinators.

The base camp was described as a "media circus." The rain continued.

Day Four: The search resumed at 10:00 a.m. By then the search teams that had responded to the mutual aid call had been on scene for 16 hours without being used. Now their objective was to apply a strategy described as a "staggered blanket search" by the search coordinators. The searchers called it an "act of desperation." They were told to line up in a "human chain" but to proceed at staggered intervals rather than in a line. The searchers had never attempted it before and confusion reigned.

Because of media attention, people describing themselves as psychics or astrologers offered help. Some appeared on the scene while others telephoned. Many of their predictions were taken seriously because several search teams were dispatched to investigate psychics' visions or premonitions.

Sometimes the teams were accompanied by the psychics. One psychic, who telephoned from across the country, asked a search coordinator to go to a specific location and wait for further instructions to be delivered telepathically. The coordinator complied, but no messages were received. The rain finally let up.

Day Five: After two days of unsuccessfully searching the area where the news carriers had reported seeing a boy of Andy's description, the search coordinators redefined the locale around the boy's home as the primary search area.

A tracking team was contacted to assist in the search. Members of the team feared that clues had been destroyed after four days of grid searching, but agreed to assist. However, when they arrived on the scene they were told to go home. Instead of leaving they began to conduct their own search, despite warnings that they would be arrested were they to enter the woods without authorization.

After several hours of searching, the team found sneaker tracks in a remote boggy area that had not been previously searched. They radioed this information into the search base, and were told to leave the area. The clues were apparently ignored.

The psychics returned. During the afternoon, search coordinators suspended activities for three hours while two psychics were flown over the area by helicopter. The psychics believed that they could get a better "fix" on the boy's location from an aerial perspective. Their efforts proved fruitless.

That evening, the emergency management official capitulated to the family's request for military assistance. A call was made to the Canadian Minister of Defense. The request was granted, but troops would not arrive until Day 7. It would become the busiest day of the search, with nearly 1200 searchers deployed.

Day Six: The number of searchers dwindled to 800, although the number of curiosity seekers milling around the search base continued to grow. The media were present in full force.

Almost all searching had been confined to the area within approximately 1 mile (1.6 km) of the boy's residence. At this point the search was extended to areas formerly considered low priority (because they would have required the subject to cross highways or pass through built-up areas).

Many people continued to conduct their own searches, ignoring threats to stay out of the woods or be arrested.

Day Seven: Four hundred military personnel arrived on the scene. Using a sweep pattern, they searched everything that had been covered previously, then proceeded to expand the search to about 2 miles (3.2 kilometers) from the place last seen.

Day Eight: A military search team found Andy's sneakers in the same, boggy location

where the freelancing tracking team had found sneaker tracks on Day 5. Some two hours later, at 5:30 p.m., Andy's body was found about 110 yards (100 meters) from his sneakers. An autopsy revealed that he had died from hypothermia sometime between Day 4 and Day 6 of the search.

Epilogue: Soon after the search was over, a television documentary aired that sharply criticized the manner in which the incident had been handled. They listed a number of mistakes in search tactics, including the failure to confine the search area early in the incident. Most telling perhaps, was their discovery of a neighbor who had seen Andy traveling east, in the direction of the swimming site, at about 4 p.m. This woman had been unaware that the searchers were operating according to erroneous information, that is, that Andy had been heading north about 2:00 p.m. Despite the fact that she lived next door to Andy, no one had approached her during the search to ask her any questions. As the documentary noted, searchers had failed to conduct an adequate investigation.

A local magazine published a lead article similarly criticizing the management of the search, particularly the role of the emergency management office that was responsible for the volunteer search teams.

Finally, and perhaps most telling of the stress involved in this tragic event, nearly every person who played a significant role in coordinating the Andy Warburton search subsequently dropped out of emergency management. One committed suicide.

Questions for Discussion:

1. How did each of the nine critical mistakes, as listed in Chapter 1, emerge in the search for Andy Warburton?

2. Given the mistakes made in this search, which — in your opinion — was the most critical?

3. What are some of the symptoms of a search that is not being well managed?

4. Should volunteer search teams be given the responsibility of managing a lost person incident?

CHAPTER 3

MANAGING AND LEADING

Management is commonly defined as "getting things done with and through people." More technically, it means **accomplishing the organization's objectives through the effective and efficient use of people and resources**. In this chapter we will describe basic management principles that are most suitable for controlling emergency incidents. In the next chapter we will present the Incident Command System, which provides the management framework underlying this manual.

CHAPTER OBJECTIVES:

When you finish studying this chapter, you should be able to:

1. Describe the components of an emergency incident that any management system must address.

2. Describe the advantages of management by objectives. Explain why and when managers must delegate authority.

3. Define four different styles of leadership and describe the situations in which each may be appropriate.

4. Describe the various functions that managers perform.

Managing an Emergency

Before we describe the principles of management, it should be instructive to consider those components of an emergency incident that any management system must address.

First, by definition, **an emergency involves some crisis or unpredicted event that threatens human safety**. Because of this concern for the well-being of the victims of an emergency, managers must effectively organize the efforts of responders to resolve the incident as quickly as possible. Moreover, the context of the emergency may also to be hazardous to the responders who are attempting to deal with the incident.

The management system must therefore have as its top priority a concern for human safety, including both victims and responders alike.

Second, emergencies usually involve a high degree of uncertainty that must be reduced quickly. **Information is the means by which uncertainty is reduced**. Because management decisions made early in the incident will have the most impact on its outcome — including the length of time it takes to resolve the emergency — it is imperative that decision-makers have accurate information available as soon as possible.

This will entail (a) initiating and maintaining a thorough investigation, (b) being prepared for decisions involving resource availability, (c) employing effective information gatherers in the field (for example, clue-sensitive searchers), and (d) maintaining direct and reliable communications between management and field personnel, through which information can be conveyed.

Third, because emergencies are time-critical, the efficient use of resources is imperative for emergency management. Even when supplies and equipment are plentiful, which is rarely the case, the amount of time that field personnel can be effectively employed is always limited. **In the case of the lost person incident, searcher hours are a non-renewable resource**. Wasting searcher hours by using them inefficiently or by sending people to the wrong locations are irreversible errors that may have a negative impact on the outcome of the incident. Consequently, the most important management decisions will pertain to the issue of how resources will be allocated.

Finally, emergency incidents frequently require interaction among management personnel who do not normally work together on a daily basis. **During an emergency there is no time for sorting out management responsibilities**. The management system

employed must therefore include clearly defined job descriptions that are common knowledge to all who could conceivably be involvement in incident management.

Each position must have unique tasks, obligations, authority, and responsibilities that are complementary to other positions, with a minimum level of redundancy. **There must be one individual on scene, the Incident Commander, who has authority over everyone and is therefore ultimately responsible for all management decisions, regardless of who made them**. The chain of command must be decided immediately once the incident commences and made visible to all management, support, and field personnel.

Basic Management Concepts

Management science is an old and well-studied discipline comprising dozens of theories that are sometimes inconsistent or in conflict. However, there are a number of management principles that have proven to be reliable methods of achieving organizational objectives, and which are not bound to any particular theory. Moreover, some of these principles are especially suited to the requirements of emergency management and have therefore been incorporated into this manual.

Management By Objectives (MBO). By necessity, emergency management must be oriented toward achieving specific results within a specific time span. This orientation is aided and abetted by the criteria contained in the MBO approach, as summarized below in Figure 3.1.

Figure 3.1

Management By Objective

MBO Criteria is:

- **time referenced**
- **attainable**
- **measurable**
- **accountable**

Briefly, MBO requires that managers specify in writing the objectives they want to accomplish during a specific time period. In addition to being **time-referenced**, the objectives must be **attainable**, in the sense of being realistically achievable under the circumstances, and they must be **measurable**.

Regarding measurability, the objectives must be stated in such a manner that there can be no question after the fact as to whether or not they had been achieved. Therefore, MBO includes the important management concept of **accountability**. For example, the CEO of General Motors might set objectives for his corporation to sell a specified number of automobiles by the end of the fiscal year. This

"strategic" plan then directs the "tactical" objectives contained within the respective "action" plans set by the individual section heads in regard to production, sales, marketing, personnel, and so forth. At the end of the year, the objectives contained within the plans are reviewed with respect to the degree to which they had been achieved.

During the lost person incident, the on-scene Incident Commander (IC) is comparable to a corporation's CEO, while the Agency Administrator, who is normally not on scene, provides policy, directives, and constraints within which the IC is expected to function (see Chapter 4). In this regard, the Agency Administrator is comparable to a corporation's Board of Directors. The IC's strategic plan is typically to locate the lost subject within that operational period, which is usually 12 hours if not sooner. Other management personnel under the IC's authority will be tasked with devising an action plan to accomplish that objective.

Delegation. Delegation is the process of assigning some level of decision-making authority to subordinates. Because of factors related to time and urgency, successful management of emergency incidents requires a relatively high level of delegation. This means that subordinates are normally allowed to make decisions within their area of responsibility, without having to consult with superiors. Barriers to this process are shown in Figure 3.2.

Delegation is an especially important component of the Incident Command System (which is the subject of Chapter 4) because of the fluid manner in which the size of the management staff grows to match the size of the incident.

Conversely, **micro-management** is the process of supervising or performing management functions that are normally performed by subordinates. **Micro-management is inefficient, counter-productive, and demoralizing to those people whose authority is being usurped.**

Unfortunately, while the CEO of General Motors would not consider supervising the welding of auto parts, it is not uncommon, during a lost person incident, to see an IC take over the job of assigning tactical resources to the field, or micro-managing similar operational tasks that should normally be the responsibility of subordinate search managers.

During any emergency incident, the temptation for micro-management can be high, requiring discipline, trust, and clearly defined management roles and responsibilities.

Figure 3.2

Barriers To Effective Delegation

- **The fallacy: "If you want something done right do it yourself!"**
- **Lack of confidence in subordinates.**
- **Fear of being perceived as lazy.**
- **Vague job definitions.**
- **Fear of competition from subordinates.**
- **Reluctance to take the risks involved in relying on others.**
- **Unwillingness to share the credit for success.**
- **Failure to adequately train subordinates.**

Span of Control. Related to the issue of delegation is the concept of **span of control, which is the number of people who report directly to a particular supervisor**. There will always be a limit to the number of subordinates whom a manager can effectively supervise while working on the achievement his or her objectives.

There has been much discussion about the "ideal" span of control for various types of organizations, but for emergency incidents the optimal number is considered to be **five**, with an upper limit of around **seven** (Figure 3.3). When the span of control rises above these numbers, it is time to delegate management authority to subordinates, who, in turn, will be subject to their own limits in span of control. This accounts for the hierarchical or pyramid shape of most organizational charts.

Figure 3.3

Ideal Span of Control

> **One Manager for every Five Subordinates, a "1 to 5" Ratio.**

It should be pointed out that span of control pertains not only to emergency managers in the command post, but to virtually anyone involved in supervising the efforts of others during the incident, including leaders of search teams in the field. For example, it is not uncommon for ten or more people to be assigned to a single grid or "sweep" team, all under the guidance of a single leader. Indeed, in one search for a lost child, more than 100 people were assigned to one such team. The resulting line was approximately 0.3 miles (0.5 kilometers long). The movements of searchers, who were mostly untrained volunteers, were "coordinated" by a team leader who controlled them through signals conveyed with a bullhorn. Clearly, in this the instance, the optimal span of control had been far surpassed. It should come as no surprise that this poorly-coordinated, massive "team" found nothing.

Unity of Command. The principle of unity of command simply states that no individual in the organization may have more than one direct supervisor or boss, therefore . . .

"one man – one master."

When two or more managers are involved in providing directives to the same people, ambiguity of authority results and confusion abounds. Such confusion is most likely to occur when there is not a clearly specified chain of command. Unity of command is especially important for large emergency incidents involving more than one agency or organization that are required to work together efficiently under unusual circumstances. Here, disputes over "who's in charge" (that is, who may give orders to whom) often occur when all of the participating agencies have not signed off on the same incident management system.

Leadership

Leadership is that important part of management involving social influence: getting people to perform those activities that contribute to the organizational objectives. Although there are various styles of leadership (described later), the demands of emergency incidents require adapting one's style to rapidly changing contexts or situations. Situational leadership involves an accurate assessment of the type of leadership that is required for a given situation, and an ability to respond appropriately. For example, a group of highly skilled individuals working on a clearly defined task is not likely to respond favorably to a leader who insists on giving directives in a continuous and rigid manner. Under these conditions, a good leader would probably choose to rely on the expertise of his or her subordinates, adopting a more democratic style in which group consensus is polled, and making sure that everyone stays on track.

However, this same leader might decide to adopt a more formal and directive role when subordinates are less skilled, when they are not well informed about task objectives, or

when there exists some disagreement in the group about how the task should be performed.

Generally, management theorists and behavioral scientists have identified **four major leadership styles:**

1. **Directive leadership**. The leader tells people exactly what is expected from them and provides guidance while they are performing the task. This style may be appropriate when roles are not clearly defined, workers are not well trained for their tasks, or whenever subordinates require constant supervision.

2. **Supportive leadership**. The leader treats subordinates as equals in a friendly manner, with most communications aimed at maintaining morale and group cohesiveness, rather than being task-oriented. This style may be appropriate when roles are well defined and subordinates do not require direct supervision. It requires good working relations among subordinates as well as between subordinates and leaders.

3. **Participative leadership**. The leader consults with subordinates and carefully considers their input before making decisions. Many situations exist that may necessitate such group involvement, especially during emergency incidents. It is a style that is appropriate when the decision is especially serious, such as when to suspend a search, or

when the consequences of poor decisions can be highly detrimental to the achievement of incident objectives, such as how to apply resources early in the incident. Employing a participative style of leadership is appropriate whenever sufficient expertise or knowledge exists among subordinates to contribute to decision making.

4. **Achievement-oriented leadership**. The leader sets challenging goals and attempts to motivate subordinates to aspire for those goals as if they were their own. The achievement-oriented leader sometimes relies on his or her personal charisma, or the ability to influence others through the appeal of his or her personality, as a source of motivation. This style of leadership may be appropriate when there are major barriers to completing the organization's objectives, when an unusually high level of motivation may be required for success, when there is a low level of morale or group cohesiveness, or when less impelling leadership styles have failed.

Although managers will all have their own, favored styles of leadership, they must know how to react to the constraints imposed by situations, including the characteristics of the subordinates whom they supervise and the nature of the task to be performed.

Management by Wandering Around (MBWA). MBWA is not so much a management principle as an indicator that good management principles are being employed. Managers who delegate authority and respect the span of control will usually have time to periodically move around the organizational setting, whether it be a factory that manufactures automobiles or a search base during a lost person incident. **Effective leaders must be <u>visible</u> to the subordinates under their control**.

Visible leadership is not only good for motivation and morale, it also gives the manager an opportunity to spot potential problems that others have missed. However, when problems are identified, the manager must continue to respect the chain of command and to specifically avoid micro-management.

For example, an IC might decide to leave the command post for a few minutes in order to see how well the logistic functions are being handled. She might visit the feeding area and have a cup of coffee with searchers just in from the woods, listening to them describe their tasks, while noting their level of fatigue. Afterwards, she might visit searchers in the staging area who are waiting for assignments, answering questions they may have about the incident and perhaps even stifling rumors. From there, she might wander out to the parking area and observe the manner in which traffic is being directed. Indeed, she might discover that traffic is not being directed at all, and that drivers are being allowed to park their cars in a haphazard fashion, possibly blocking access by emergency vehicles.

In identifying the parking problem, she should <u>not</u> grab the first idle person she saw and assign him traffic duty, but should rather inform the Logistics Chief of the situation, communicating the expectation that it be handled immediately. Generally, much can be gained — and many problems can be avoided or quickly corrected — from such "wandering around."

MBWA is a popular technique of managers employing widely different leadership styles in all types of organizations. It is especially appropriate for the management of emergency incidents. This is an excellent role for seasoned leaders to perform even when they are not otherwise involved in search management. They contribute to the IC by being extra "eyes and ears" in the on-going assessment process.

What Managers Do

What follows is a non-exhaustive list of the major management functions:

Managers plan. Planning, or the formulation of future courses of action, is the primary management function. It gives direction and purpose to the organization, coordinating everyone's efforts toward achieving specified goals. In this regard, good managers are <u>proactive</u> (they anticipate problems before they occur) rather than <u>reactive</u>.

Managers make decisions. Good decisions require a well informed consideration of alternative courses of action. Good managers gather whatever information is available, including the opinions of other managers and informed subordinates, before committing the organization to a particular action.

Managers organize. For an organization to run efficiently, there must be division of labor, so that everyone's efforts contribute significantly to achieving group objectives. Managers assign roles, tasks, and responsibilities in a manner that ensures human resources are not wasted or overloaded.

Managers staff. In order to ensure that tasks are performed competently, managers must recruit and train people who are able to fill the organization's various positions.

Managers communicate. In addition to assigning tasks to subordinates, managers must communicate clearly with their subordinates the information that they need to perform their jobs, including technical information, policies, rules, and instructions. They are also receptive to feedback and other types of input, for which clear avenues of communication are made available.

Managers motivate. The more people are motivated to achieve the organization's goals, the more likely those goals will be attained successfully. Managers can help motivate their subordinates by satisfying their needs, meeting their expectations, and providing valued rewards. For volunteer organizations, such as are commonly involved in emergency incidents, an important component of motivation will usually involve public and sincere acknowledgements of individual contributions.

Managers lead. While not all leaders make good managers, all managers must by necessity be leaders. In addition to providing tangible or intangible rewards, managers must inspire their subordinates by serving as role models and by adapting their leadership style to the requirements of the situation (situational leadership).

Who Should Manage?

Selecting competent managers is one of the most important and distinctly difficult tasks that an organization must accomplish. Too often, the person who has demonstrated good leadership skills in the field proves to be a poor manager, and history is replete with examples of successful military generals becoming dismal political rulers. While leadership experience may be considered a necessary but not sufficient qualification for management, it should be remembered that some of the best managers (including a few U.S. Presidents) are people with little prior experience as leaders.

Complicating the selection of good managers is the so-called **Peter Principle**, which is the observation that people tend to eventually become promoted to positions that are beyond their level of ability or competence. Clearly, there is no simple formula for choosing managers, as past performance and demonstrated success are not always reliable criteria. How, then, should managers be selected? We suggest that people be selected for emergency management who demonstrate three characteristics: ability, knowledge, and motivation. Ability refers to the attitudes, traits, and social skills of the manager.

An emergency incident manager should be someone who is action-oriented and able to stay focused on obtaining results, rather than allowing himself/herself to become sidetracked on nonessential issues. Managers and leaders need good interpersonal and communication skills, coupled with an ability to give clear directives in a manner that encourages a cooperative and positive response by subordinates. They should be able to employ whatever leadership style is appropriate for the situation. **Ultimately, a good manager will be especially effective functioning as a participative leader, who knows when to obtain group involvement in the decision making process.**

With respect to knowledge, a good manager should have a firm grasp of the fundamentals of search theory, as described in this manual.

Managers should also have sufficient technical skills and experience to be able to supervise the work of others who are attempting to apply those skills. They need not be experts in all possible areas, few people are, but they should be knowledgeable enough to spot problems and to know when to consult with others who have the relevant expertise.

Finally, emergency managers must be motivated to lead, with no hesitation about taking charge of a life-threatening situation, and a readiness to impose their will on others, if necessary, to move the mission forward. They must be prepared to make decisions for which they will be held accountable, and be willing to sacrifice working in the field, where the action is, for the relative tedium of the command post, with its alternating periods of stress and boredom.

We never said search management would be fun but it can be enormously gratifying. Not everyone can do it. Managers often have to know more about the tasks they are handling than their subordinates. Frequently it takes more knowledge and experience to say "No" than to say "Yes."

Summary

Management means accomplishing an organization's goals through use of people and resources. Emergency incidents present special requirements for managers in that management decisions are time critical and poor decisions can easily impact negatively on the health of lost subjects or the safety of emergency responders. Because emergencies involve a high degree of uncertainty that must be resolved quickly, managers must employ an effective system of information gathering and processing. Moreover, the management system employed must contain clearly defined job descriptions for management personnel so that a coherent chain of command can be initiated as soon as possible once the incident begins.

Basic management concepts, that are appropriate to managing a lost person incident, include: management by objectives, in which all actions follow directly from clearly specified incident objectives, and delegation of authority, meaning that subordinates in the chain of command are permitted to make decisions within their area of responsibility. Respecting the span of control, or the number of people who can be effectively supervised by one person, is also an important component of emergency management. The related concept of unity of command ensures that no individual may have more than one direct supervisor or boss. **Note that "unity of command" should not be confused with the concept of "unified command"** discussed in Chapter 4, which is an Incident Command System concept that relates to joint planning across agencies involved in an incident).

The principle of <u>situational leadership</u> states that the most effective leadership style is one that is most appropriate to the present situation. <u>Directive</u> leadership may be required when workers are not well trained or need direction about how a task should be accomplished; <u>supportive</u> leadership may be called for when tasks are well defined and workers are familiar with their jobs; <u>participative</u> leadership is appropriate when a difficult decision must be made and there are competent subordinates available to provide input; and in some situations, <u>achievement-oriented</u> leadership may be necessary when workers need to be inspired to strive for challenging or difficult goals.

The chapter ended with a discussion of exactly what it is that managers do, and the criteria by which competent SAR managers should be selected. The various functions of management were described as <u>planning</u>, <u>decision making</u>, <u>organizing</u>, <u>staffing</u>, <u>communicating</u>, <u>motivating</u>, and <u>leading</u>. It was proposed that individuals should be selected who have the <u>ability</u>, <u>knowledge</u>, and <u>motivation</u> necessary for incident management.

Ability refers to the attitudes, traits, and social skills necessary for managing others; knowledge refers to having the relevant technical skills and experience in order to perform their management tasks and to supervise the work of others; and motivation refers to having the willingness to lead and to be held accountable for one's decisions. In the next chapter we will see how basic management concepts have been applied to one very effective system for managing emergencies: the Incident Command System.

Questions for Discussion:

1. Why do some good leaders make poor managers?

2. During an emergency incident, what types of situations might require each of the four leadership styles?

3. What kinds of delegation failures are most likely to occur during a lost person incident?

4. Why is it important for a search manager to show "visible" leadership?

5. Considering the various management tasks that must be performed during a lost person incident (e.g., gathering information, deciding where to search, assigning searchers to the field, transporting them to their locations), is there a way to divide tasks into <u>types</u> of functions such that managers have non-overlapping areas of responsibility?

6. How can members of volunteer SAR groups be motivated to strive for and maintain a high level of performance?

CHAPTER 4

THE INCIDENT COMMAND SYSTEM

In the last chapter we discussed the importance of employing good management principles during an emergency incident. In this chapter, we will describe why and how these principles should be integrated into **a management system designed specifically for emergency incidents**. We will introduce an especially effective approach to managing emergency operations: the Incident Command System (ICS).

CHAPTER OBJECTIVES:

When you finish studying this chapter, you should be able to:

1. Discuss the functions and structure of an effective search management system.
2. List and discuss the critical components of the ICS.
3. Describe the functions and responsibilities of the IC and each member of the Command and General Staffs.
4. Explain how the modular organization of the ICS allows for an orderly expansion of the incident that respects the span of control.

What Is a Management "System" and Why Do We Need One?

For people assigned the responsibility of coordinating an emergency incident, merely being familiar with good management principles (as described in Chapter 3) will not usually suffice. We require a system or structure that will provide a specific management **organization**, a common **terminology** familiar to those who are involved in the incident, and a set of clearly defined **procedures** for accomplishing management tasks.

Moreover, the management system we employ must be **modular** and readily adaptable to **changes in incident size**. Once a search operation begins, it can grow rapidly within mere hours. Indeed, within only a day or two, a lost person incident can develop into a large, multi-agency affair involving hundreds or even thousands of people (as we saw with the Andy Warburton search in Chapter 2). Conversely, once a large incident is terminated — for whatever reason — it will be necessary to **downsize** the operation in an orderly and safe manner. An effective incident management system must therefore allow for a logical and systematic expansion from the initial response into a major operation. It must also provide **a method for demobilizing,** that is, releasing resources and decreasing management staff, once the subject is found or the incident is suspended.

The combination of **common terminology** and **modular organization** used by ICS is illustrated in Figure 4.1. Standardized organizational levels are designated for incident managers that are filled by standardized position titles.

Figure 4.1

ICS Management Position Titles

Organizational Level	Title	Support Position
Incident Command	Incident Commander	Deputy
Command Staff	Officer	Assistant
General Staff (Section)	Chief	Deputy
Branch	Director	Deputy
Division or Group	Supervisor	n/a
Unit	Leader	Manager
Strike Team or Task Force	Leader	Single Resource Boss

Interagency Coordination

Many emergency incidents, including the search for a lost person, will involve more than one agency or group working together. During the search for a lost person, such groups may include search teams from other jurisdictions, as well as firefighters, ambulance attendants, canine teams, equestrian units, government or civilian helicopter services, Civil Air Patrol, or other agencies providing specialized search resources. It is imperative that the individual efforts of all participating agencies be coordinated in an efficient manner. The management system employed must specifically anticipate the need for interagency cooperation and coordination.

ICS: The Incident Command System

The need for ICS became apparent through problems experienced with communication and coordination in multi-agency responses to Southern California wildfires that claimed lives and property in the 1970's. While initially developed for federal, state and local fire agencies to better manage wildland fires, ICS was designed from the beginning to be flexible enough to handle all forms of emergencies. In addition to wildfire management, the ICS provided an improved method for responding to all kinds of disasters like floods, aircraft accidents, earthquakes, hurricanes, and other civic emergencies. ICS has proven to be so successful for handling emergencies that it is now also used for planning conventions and other activities requiring the coordination of large numbers of people. Because of this flexibility, ICS has become the *de facto* standard for incident management throughout North America.

In the United States, ICS training at various levels is now mandatory for all emergency responders and managers under the National Incident Management System (NIMS). NIMS was developed to ensure a unified approach to incident management under a multi-agency response. NIMS ICS is formally described as "a standardized, on-scene, all-hazard incident management concept." The U.S. Homeland Security Presidential Directive No. 5 requires that ICS be used by all federal agencies. For state, county, local and tribal governments, institutionalizing ICS is strongly encouraged while implementation of ICS is now a prerequisite for obtaining federal grants.

On-site, the IC is in charge of ICS, but even he/she must answer to someone. The governmental or corporate official who establishes policies, who delegates the authority to the IC and who has the ultimate responsibility for authorizing and accounting for incident funding, is the Agency Administrator. The **Agency Administrator** generally functions off-site, and will be discussed in detail in the Chapter 26.

The 8 Components of ICS, the Incident Command System

1. Common Terminology:

The ICS stresses the importance of using terms whose meanings are similar or "common knowledge" to all responders involved in the incident, especially management personnel. Speaking the same language facilitates communication and reduces confusion, redundancy, and wasted effort.

The terminology employed in ICS refers to three general components of the emergency incident:

I. **Functions**: terms for the management tasks that must be performed. The five major functions are: command, planning, operations, logistics and finance/administration (see Figure 4.2). These functions will be described in detail later in this chapter.

II. **Resources**: terms for the various types of personnel and equipment employed during the incident. Examples include "crew," "strike team," and "task force."

III. **Facilities**: terms for the designated locations in and around the area where incident-related tasks are performed or services are provided. Examples include the "incident base," "command post," and "staging area."

Figure 4.2

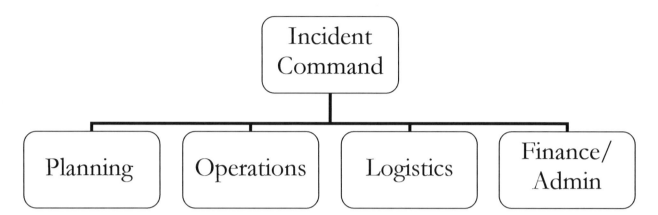

Modular ICS: The Five Major Functions

2. Modular Organization:

The organizational structure develops in a systematic fashion depending upon the size of the search. For example, the management staff involved for each section in Figure 4.2 may expand progressively from two or three individuals who perform all of the management functions during the initial response, to a full contingent of section chiefs, each of whom may establish units and appoint unit leaders as the need arises. In turn, the unit leaders may also make further appointments if necessary.

In this context, **"modular" refers to the fact that each section—Planning, Operations, Logistics, and Finance/Administration— is a self-contained module that may grow independently of other sections.** Sections and sub-sections can be added or removed "as needed." Use only what you need!

Additionally, the IC may similarly appoint officers to assist with his or her responsibilities, which are discussed in detail later in this chapter, as the incident requires.

For example, one of the IC's responsibilities is to manage media relationships. The IC may be able to do this unassisted during the initial response, but as more reporters arrive on the scene the IC may decide to appoint a Public Information Officer (PIO), someone qualified to handle media questions and release updates to the public.

3. Integrated Communications

According to ICS, incident communications should be managed through an on-scene communications center established for the use of operational and support resources involved in the search. This is especially important during a large search. Communications are handled by the Communications Unit, which is part of the Logistics Section.

The Communications Unit is responsible for all communications planning, which may involve the use of handheld radios, repeaters and other relay methods, satellite communications, packet radio, citizen's band, cellular telephones, public address systems, and other communications systems.

Also part of the communications plan are the **designated radio frequencies for different functions during the incident**, such as field or air operations and logistics. These should be included, with the entire communications plan, as part of the overall **Incident Action Plan**. A common frequency creates a working radio network that allows people operating within a particular function to communicate without having to contend with crowded or "jammed" frequencies. However, all radio communications on scene, regardless of frequency, must be monitored by the Communications Unit and entered into the radio log.

By integrating communications in this manner, the IC and other search managers have constant access to the "big picture" with respect to events as transmitted over the radio. These important milestones can include such things as the discovery of clues, the ETA of aircraft, or vehicle breakdowns. Moreover, integrated communications provides search managers with the capability of talking to

virtually any person involved in the incident, regardless of the person's location or the radio frequency they are using.

ICS also stipulates that, in order to reduce confusion and miscommunication, all voice radio transmissions during the incident should be in clear text or plain language. Radio codes such as the ten-code system should be specifically avoided since the meaning of codes like "10-50" may vary across agencies. Communications should also be confined to essential messages to keep the frequencies open.

4. Unified Command Structure

A lost person incident may involve **more than one jurisdiction**. For example, the place where the subject was last seen may lie near the border between two countries, counties, states, or provinces, or near the edge of a national park or forest. Alternatively, a search may begin well within one jurisdiction, such as in a state or national park, but later indications may suggest that the subject has traveled into another jurisdiction, such as a rural county adjacent to the park. In such instances, there is the potential for jurisdictional disputes between agencies.

These disputes are not necessarily due to base motivations to protect one's "turf," but may arise because agencies are legally accountable for the safety of persons within their boundaries. With the potential for litigation after an unsuccessful search, agency administrators may be reluctant to surrender incident control to agencies from other jurisdictions.

In order to avoid such problems, ICS stipulates that **the management of a multi-jurisdictional incident should be <u>unified</u>, that is, each agency having a jurisdictional claim should be allowed to participate in the command and control of the search**. Specifically, through a joint planning process, representatives from each agency cooperate in the determination of search <u>objectives</u> as well as the selection of specific <u>strategies</u> designed to accomplish those objectives. Then, through mutual agreement, one individual is appointed as the incident Operations Section Chief (OSC). The OSC, whose full responsibilities are described later, has the task of implementing the search plan by making tactical decisions and assigning resources to the field. In place of organizational rivalry, a unified command structure provides a template for mutual aid, preferably already outlined in Memoranda of Understanding between the cooperating agencies.

5. The Incident Action Plan

The Incident Action Plan is a plan for finding the lost subject. The plan should be initiated as soon as possible during the incident, particularly the incident objectives, as they will determine all operational decisions regarding the number and type of resources to use, where to deploy them, and what tactics to employ.

The Incident Action Plan (IAP) consists of the objectives and strategy along with an organizational chart, tactical assignments, and maps. There may also be additional attachments as the incident requires, including a communications plan, a medical plan, and a transportation plan.

An Incident Action Plan is developed as soon as practical after the search starts and is developed in each <u>operational</u> period (normally 12 hours, but may be less if conditions dictate) for use in the following operational period.

6. Manageable Span of Control

The ICS formally prescribes that the manageable span of control (the number of people who can be effectively supervised by one person, see Chapter 3) must be respected during all phases of the incident. Indeed, the span of control will determine the need for expanding specific units or sections as the incident grows. An important principle is to anticipate such expansions and to make the appropriate appointments <u>before</u> the supervisor becomes overwhelmed. Again, efficient management means being <u>proactive</u> toward potential problems rather than <u>reactive</u>.

Maintaining **adequate span of control** throughout the ICS organization is very important. Effective span of control on incidents may vary from three (3) to seven (7).

A ratio of one (1) supervisor to five (5) reporting elements (direct reports) is recommended. If the number of reporting elements falls outside these ranges, then expansion or consolidation of the organizational structure may be necessary.

7. Designated Search Management Facilities

There are various types of facilities that can be established in and around the search area. The determination of the kinds of facilities to establish, as well as their respective locations, will be based upon the requirements of the incident and the direction of the management team. The following facilities are defined for possible use:

- Incident Base. The Incident Base is the location where primary support activities are performed and supplies and equipment are stored. It normally contains other incident facilities such as the command post and staging areas.
- Command Post. The Command Post is the location at which all search operations are planned, managed, and directed.
- Camps. Camps are locations where resources may be temporarily placed outside of the incident base, in order to better support search operations.
- Staging Areas. Staging Areas are established for temporary location of available resources that can be activated on a three-minute notice.
- Helibases. Helibases are locations in and around the search area where helicopters may be parked, maintained, fuelled, and loaded with personnel or equipment.
- Helispots. Helispots are locations at which helicopters can land and take off to load or unload personnel or equipment.

8. Comprehensive Resource Management

ICS has standardized organizational components (see also Figure 4.1), which in descending order, include as needed:

Sections: The organizational levels with responsibility for a major functional area of the incident (for example, Planning, Finance/Administration, Operations, Logistics). The person in charge of each section is designated a Section Chief.

Branches: Branches are used under a Section when the number of Divisions or Groups extends the span of control. Branches can be either geographical or functional. The person in charge of each Branch is a Director.

Divisions: Divisions are used under Sections or Branches to **geographically** divide an incident. The person in charge of each Division is designated as a Supervisor.

Groups: Groups are used under Sections or Branches to describe **functional areas** of operations, such as all the K9 resources at the incident. The person in charge of each Division is designated as a Supervisor.

Field Resources which actually do the searching fall into three categories:

1. <u>Single Resource</u>: The smallest unit that can **operate independently** in the field. This could be a search crew, a tracking team, a dog team (handler plus search dog), a helicopter, an all-terrain vehicle, an ambulance, or any resource that can be assigned as a primary tactical unit. Single resources pertaining to equipment or vehicles include the individuals who operate them.

2. <u>Task Force</u>. A task force is any combination of single **resources of various kinds and types** (not all the same) that can be temporarily assembled for a specific task. A task force could be a combination of search crews, dog teams, all-terrain vehicles, and other resources that work together in order to accomplish a particular objective. All resources within a task force must have common communications, and each task force must have one leader. A task force is established to meet a specific tactical objective. Once the objective is met, the task force can be disassembled or demobilized as single resources, or reorganized into another task force.

3. <u>Strike Team</u>. A strike team consists of a number of **resources of the same kind and type** functioning together under a single leader who coordinates their activity. These resources could either be search crews, dog teams, all-terrain vehicles, or any one kind of resource type that may be aggregated in order to accomplish a particular objective. Like the task force, the strike team should have common communications.

Strike teams and task forces should be used, whenever possible, to optimize the efficiency of resources, to increase the management control of a large number of single resources, and to reduce the communications load.

<u>Tracking Resource Status</u>. The Planning Section is tasked with maintaining an accurate, up-to-date picture of resource readiness by assigning a status condition to each resource. Three common conditions should be tracked by a workable system, like index cards, where the resource can be moved between these different states of readiness.

The Three Resource Status Conditions:

I. **Assigned**: Currently performing an active assignment.

II. **Available**: Ready for immediate assignment.

III. **Out of Service**: Not available for service at this time.

All changes in resource locations and status conditions need to be promptly communicated to the Planning section, which may in turn record the change on a physical "T-Card" resource status board or a computerized system that **graphically depicts the resource status** of the incident at any given moment in time.

Resource Typing

While resource types have been around since the advent of ICS, new to the system under the NIMS mandate is SAR "resource typing." Resource types were developed to assist neighboring jurisdictions in requesting help when local resources are overwhelmed. Under this scheme, resource types vary from Type 1 (the most capable) to Type 4 (the least capable), allowing the requesting agency to locate and pick the appropriate level for the particular incident. Besides rating capability, resources are also classified by "Category," based on their most useful function, and by "Kind," based on broad descriptive classes like teams, equipment, personnel, supplies, etc. Typing definitions are dynamic and will continuously be updated and revised as

necessary. The link to the NIMS resource typing classifications is at: http:// www. fema.gov/emergency/nims/mutual_aid.shtm.

Incident Typing

Under ICS, incidents are also typed. The most complex incident (Type 1) would require a commitment of national resources to effectively manage the operation. The least complex incident (Type 5) would require no more than six personnel and would be resolved within one operational period or less, with no written Incident Action Plan. An example of a Type 5 incident would be a vehicle fire. Lost person incidents would typically be classified as Type 3 or Type 4, requiring Command and some General Staff functions to be activated over one or more operational periods.

The Organizational Structure of ICS

According to the ICS, there are **five major management functions** that must be performed. These functions are **Command, Planning, Operations, Logistics, and Finance/Administration** (Figure 4.2). The unit or group contained within one function is termed a section. It may not be necessary, especially early in the incident, for each function to be performed by a different individual. For example, the IC may decide to perform the operations function—in addition to command—during the initial response. However, any function not assigned to another individual remains the responsibility of the IC. What is important is that a function be performed effectively while not exceeding the individual's span of control.

When individuals are appointed to perform specific functions, they are referred to as **Section Chiefs**. As discussed earlier, chiefs may appoint additional individuals to assist with the management of that particular section. A Planning Chief, for example, may decide to appoint someone as a lone investigator or to lead an Investigation Unit. **Together, the section chiefs constitute what ICS terms the General Staff.** The IC and General Staff will stay on duty for one operational period.

Command

The most important component of search management is an effective IC. In general, the IC provides leadership and direction, makes, reviews, and approves decisions, oversees all other management functions, and accepts responsibility for the manner in which the search is conducted.

Specific **responsibilities of the IC** include:

- Evaluating the urgency of the incident and determining the nature and magnitude of the initial response.
- Appointing section chiefs.
- Selecting the location of the incident base and command

post, and approving the locations of other incident facilities.

- Initiating or approving the requisition of resources.
- Preparing the Incident Objectives.
- Establishing consensus with respect to decisions concerning search strategy and tactics.
- Carrying out policy, briefing agency administrators, communicating with dispatchers.
- Soliciting assistance from appropriate technical specialists when special problems arise.
- Interfacing with the representatives of external agencies involved in the incident, unless the IC appoints a liaison officer.
- Ensuring the safety of personnel by identifying and mitigating hazards.
- Dealing with the media, the subject's family, persons exercising political influence, and other individuals external to search operations.
- Organizing and conducting an incident critique if appropriate.

The Command Staff: Just as section chiefs may appoint unit leaders to assist them with the performance of their respective functions, the IC may appoint <u>officers</u> to assist with the command function (Figure 4.3). These Command Staff officers include:

Safety Officer: Assesses hazards and develops measures for assuring safety. The Safety Officer has emergency authority to halt a specific operation that he/she deems to be unsafe. In an incident involving numerous hazards, the Safety Officer would likely appoint however many assistants are necessary to ensure safe operations. The Safety Officer may stop an activity, but usually has no authority to initiate one.

Public Information Officer: Summarizes, for public consumption, information pertaining to incident cause, size, current situation, resources committed, and other matters that may be of general interest. The Public Information Officer is normally the point of contact for the media as well as government officials seeking information. In addition to releasing information to the world outside the search, the PIO can also play an important role internally by periodically briefing and updating general staff on the incident status and on how the operation is being perceived externally.

Liaison Officer: Serves as the contact person for agencies that are providing assistance during the incident. As a representative of the IC, the Liaison Officer has the authority to discuss all aspects of the incident with such agencies, and to provide them with whatever information and assistance that they need.

A high level investigative team, like the FBI, may be assigned directly to the IC as part of the command staff for inter-state or other incidents of national interest. However, for SAR missions, the investigation and interviewing process would typically be done by local law enforcement reporting back to the Planning Section Chief.

Figure 4.3

Modular ICS: Command Staff

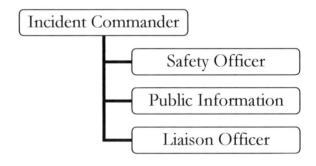

Planning

The Planning (also called the "Plans") Section is responsible for gathering information relevant to the incident, tracking the status of search resources, keeping a current record of search progress, and formulating strategies for finding the lost person. Generally, any operational task involving the **collection or exchange of information** is considered to be a planning function. The Planning Section collects situation and resource status information, evaluates it, and processes it for use in developing action plans. **Planning then disseminates information** in the form of the Incident Action Plan, formal briefings and through map and status board displays.

Some specific **tasks of the Planning Section** include:

- Preparing the Incident Action Plan.
- Preparing and maintaining all incident documentation.
- Acquiring investigative data (information about the missing subjects and why they might have become lost).
- Developing strategies and priorities about where to search for the subject. These strategies will normally be driven by the Incident Objectives, and will pertain to the current operational period.
- Developing alternative strategies.
- Briefing and debriefing tactical resources (because this involves the exchange of information).
- Obtaining and analyzing maps and aerial photographs.
- Maintaining a list of all resources assigned to, or requested for, the incident.

- Anticipating the need for additional search resources.
- Planning for demobilization.

Planning Section Chief: The demand for information is most intense at the beginning of the incident. This is when an initial set of search strategies must be devised. For this reason, the Planning Section Chief (PSC), sometimes abbreviated to "Plans Chief," should normally be appointed as soon as possible. He/she will need to collect pertinent information about the missing subject, including interviews with witnesses or family members.

Based on this data, appropriate maps will need to be procured, a search area defined and divided into manageable segments, and a consensus of the areas most likely to contain the subject will need to be created. Simultaneous with these tasks, the Planning Section will need to be assessing the adequacy of search resources while logging them in as they arrive.

As the incident develops and more information needs to be obtained, processed, and recorded, the Planning Section can easily become overwhelmed. For this reason, the Planning Section Chief under ICS has the authority to appoint leaders for four primary units:

1. Resources Unit- Tracks all search resources, including personnel who

have signed in and out of the incident, and their current status.

2. Situation Unit- Gathers and processes information pertaining to search progress, such as tracking coverage and identifying the locations where clues have been found. The Situation Unit may maintain current information on a "status map" to facilitate search planning. With the advent of digital mapping capability, mapping display technicians would be assigned to the situation unit. The Planning Section Chief might also assign the investigator to the situation unit or create a separate unit to oversee that function.

3. Documentation Unit- Ensures that accurate records and forms are available and maintained. Such documentation will be used during the incident for planning purposes as well as for post-incident reviews.

4. Demobilization Unit- Prepares the demobilization plan that includes specific instructions for everyone— management and resources—on the actions to perform when the incident ends.

Operations

The Operations Section is responsible for organizing tactical operations and committing search resources to the field and consists of: the following specialties:

Operations Section Chief: The Operations Section Chief (OSC) is responsible for translating incident strategies into tactical operations and managing all activities of search resources that are currently deployed. Generally, the OSC will work closely with the Planning Section Chief during the development of the Incident Action Plan, because it is the Operations Section who will implement the plan. Similarly, the OSC will consult with the Logistics Section regarding communications, transportation, and support of tactical operations. Specific tasks of the OSC include:

- Developing tactics on how to search for the subject.
- Committing specific search resources to the ground, air, and water.
- Advising the Planning Section Chief on the feasibility of alternative strategies, given the tactical resources available.
- Actively participating in the development of the Incident Action Plan.
- Changing resource assignments during the current operational period due to

shifting requirements as the search progresses.

Air Operations: All air operations, whether used for tactical or logistical purposes, are coordinated by the Operations Section. When the managing of air operations becomes complex, such as when helicopters are providing both tactical and logistical services, and fixed wing aircraft are also being deployed, the OSC may choose to appoint an Air Operations branch director to coordinate these activities. If many aircraft are involved, then the "Ops Chief" might create two section "branches" and appoint a director for each functional type of aviation resource (fixed wing and rotary wing) in place of a single Air Ops unit.

Of all the management functions, the Operations Section is most likely to vary from incident to incident, depending on the requirements of the search and the availability of specific resources. One incident may consist of a list of single resources, all managed directly by the OSC or IC, while another may involve strike teams or even task forces for which leaders have been appointed. In Figure 4.4, for example, the OSC has four ready resources under direct control, including two hasty teams, a task force, a K9 strike force and possibly a helicopter. In this example, a local SAR dog association has provided a large contingent of air scent dog teams, so the OSC has decided to deploy them as a strike team rather than as single

resources. Being a strike team, they will have a designated leader and a common communications system. Moreover, the leader can serve as a technical specialist to the OSC, with respect to how the dogs can be effectively deployed toward meeting search objectives.

Logistics

The Logistics Section is responsible for providing all support needs to the incident (except for air, which is managed by the Operations Section). Logistics provides and maintains facilities, transportation, supplies, equipment, food services, sanitation, shelter, and medical services. In other words, all ground resources, including people, are ordered by the Logistics Section. Logistics will be managed by the Logistics Section Chief (LSC), who should normally be appointed early in the incident when the base is being established and important facilities, such as the command post and communications center, need to be set up (see Chapter 21). The Logistics Section Chief may appoint leaders for any of six separate units as the need arises:

1. Supply Unit: Orders, receives, stores, and processes all incident-related resources, personnel, equipment, and supplies. **This also includes tactical resources, on the request or approval of the IC.**

2. Facilities Unit: Establishes, maintains, and demobilizes all facilities used in support of the incident. The Facilities Unit will also provide personnel support services, including sleeping areas, sanitation services, showers, and, when necessary, security.

3. Ground Support Unit: Prepares the traffic plan and maintains and repairs tactical vehicles and equipment, including fuelling and transportation services, and may even provide drivers. The Ground Support Unit will keep the Resources Unit (Plans Section) informed with respect to changes in the status of vehicles and other tactical resources within their control.

4. Food Unit: Determines food and water requirements, plans menus, orders, prepares, and serves food, and generally maintains the food service areas, including remote feeding locations.

5. Medical Unit: Develops the Incident Medical Plan for handling medical emergencies involving incident personnel (not the missing subject, whose medical treatment will normally be under the supervision of the OSC). The Medical Unit will establish identifiable first aid stations and provide suitable transportation for personnel requiring immediate evacuation to a hospital or other medical facility.

6. Communications Unit: Integrates all communications planning, which includes the use and assignment of equipment and common frequencies.

Finance/Administration

The Finance/Administration Section is established when the agency involved perceives a specific need for financial services. Often financial considerations can be handled by the IC or by the appointment of a technical specialist assigned to the Planning Section. However, on larger incidents, or when there are special problems related to finance, the IC may appoint a Finance/Admin Section Chief, (FASC) , who may appoint leaders of four separate units:

1. Time Unit: Ensures that personnel and equipment time recording documents are prepared in accordance with agency requirements.

2. Procurement Unit: Administers all financial matters pertaining to vendor contracts with respect to rentals and supplies.

3. Compensation/Claims Unit: Processes Compensation-For-Injury

and Claims, such as ensuring that all worker's compensation forms are completed. This unit will also process claims regarding lost or damaged property.

4. <u>Cost Unit:</u> Provides cost analysis data for the incident, when required, such as estimating and recording costs of resource use.

The ICS Organizational Chart

An important component of the Incident Action Plan is the Organizational Chart, which graphically depicts the management structure for a specified operational period. Figure 4.4 presents one possible structure. In order to illustrate the various management <u>functions</u> that need to be performed, all the officers of the Command Staff have been indicated, as well as all the units assigned to sections of the General Staff. Again, not all of these unit leaders or staff officers need to be assigned, especially during the first operational period. This particular chart would suggest a fairly large incident with many personnel and resources to manage and information to process. Indeed, a search of this size would likely have many more tactical resources under control of the Operations Section than are depicted in this example.

Normally, the Organizational Chart during the initial response would be much simpler than is shown in Figure 4.4. One popular configuration is to "roll" with an IC and a Planning Section Chief. In this case, the IC performs the Operations function, perhaps by tasking hasty teams, or trackers to "sign cut" for indications as to which direction the subject may have traveled from the Place Last Seen (PLS) or the Last Known Position (LKP), while the Planning Chief prepares maps and other materials while obtaining information about the missing subject from the assigned investigator. The Planning Section Chief would also document initial and subsequent search activities, with the option to create a Documentation Unit to handle that function.

The IC should also appoint someone to serve as Communications Unit Leader, in order to place the base station radio in service. Meanwhile, the IC may conscript one or more individuals to assist with other components of the logistics function that need to be performed immediately, for example., establishing base facilities. Other management configurations are equally possible, depending on the responding agency's capabilities and the nature of the incident. Note that Figure 4.4 does not include Branches, Divisions or Groups. Given the flexibility of ICS however, they can be added to correctly manage the span of control when needed.

Figure 4.4

Modular ICS: A "Large Search" Organizational Chart

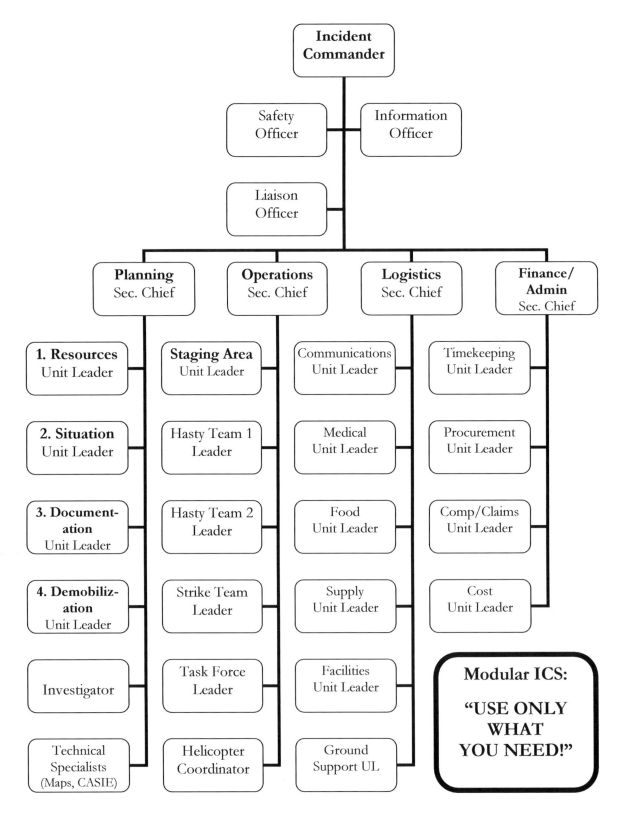

necessary to maintain span of control. The governing principle is to **"think functions, not people."**

> ## What matters is that the FUNCTIONS ARE PERFORMED,
> ### regardless of who does them.

One individual may be performing multiple functions until the workload increases to a point where "job-shedding" occurs. At that point additional appointments may be necessary to maintain span of control. The governing principle is to **"think functions, not people."**

Agency Representatives

Not shown in the organizational chart in Figure 4.4 is the position of **Agency Representative**. This individual is assigned from an assisting or cooperating agency and has the authority to make decisions on matters affecting that agency's participation in the incident. Agency Representatives report to the Liaison Officer or to the Incident Commander in the absence of a Liaison Officer.

ICS Training

All personnel likely to perform on a search (or other incident) management team must complete a set of ICS courses appropriate to the expected management level. Classes in ICS procedures can be arranged in-house for a group or taken on-line individually through FEMA's Emergency Management Institute, as this chapter has only provided a brief overview.

Summary

In this chapter, we discussed the need for employing an effective emergency management system during the lost person incident. We introduced the Incident Command System (ICS) and described its application to a single-jurisdictional search during the first operational period. The eight critical components of ICS were discussed, as well as its organizational structure. Generally, ICS has proved to be a very flexible system, adaptable to rapidly changing management requirements as the incident develops. In particular, its modular structure allows search managers to stay within their span of control, by providing them with the power to delegate authority to the appropriate assistants, as necessary.

Questions for Discussion:

1. What sorts of problems will a SAR agency, or group that has never employed a management system, encounter when trying to adopt the ICS?

2. What are the hazards of modifying ICS, such as changing terminology or job descriptions?

3. Why is it important to separate the operations function from the planning function?

4. Why is it a good idea for there to be a consensus on search strategy and tactics? For example, why should the OSC contribute to the selection of strategies, and the Logistics Chief participate in a discussion of tactics?

5. What problems may occur if the search's IC is not search management qualified?

CHAPTER 5

THE OPERATIONAL PREPLAN

As mentioned in Chapter 1, being **unprepared for a search incident** is one of the most critical—though frequent—mistakes that search managers can make. Many of the problems <u>and</u> solutions encountered during a search are foreseeable, such as requirements for special resources, or the arrival on scene of large numbers of spontaneous volunteers. **Being predictable, these problems can be anticipated** and dealt with to some extent <u>before</u> the incident actually happens. The means for accomplishing this end is the Operational Preplan.

CHAPTER OBJECTIVES:

When you finish studying this chapter, you should be able to:

1. Describe the importance of preplanning prior to a search incident.
2. Discuss the process of preparing a preplan.
3. List the components of a preplan.

Pre-Planning Documents

Generally, there are three categories of SAR planning documents that are maintained prior to the start of an incident:

1. <u>Agency documents</u>: These are manuals, directives, memoranda, and other documents that pertain to agency policies, authorizations, job descriptions, responsibilities, mandates, inter-agency agreements and legal constraints. These documents provide the umbrella under which all other documents and manuals, including the preplan, are prepared.

2. "<u>How to</u>" manuals: These are resource documents that provide instructions regarding operational procedures and standards, such as how to search, SAR reference manuals, field operations guides (FOGs), what to carry in the field, how to tie knots, and other training manuals. These documents provide the guidelines that SAR personnel use while becoming proficient in certain skills. Although such training documents may be referenced in the preplan, they are not normally part of the preplan itself.

3. <u>The Operational Preplan</u>: This document provides incident management personnel with information, instructions, checklists, standard operating procedures, and technical data that will be referred to during the actual conduct

of the search. The preplan provides a good skeletal structure for the Incident Action Plan.

Why Prepare a Preplan?

Few would deny the merits of preparing for the <u>tactical</u> and <u>strategic</u> operations that will be performed during a search incident, such as how to conduct search patterns, or how to keep track of coverage. This information is usually contained in the various training manuals and books — such as this one — that are often valued and studied by conscientious SAR responders. Yet it is not uncommon to see experienced search managers, during the initial phase of the search, thumbing frantically through phone books, looking for names of contact people, or scanning the Yellow Pages for suppliers of food or other logistical resources. And few search critiques have not included mention of **at least one significant oversight** committed during the search, such as forgetting to call the fire department to provide safety support for a helibase, or failing to inform the local airport that SAR aircraft would be appearing on their screens.

Preplanning means being ready for all decisions that will have to be made and having available the information that will need to be accessed during the conduct of the search. The operational preplan is the document that contains this information. Because it must always be current, the preplan should be reviewed frequently, especially after

each incident, and updated when necessary as new lessons are learned or changing conditions are experienced.

Developing a preplan should be a group effort. The process of preplanning can be one of the most important activities a SAR agency or team can perform. Indeed, the activity of discussing and reviewing the preplan periodically can be just as valuable as the document it produces.

Some additional benefits of a preplan include the following:

<u>A preplan reduces stress load</u>. During a search, many important decisions have to be made under conditions of high stress, such as during the initial response, or when someone needs immediate medical evacuation. Under these circumstances, the possibility of making poor decisions——or overlooking something important——increases dramatically. A good preplan can guide search managers through difficult times by specifying the decisions that have to be made, suggesting alternatives for those decisions, and providing the information the manager needs to make the best decision under the circumstances.

<u>A preplan facilitates a realistic assessment of SAR resources</u>. Are available resources adequate to accomplish the objectives mentioned in the preplan? For example, if the preplan specifies that, during the initial phase of a search, efforts should be made to

determine the direction of the subject's travel, then it becomes important to ask whether searchers are sufficiently trained in tracking or sign cutting in order to accomplish this task. The preplan helps identify those areas where further training may be necessary, or when special resources need to be identified and recruited. Many otherwise well trained searchers have had little or no instruction in how to assess and report how well they have searched. This is one area that deserves emphasis through initial and recurrent training.

A preplan orients personnel to operational procedures and policies. To the SAR recruit, a preplan provides a thumbnail sketch of how search incidents are conducted, why certain tasks are performed, what training manuals and other documents are considered important for SAR operations, and, by implication, what role the recruit may expect to play in the organization.

For agency administrators, who may have responsibility for public safety (parks) or missing persons' investigations (police), but are not themselves directly involved in SAR operations, the preplan can be an excellent means for becoming informed of how incidents are conducted, and for identifying possible conflicts with agency policies. For experienced SAR responders, periodically reviewing the preplan is an excellent method of staying up-to-date regarding operational

procedures, especially when there are significant time lags between incidents.

What's In a Preplan?

1. Checklists. These are itemized sequences of critical activities in the proper order. See Figure 5.1 for an example. Note that some items referenced in Figure 5.1, such as the theoretical search distance, the statistical search distance and OPOS, have not been discussed yet, but they will be later. A checklist ensures that critical steps are not forgotten. Activities for which a checklist should be considered include:

- Hazardous operations (for example, helicopter safety).
- Call-out procedures.
- Planning activities in which oversights or errors can be critical.
- Complex tasks involving group effort (for example, erecting a radio tower).
- Vehicle and equipment maintenance during an incident.
- Any activity that is infrequently performed or for which trained personnel are scarce.

2. Resource lists. Phone numbers of contacts for acquiring personnel, vehicles, equipment, supplies, food, or other resources are an important component of any preplan. Each resource should be described in terms of capabilities, requirements, and limitations. For

example, search resources can be described in terms of their kind and type (air scent dog teams, man-trackers, etc.) and the amount of time they will require to become mobilized.

Similarly, food suppliers can be listed in terms of food type, quantity, hours of service available, and procedures for pickup or delivery. The Plans and Logistics sections are especially likely to have resource lists, which should be periodically reviewed and updated between incidents.

3. <u>Names of referenced documents</u>. Training manuals and agency documents that will guide operations during the incident should be included, with page references, where appropriate. For example, if the ICS is to be used, then the appropriate ICS manual should be referenced. The contents of such documents should <u>not</u> be contained or described in detail in the preplan, except where modifications or additions have been made.

4. <u>Standard Operating Procedures</u> (SOP's). Any accepted procedure that is not sufficiently described in other documents should be included in the preplan. For example, procedures for receiving the first notice, initiating a callout, determining incident priority, mobilizing and demobilizing resources, and conducting an incident critique are all good candidates for inclusion in the preplan. Other SOP's might include

communications protocols, instructions on how to protect the PLS or to acquire a scent article, procedures for dealing with the subject's family or other external influences, or for handling subject fatalities. Standard operating procedures will usually reflect the specific characteristics and requirements of the SAR group or agency, which may differ markedly from other groups.

5. <u>Memoranda of Agreement</u> (MOA). Any documents on which agencies or organizations have agreed to cooperate with or support the agency's SAR incidents should be attached to the preplan. Examples of such organizations include the Civil Air Patrol, Red Cross, fire departments, ambulance services, equestrian groups, snowmobile associations, and all-terrain vehicle or 4-wheel-drive clubs. Similar MOA's may be signed between volunteer SAR groups and those agencies that deploy them, such as a park services or police authorities. All MOA's should include specifics of the duties, authorities, and responsibilities of each agency involved. Any relevant financial or liability issues and approval process should also be specified.

6. <u>Miscellaneous information that will be needed during an incident</u>. Examples include radio frequencies available for use, map lists, lost person statistics, planning formulas, and supply lists.

Figure 5.1

Example of a Planning Checklist
(to be included in a Preplan)

1- ☐ Gather sufficient **Search Data** to plan the search.

2- ☐ Consult Lost Person **Behavior & Distance Traveled** tables.

3- ☐ Determine the **Urgency** of the incident.

4- ☐ Compute the **Theoretical Search Area** for this subject's type.

5- ☐ Compute a **Statistical Search Area** for this subject type.

6- ☐ Establish the Subject's **Direction of Travel** from the IPP.

7- ☐ Identify all **Potential Boundaries** (water, cliffs, etc.).

8- ☐ Identify points where **Confinement** should occur.

9- ☐ Identify **Travel Aids** (drainages, roads, trails, survey lines, etc).

10- ☐ Create plans that flow from the **Incident Objectives**.

11- ☐ Divide the search locale into **Manageable Segments**.

12- ☐ Set **Priorities** using a **Consensus** for which segments should be searched first.

13- ☐ Allocate resources in a way that **Maximizes OPOS**.

14- ☐ **Diversify Resources** with respect to location, tactics, and type.

15- ☐ Select necessary resources for the **Next Operational Period**.

Further Pre-Planning Considerations

Perform a SAR vulnerability assessment: What type of lost person incidents have actually occurred in the past? What kinds of people use the area? Where do they go? What do they do? How do they get into trouble? What kinds of strategies and tactics have proved effective? What kinds of problems (for example, geography, logistics) have been encountered when searching for them? What types of training or other forms of preparation would help to mitigate these problems?

Forecast and analyze potential problems: What kinds of problems could happen? What types of incidents or problems are you less prepared for — simply because they haven't happened yet? What are the worst case scenarios? What types of special resources could be enlisted in order to deal with these problems? Consider all reasonable possibilities and discuss methods and procedures for handling them.

Identify agency policies that may impact on the preplan: There will always be policies that guide, and sometimes override, decisions that will be made during an incident. Many such policies pertain to expenditures and procedures regarding the ordering of resources, such as helicopters, portable toilets, or equipment. In national or state parks, there may be policies regarding environmental protection or the maintenance of visitor services during a lost person incident. Volunteer SAR organizations often encounter policies from jurisdictional police authorities regarding the use of civilian dog teams or divers, the handling and recording of evidence, and investigation procedures. During the preplanning process, all relevant policy documents should be reviewed, discussed, and clarified, when necessary.

Implement Risk Management Policies or Guidelines, especially for Operations: Make it clear that resources should never be assigned to tasks for which they are not trained or which will expose them to unreasonable danger. The simplest and most effective method of handling excessive risk is to not take it.

The Structure of the Preplan

As noted earlier, the specifics of a preplan will differ widely between SAR groups or agencies. What follows is a suggested structure that might be considered during the preplanning process.

1. Purpose and objectives of the preplan: A concise statement that will orient readers to the document's purpose and intended use.

2. Incident priority guidelines: If the organization sets priorities with respect to whether an incident should receive a full callout versus a measured or limited response, then those priorities should be articulated. Guidelines for determining the relative urgency of an incident should be specified.

3. First notice procedures: Who is contacted when an incident commences? What alternative contact persons are there? What is the procedure for calling SAR responders and other resources during the initial response? Who else needs to be notified?

4. Procedures for conducting an investigation: Who gathers information about the missing subject? Who interviews witnesses and family members? Specific agency guidelines should be considered.

5. Strategies for finding the subject: These are considerations for defining the scope of the problem and determining courses of action. For example, how large an area should be searched? How thorough should the search be? When search strategies are determined by training manuals or other documents (such as this manual). Those documents should be referenced in the preplan, with strategies briefly summarized, at most.

6. Search tactics: What methods or actions should be employed in order to find a lost person, or to rescue a subject. Again, the relevant documents should be referred to and briefly summarized in the preplan.

7. Emergent authorities and responsibilities: These refer to possible conditions that may require alterations as an incident develops, such as a possible change in jurisdictional boundaries, or any event that increases the complexity of an incident.

8. Organizational structure: How should an incident be managed? Relevant manuals should be referred to under the National Incident Management System (NIMS) to employ the ICS structure.

9. Incident facilities: Locations and resources available for possible facilities. Specifically, the locations of any buildings or structures in the jurisdictional area that could be used for command posts or other facilities should be identified. Some examples include fire halls, Red Cross facilities, schools, emergency shelters, or camps.

10. Radio communications: Procedures for acquiring and using handheld radios and other communication devices. This could include a list of available frequencies, suggestions about how the frequencies should be distributed, and possibly a list of licensed amateur radio operators (Hams).

11. Briefing and debriefing procedures: If forms are used (highly recommended), then they can be included as a preplan appendix.

12. Medical considerations: Procedures for dealing with searcher injuries could be outlined, including phone numbers of ambulance services and hospitals. The availability of helicopter landing sites at hospitals could be specified.

13. Fatalities: What happens if the subject is found deceased, or dies during the rescue? Procedures should also provide for the possibility of criminal activity or the involvement of a coroner or medical examiner.

14. Rescue/evacuation: Rescue capabilities and limitations should be considered. The needs for special resources, such as technical rescue or high angle rescuers, should be considered.

15. Mission suspension or de-escalation: How will the determination be made to suspend the incident when the subject has not been located? What criteria should be considered? What level of authority will be required to make such a decision?

16. Demobilization procedures: What procedures should be used when bringing resources back from the field and sending them home? What to do about fatigued searchers or search managers who cannot safely operate their motor vehicles?

17. Documentation: Forms and other paperwork should be attached to the preplan as appendices, including items like technology standards such as which software, and version thereof to be used, to help simplify keeping up with changes and increase response efficiency.

18. Critiques: Procedures for constructively reviewing the mission should be considered.

19. Special problems: Depending on circumstances, many other considerations may be included, such as:

- Restricting airspace.
- Aircraft crash consideration; private, commercial and military.
- Safeguarding victim's valuables.
- Resource protection & environmental constraints.
- Cost accounting procedures.
- Manifesting, timekeeping, etc.
- Preventative actions.
- Press briefings and media spokesperson identification. Preventative actions.
- Critical Incident Stress Management.
- HAZMAT and blood-borne pathogen exposure.

20. Appendices: The following may be included in the preplan as appendices. They can be referred to independently and are easily revised.

- Resource lists.
- Phone lists.
- Equipment lists.
- Radio frequency lists.

- Organizational chart.
- Cooperative commitments and Memoranda of Agreement (MOAs) and Memoranda of Understanding (MOU's).
- Copies of relevant Forms.

Preplanning means being ready for practically anything that could happen, regardless of whether it has happened before. Having a useful preplan reduces stress load during stressful moments, when memory lapses or oversights are most likely to occur.

Figure 5.2 summarizes the characteristics of a good preplan.

Figure 5.2

Characteristics of a Good Preplan

- **Simple in structure.**
- **Easy to read and understand.**
- **Easy to update.**
- **Flexible and adaptable to varying situations.**
- **Current, accurate, and useful.**
- **Is used often enough that it becomes the de facto process for search incidents.**

Summary

We described three types of manuals or documents that SAR organizations use for planning purposes: (1) various agency documents that contain policies, mandates, and legal considerations, (2) training manuals that SAR responders use to acquire and maintain their skills, and (3) the operational preplan. The preplan contains descriptions of standard operational procedures, resource lists, checklists, and whatever technical information search managers will refer to during an actual search incident.

Preparation of a preplan facilitates a realistic assessment of SAR resources and identifies training needs. The preplan also orients both new and experienced personnel to the organization's operational procedures. Overall, a good preplan promotes efficient and cost-effective search incidents, and, ultimately, protects the safety of subjects <u>and</u> SAR responders.

Questions for Discussion:

1. What additional kinds of checklist and resources lists, besides the ones mentioned in this chapter, could be added to your preplan?

2. Many SAR organizations have informal or "handshake" agreements with various agencies and clubs for mutual aid during a search for a lost person. What advantages are gained by putting such arrangements into writing and asking everyone to sign off on a memorandum of agreement?

3. How is it possible to forecast problems that <u>could</u> occur during a lost person incident, but which have not happened previously?

4. It is often said that the process of preplanning is just as important as the document it produces. Explain.

CHAPTER 6

SEARCH AND RESCUE RESOURCES

As discussed in the last chapter, a SAR resource list is an essential part of any preplan. Lists of operational and logistical resources, including personnel, vehicles, equipment, supplies, and services, must be diligently created, reviewed, and updated. In this chapter, we will take a closer look at the **kinds of resources that may be deployed** during a lost person incident.

CHAPTER OBJECTIVES:

When you finish studying this chapter, you should be able to:

> 1. Discuss categories, kinds of search and rescue resources.
> 2. Describe their functions, capabilities, and limitations.
> 3. Discuss the importance of identifying and evaluating SAR resources.

SAR Resources

The National Incident Management System (NIMS) includes evolving definitions of resource types. Since these designations are dynamic and subject to updating, NIMS resource types should be reviewed periodically. What follows is a non-exhaustive list of various types of resources that may be employed during a lost person incident.

Aircraft

Helicopters. Besides being employed for searching, often their most important function on a search, helicopters (rotary-wing aircraft) are useful for transporting personnel to remote locations, as well as transferring supplies and equipment. They are also useful for evaluating the search area, especially during the initial phase of the incident.

Advantages of Helicopters include:

• Can search large areas very quickly.

• Can fly "low and slow" over high-priority search areas.

• Can usually land in or near the search base.

• Can be a platform for specialized search technology like Forward Looking Infrared Radar (FLIR).

• With appropriate clearance, can fly "low and slow" dispersing the vegetation canopy to aid in air-to-ground viewing.

• Can often provide the most efficient rescue platform.

• Can be used for transport of equipment and personnel.

• Can be equipped with FLIR, "night sun," and video cameras.

• Can be used for long-line support or short-haul external load extractions.

• Can employ a PA system to call the subject.

• Can direct ground crews to a subject spotted from the air.

Limitations of Helicopters include:

• Usually require frequent refueling.

• Unless specially equipped, typically will not fly at night.

• Subject to weather conditions like cloud ceiling, icing and factors affecting visibility.

• Require special facilities (for example, helibases), support resources (for example, fire department), and training requirements for personnel (for example, safety for crew and observers).

• High cost per flight hour.

Fixed-wing aircraft: Small, fixed-wing aircraft may be useful for search area evaluation, or for actual searching when there are large, relatively open areas to cover, or when the search subject or clue is large like an aircraft or vehicle. These are often military aircraft, or provided by SAR groups such as CAP (Civil Air Patrol) or CASARA (Canadian Air Search and Rescue Association). Regardless of whether fixed-wing aircraft are actually deployed, CAP and CASARA are excellent sources of training for air spotters and other skills useful to land SAR organizations.

Advantages of Fixed-Wing aircraft include:

• Can search very large areas very quickly.

• Depending on the aircraft, may have more spotters than a helicopter.

• Many such resources are available and prepared specifically for SAR.

• Can provide a platform for specialized search technologies like FLIR.

• Can function as an airborne radio-relay, especially in areas of mountainous terrain.

• Can provide a shuttle for critical resources into an airfield near the search area across medium distances.

• Can stay airborne longer than helicopters.

Limitations of Fixed-Wing aircraft include:

• In areas where there is tree cover, or other factors restricting visibility from the air, or in mountainous terrain, fixed-wing aircraft generally must fly too high and too quickly to provide a high probability of detecting a lost person.

• May require special air operations procedures for their coordination especially if more than one aircraft is being deployed.

• Airports may be some distance from the search base, which delays briefing and debriefing by the Plans section.

• Like helicopters, fixed-wing aircraft are subject to weather conditions and other factors affecting visibility.

Search Dogs

Generally, there are two kinds of dogs employed in search and rescue: the air scent dog and the trailing dog. The SAR dog's type will depend on its natural ability, disposition, and the type of training it receives from its handler. Appendix B provides a compilation of traditional sources of information on K9 types and scent detection. Incident planners and managers should be aware of the fact that research on the capability of K9 resources is on-going and human understanding of scent propagation and detection is an ever evolving

science. Ideally, a person well versed in various uses of SAR K9's should be available for consultation in the Command Post and for briefing and debriefing K9 teams.

While nighttime can be challenging to handlers, it should not be overlooked as an opportune time to deploy search dogs. Wind at night with no solar convection helps maximize scent detection and temperatures lower than those in daytime help increase endurance in the summer months. With typically fewer human searchers working at night, search dogs have fewer scent targets to sort out and fewer sources of contamination to deal with during those hours.

Air scent dogs. The air scent dog is the type most frequently encountered. This dog finds lost people by picking up traces of human scent that are drifting in the air, and looking for the "cone" of scent where it is most concentrated. The dog will not normally discriminate scents, so there is the possibility of false alarms if other searchers are nearby, or if people have recently been in the area (a segment should be "aired" of human scent for a minimum of 30 minutes before a dog team enters it). The success of the air scent dog will be affected by a number of factors, including wind conditions (direction and speed), air temperature, time of day, terrain, and presence or absence of contamination (such as auto exhaust or factory smoke). Early mornings or late afternoons on cool, cloudy days, when there is a light wind, are often ideal conditions for air scent dogs to work.

<u>Advantages of air scent dogs</u>:
• Are easily integrated into the search: can be assigned to segments.
• Because they may work "off lead" they can search difficult areas more easily than human searchers, and will complain less.

<u>Limitations of air scent dogs</u>:
• May be less effective in the middle of clear, still days when temperatures are high.
• May be less effective in steep cliffy areas and narrow restricted canyons.
• Are best worked in split operational periods of 4 to 6 hours early in the day and 4 to 6 hours late in the day or at night.

Trailing dogs. These dogs are most often Bloodhounds. While many dogs can be trained to follow a specific scent, Bloodhounds are naturally gifted with this ability and have been known to pick up scent trails that are more than a week old. A trailing dog attempts to follow the actual route taken by the subject from a last known position. With an adequate scent trail, trailing dogs are capable of leading searchers directly to the subject in a "walk-up" find. Even when that is not possible, a trailing dog can often make a crucially important contribution by determining a subject's **direction of travel** from their last known position.

Trailing dogs are normally trained to be <u>scent discriminating</u>, which means that they require

a scent article belonging to the subject, protected from contamination from other human scents or by other strong odors, such as perfume or chemicals. These dogs are typically able to discriminate the lost person's unique scent from all other human scents, however mixed scents from other family members or institutional settings can be a source of confusion if not neutralized.

Absorbent fabric that has had prolonged contact with the subject's skin makes an ideal scent article, such as pillow cases, pajamas, and other articles of clothing which the subject has recently worn. Ideally, such items should be obtained by the dog handler from the subject's home. However, as this is often impractical, it may be necessary for someone else to obtain the scent article. If so, that person should avoid actually touching the article, if possible, but rather use some implement (e.g., coat hanger) for picking up the article and placing it into a sealable (and unscented) plastic bag, such as Zip-Loc (some dog handlers prefer ordinary brown bags; do not, however, use plastic garbage bags, as they may contaminate the scent).

If there is an unlocked automobile belonging to the subject, it may be possible to obtain a scent article from that in a similar fashion. Indeed, some trailing dogs may even be able to obtain the scent from the subject's footprint or from the car seat of the subject's vehicle. This is another good reason to protect the PLS or LKP by flagging the area to prevent people from wandering through it, touching possible scent articles. The operation of vehicles in the immediate area should also be prohibited to eliminate the contaminating effect of exhaust fumes.

Incident managers should brief trailing dog handlers as soon as practical to allow them to evaluate the prospective scent articles, potential contamination, age of the trail and expected effectiveness given the prevailing conditions and the level of experience of the responding team (handler and canine).

Advantages of trailing dogs:

Can be an excellent resource for finding the subject quickly when employed early in the search.

- Being scent discriminating, the search area doesn't have to be "aired out."
- Usually function independently for long periods.
- Often a good resource for determining the subject's direction of travel from the last known position.
- May lead the K9 handler directly to the lost subject.
- Work well at night when other teams may have been retired until daybreak.
- May be used in a tracking mode to "cut sign" in an attempt to pick up the subject's scent trail when a definitive PLS or LKP is not known.
- The inability to find a scent trail can serve as a "negative" clue that may change the direction and focus of the search.

Limitations of trailing dogs:

- Normally requires a specific point at which to begin (PLS/LKP).
- Normally requires a useful, uncontaminated scent article.
- Does not usually provide measurable estimates of POD when subject is not found, as they are not confined to designated segments.
- Sometimes difficult to integrate into rest of search (crosses various segments).

- Less effective after time has elapsed and scent has faded or area has been contaminated.
- May not be able to search effectively at midday in hot, dry environments.

Other specialized types of K9 resources

- Disaster/debris K9 (FEMA).
- Water/drowning cadaver K9.
- Cadaver/decomposition K9.
- Evidence sensitive K9 (drugs, weapons , explosives)

Sources for various kinds of search dogs:
Volunteer SAR units, local law enforcement departments and conservation officers.

Trained Ground Searchers

Human trackers: These highly trained searchers follow the route taken by the subject from the last known position or point (LKP) by locating tracks and other **disturbances** ("sign") left by the subject. The technique is referred to as "man-tracking" or often just "tracking" and was pioneered by retired Border Patrol supervisor Jack Kearney.

Advantages of human trackers:
• Highly efficient if a good and undisturbed starting point (PLS) exists.
• Can quickly determine the subject's initial direction of travel.
• **Binary sign cutting** can rule out large portions of the search area (more details on

binary techniques are found in Chapters 7 and 14, and illustrated in Figure 7.3).

Limitations of human trackers:
• Less effective after "sign" has been destroyed by other searchers
• Much less effective after heavy rains or, in some soils, heavy winds.

Sources for human trackers:
• Volunteer SAR units.
• U.S. Border Patrol.
• Some local law enforcement departments.

Hasty Teams: These are small, highly mobile, clue-sensitive groups of trained searchers conducting initial search tasks.

Advantages of Hasty Teams:
 • Can quickly check high probability locations.
 • Can locate clues for use in search area establishment.

Sources for Hasty Teams:
• Local agency or volunteer units.
• Running Clubs. Trail Runners are specialized hasty teams consisting of 10k and marathon runners in optimum physical condition who can cover moderate terrain very rapidly.

Grid searchers: These are ground searchers who pass through an area in a parallel fashion, described as a "line" or "sweep," with a specified spacing between them. Their relative thoroughness (the percentage of clues they can be expected to find) is determined largely by their spacing, the type of terrain they're searching in, the size and appearance of the missing person or object, the local environmental conditions and searcher training in clue detection.

Advantages of grid searchers:
• Can provide thorough searching when necessary (close spacing).
• Persons with less training may be usefully employed in grid teams.

Limitations of grid searchers:
• May destroy clues.
• Tend to move relatively slowly.
• Can be very inefficient when spacing is too narrow for conditions.
• Certain terrain can make grid searching impossible.

Sources of grid searchers:
• Local units, such as rescue squads, Explorer SAR units, other agency or volunteer units.

Special Competence Resources

Special Competence Resources are searchers with training or skills relevant to a specific type of SAR environment or task. Some examples include:

Rough terrain responders: These units have skills and technical equipment to operate effectively in mountainous, hilly, or very remote environments. Sources:
• Mountain Rescue Association (MRA).
• Local rescue squads and SAR units.
• Some fire departments.

Swift Water & Underwater responders: These are units or individuals with skills and equipment to search, rescue, or recover in surf, swift water, or deep water conditions. They are trained in specialized search and recovery techniques. Sources:
• Local units or individuals from rescue squads, sheriff's dive-rescue units, or organized divers organizations (e.g. Diver's

Alert Network, National Association of Underwater Instructors, SCUBA clubs, etc.). Resources that operate underwater must be SAR-trained and NOT simply recreational level dive enthusiasts.

<u>Winter environment responders:</u> These are units with skills and equipment to search for or rescue in snow, ice, or avalanche. <u>Sources:</u>
• National Ski Patrol.
• Mountain Rescue Association.
• Local rescue squads and SAR units.
• Some fire departments.

<u>Specialized vehicle responders.</u> These are local units or individuals with vehicles capable of responding in special terrain or difficult environmental conditions, such as:
• snowmobiles.
• four-wheel drive (4WD) vehicles.
• all-terrain vehicles (ATV).
• mountain bikes.

<u>Sources for specialized vehicles:</u>
• Snowmobile or ATV associations.
• Some local fire departments.
• Mountain biking groups.
• Local SAR teams.

Note: Since many of these specialized vehicle groups can cover ground rapidly, special safety procedures are advised, like frequent check-in by radio while searching. Lesser skilled responders should be attached to more experienced drivers and observers.

<u>Subterranean responders (aka, Confined Space Rescue Units):</u> These are units with skills and equipment to search for or rescue in caves, mine shafts, or similar closed-space environments.

<u>Sources:</u>
• National Cave Rescue Commission.
• Many fire services and FEMA.
• National Speleological Society.
• Mine Safety and Health Administration.
• The Office of Surface Mining.
• Local speleological groups ("cavers").
Note: All working miners can be expected to have mine rescue skills training.

<u>Equestrian units:</u> Persons with riding or pack animals who are skilled handlers for searching remote or rough terrain, or for transporting supplies or equipment. Clue-conscious riders can be valuable resources for searching remote areas and trails.

Equestrian units and strike teams may be especially useful as long range patrols (see Chapter 21).

Sources for equestrian units:
• Sheriff's posses or auxiliary units.
• Equestrian clubs or associations.
• NASAR affiliated equine resources.

Advantages of equestrian units:
• Can travel farther and faster than searchers on foot, while carrying more equipment.
• Horses may alert riders to the presence of the lost person.
• Riders may have a better view of larger areas due to increased saddle elevation.

Limitations of equestrian units:
• They are much less effective in areas of dense vegetation, or where the terrain is difficult or hazardous for the horse to travel.
• In the hands of an inexperienced rider, the horse may destroy more clues than the rider can detect.

Depending upon the locality, swift-water rescue teams and extreme winter environment responders may need to be on the resource list. Other helpful resources which should be added to resource lists include game wardens, county, state and federal park rangers who may reside in nearby jurisdictions.

Search Management Resources

These resources are used by the search management team for controlling the search incident. Most involve obtaining necessary information or communicating information to searchers in the field.

Weather forecasts: Flight Service Stations, Air Traffic Control Centers, radio and TV news, FAA centers, military bases and the Internet can all can provide weather information. NOAA resources include the National Weather Service where staff forecasters can be reached for "spot weather forecasts." On site computers can access weather information through satellite links, by accessing various Internet sites which provide world-wide coverage of weather conditions and forecasts. Pre-planning efforts should include contact with federal, commercial and broadcast sources of weather information with appropriate telephone numbers and websites for ready access.

Communications support: In addition to the internal communications systems of responsible and support agencies and organizations, additional and specialized communication support, including relays and repeaters, is often available from:

- Ham operators clubs like ARES.
- REACT units.
- CB clubs.
- Satellite telephone services.
- Cellular phone services.
- Broadband & wireless providers.

Facility Equipment: The preplan should identify sources for the following types of special equipment needed to help manage and support the incident:

- Extra telephones and lines.
- Computer equipment and appropriate software.
- Photocopy equipment.
- Transportation (buses, etc.).
- Sanitation facilities (trash disposal and portable toilets).
- Temporary shelter (small circus tents, funeral canopies, military surplus etc.).
- Portable heaters.
- Mobile food service providers (Red Cross, Salvation Army, church and civic groups as well as commercial providers).

Developing Resource Lists for the Pre-Plan

One useful method of developing a resource list is to categorize resource needs according to the management function they will serve. For example, start with command staff and consider this non-exhaustive list:

Planning Section:

- Interviewers and investigators.
- Cartographers and other digital mapping specialists.
- Computers
- Computer operators.
- Interpreters
- Regional Incident Management Teams (IMT)

Operations Section:

- Hasty teams
- Grid teams
- Human trackers
- Dog teams
- Patrol providers
- Rescue squads

Logistics Section:

- Radio operators
- Food caterers
- Field kitchens
- Transportation
- Sanitation
- Security

List human resources by:
- Name.
- Telephone, cell phone, and pager numbers.
- Experience, skills or capability.
- Expected time to respond.
- Limitations of availability.

Summary

In this chapter we described the major types of resources employed during the lost person incident. We discussed types of <u>search</u> resources, including aircraft (helicopters and fixed wing), dogs (air scent and trailing), and ground searchers (including trackers, hasty teams, grid searchers, and various special competence types for specific SAR environments).

We also described important <u>search management</u> resources, including sources for weather forecasts, communications, and facility equipment. Finally, we suggested how resource lists could be organized in the operational preplan according to the management function which each resource is intended to serve.

For example, all search resources would normally be listed under the Operations Section. Such organization facilitates rapid access to the desired information during the incident, and helps planners assess the adequacy of resource lists between incidents.

This chapter concludes Part I of this book. In this section we've attempted to explain why effective search management is important to the success of the lost person incident. We've introduced basic management concepts and have described the manner in which they are applied to emergency situations.

Central to this discussion has been the Incident Command System, use of which is recognized as the "best-practice" for emergency incident management. ICS is a well-tested practical emergency management methodology which stresses the importance of preplanning and being proactive rather than reactive, the division of management functions (with clear job descriptions), the manageable span of control, and the efficient allocation of resources.

In Part II, we'll take a closer look at that part of management which develops strategies for finding the lost person while recording search progress as the incident proceeds. These tasks are the responsibility of the Planning Section.

Questions for Discussion:

1. What kinds of knowledge should search managers have about various types of search resources (e.g., dogs, aircraft) before they can use them effectively?

2. Why is it important to have different types of ground searchers during an incident, that is, trackers, hasty teams, and grid teams? For example, why not just train everybody to be human trackers, or members of hasty teams?

3. Apart from the suggestions mentioned in this chapter, what else might you want to know about a resource before adding it to your preplan?

4. Are there any additional resources which might be of some assistance to your agency or organization during a lost person incident?

Part II: Introduction to Search Planning

CHAPTER 7

CLUES

Not so long ago, searches were organized with the sole objective of finding the lost subject, rather than detecting the multitude of signs or clues that help determine the subject's location. As a result, clues were missed and search incidents tended to last longer, often ending with the injury or the death of the subject. **Clues provide valuable information** to assist the search managers in making informed decisions about how and where to search. In this chapter we will describe the **significance of clues** to the well-managed search mission.

CHAPTER OBJECTIVES:

When you finish studying this chapter, you should be able to:

>   1. Describe how clue detection fits into search theory.
>   2. Explain why we search for clues rather than for subjects.
>   3. Identify the four categories of clues.

Clues Reduce Uncertainty

As we stated in Chapter 3, a search for a lost person involves a high degree of uncertainty that must be resolved as soon as possible. We also pointed out that this uncertainty can only be resolved with <u>information</u>. <u>Clues</u> are the sources of information that search managers need to locate the lost person. A clue is a piece of information that contributes to the reduction of uncertainty in the search effort. More specifically, **a clue is a <u>signal</u> or <u>message</u>, whose information serves to reduce uncertainty with respect to the missing subject's location**. The ability to

find clues depends upon the sensitivity of the <u>clue detectors</u>. Much like the proverbial tree falling in the forest, a message that is not "receivable" or detectable by searchers does not constitute a clue.

To summarize, it is useful to think of a search for a lost person as an exercise in reducing uncertainty, through information that narrows down the problem of finding the subject. Among other advantages, clue orientation allows us to break down a larger problem into manageable units. For example, it encourages us to ask the right questions. That is, rather than basing the entire search strategy on the single question "Where is the subject?." We can ask more specific questions, such as:

>   A. Which direction did the subject travel from the PLS?
>   B.   What were the subject's intentions or trip plans?

C. How far can we reasonably expect someone like this to travel?

D. Which parts of the search area has the subject passed through?

E. Which parts of the search area has the subject <u>not</u> passed through?

Several implications should be apparent from these questions. First, notice how the global search problem ("Where is the subject?") is broken down into smaller problems, the solving of which can contribute to the overall solution.

While the global problem can only be answered after the subject is found, the specific questions can be addressed immediately, and, moreover, their answers have direct implications for search tactics. Appropriate tactics would include : man-tracking, interviewing, sign-cutting, and consulting statistical and archival data.

Second, notice that clue seeking is an activity carried out not only by searchers in the field, but also by investigators who interview witnesses, as well as search management personnel who consult tables of lost person behavior (described in Chapters 11 and 12). It is critical to establish **a management system for handling clues** and brief

everyone on its details. Establish a policy for "evidence harvesting," and reporting clues that are found in the field or through investigation. A **Clue Management System** should include a **clue registry log,** where clues are numbered and thoroughly described.

The Principles of Clue Orientation

- Clues are messages.
- The subject is a clue generator.
- The searcher is a clue seeker.
- The search area should contain many clues.
- The <u>absence</u> of clues is also a clue (the "no-clue clue").

<u>Clues are messages that are waiting to be detected</u>. In general, there are four simple (but very important) lost subject messages that searchers need to detect:

1. The present location of the Subject - (Subject found).
2. The previous location of the Subject - (Clue found).
3. The destination or intent of the Subject. - (Clue found).
4. The Subject was not here - (No clues found).

However, some of these simple messages are hard to detect because of difficulties in identifying the specific search area (you can read more about this in Chapter 10).

Generally, there are **four categories of clues:**

1. Physical (an item or event).
2. Documentary (a written clue).
3. Testimonial (statements by others).
4. Analytical (from reasoning).

The key to an effective clue-oriented search is to identify clues left by the lost subject and constantly monitor the search area for changes.

Some clues are fragile and may not last long. Footprints are blown away. Witnesses leave the search area. Summit logs are buried in the snow. Flashing lights are never seen. The search area is volatile. Some clues not generated by the subject, but identified as such, will add to the confusion. A set of footprints in the search area may contain different messages, depending on whose footprints they are. If they are the subject's, then the messages could be:

    • The subject was present previously, but has gone elsewhere.

    • The subject's destination can possibly be derived from the direction of travel.

The subject is a clue generator. Fortunately for searchers, only the most cautious lost subject can keep from becoming a prolific signal generator. In fact, a common problem is multiple signal generators caused by the presence of witnesses, the public and even other searchers. The problem becomes which signals belong to whom? For the searcher,

becoming familiar with the personal characteristics of the subject or signal generator is important. We search for clues because there are many more clues in the search area then there are subjects.

> **Searches require clue–seeking in addition to subject–seeking because:**
> *There are many more clues than subjects!*

This is the place for the skillful interviewer. Strategic characteristics concern primarily the time that the subject has been lost or missing (in order to estimate the search area size) and his or her intent or destination. Tactical characteristics concern primarily descriptions of the subject, and his or her clothes and gear (for identifying footprints and discarded articles).

The searcher is a clue seeker. It follows that, in order to detect clues:

a) Searchers must be in the search area, that is, deployed in the field to monitor the most probable areas.

b) An overall strategy is needed to assume that all pertinent and significant areas are identified so that clues and clue messages can be detected and acted upon.

c) Finally, there is considerable significance in that last statement, "and acted upon." Search teams need to ensure that their training programs teach searchers, that is, receivers, how to follow the detection of various common clues to their logical conclusion. Specifically, the basis for "acting upon" a detected clue should first be interpreting the message.

To **enhance message interpretation** searchers should:

1. Immediately notify the Command Post of a clue/messages received.

2. Through group action, that is, working together, try to evaluate and interpret the significance of the clue or message in the field.

3. Act upon the interpreted message in consultation with the Operations and Planning sections and the IC.

Clue detection demands intelligence, concentration, and determination on the part of the searcher. However, even the best searchers have limitations. Searchers will lose concentration when fatigued and even miss obvious clues. A useful rule of thumb is to rest searchers for at least one hour after four hours of searching, and to send them home after eight hours in the field. Searchers are best qualified to recognize and act upon clues because they train to:

  - Identify and monitor the search area.
  - Detect and act upon clues.
  - Be observant and not accept clues at face value or with preformed opinions.

The search area must contain clues. A search without the subject is an exercise in futility. In every search incident, positive steps are required to assure that the subject does not leave the search area (is "confined" within it) and that the area is extended to include all clues. Considerable understanding and training is required to detect clues. Expertise is also required by the Planning Section to clearly identify a clue when it is found and to interpret its message.

The Operations and Planning Sections need to agree to an integrated attack on the problem. This will ensure that the right resources are sent to the appropriate areas. There may be prominent non-search clues such as the subject's home, a friend's home, the local bar, or some other location miles from the search. Focus should not be limited to just the physical search area. Clues may abound in what can be called the "extended" search area, as hot spots in the Rest Of the World, which may not become searchable segments on the map but still need close investigation. The search universe must include these areas and investigative resources need to be deployed to them. Other non-contiguous points within the search universe would be the location of witnesses or other clues, such as the subject's vehicle left abandoned or towed to an impound area. Although there should always be some consideration of whether the subject is involved in a crime, criminal activity is seldom a reason for someone becoming lost or missing. Figure 7.1 depicts some examples of detection resources that are geared to finding clues versus those that are often more successful directly looking for the subject.

Figure 7.1

Detection Resources

Clue Finders	Subject Finders
Search Dogs	Grid Teams
Human Trackers	Aircraft
Hasty Teams	Dive Teams
Sign Cutters	Fwd Looking IR (FLIR)
Investigators & Interviewers	The Untrained

The absence of clues is also a clue. Knowing where the subject has not been is extremely important information when narrowing down the search area. The means for determining which parts of the search area the subject has or has not entered is called **sign-cutting** (see more on that tactic in Chapter 14).

Time As It Relates To A Sequence Of Events

All clues and messages should be time-tagged by searchers to help reconstruct the scenario that led to the lost person incident. This procedure can be time consuming, but it is extremely important as it keeps everything in perspective. The following **key times** in a search should be noted and logged:

a. When did the subject become lost or missing?

b. Projected time frame for survival.

c. Time frame for the existence of clues. (How long could they be expected to last with a given type of weather?)

d. When were the searcher resources deployed in the field?

e. How old are the clues or when were they made?

f. Time when clues were found.

Figure 7.2 summarizes the reasons for seeking clues and not just the subject.

Figure 7.2

SEARCH FOR CLUES, NOT JUST THE SUBJECT
Because:

• There are more clues than subjects.

• Clue detection reduces uncertainty.

• The information level of some clues approaches that of the ultimate clue.

But . . .

• Expect **false clues!** False sightings and misleading information occur on most searches — be prepared for them.

Check and double check for accuracy.

Recording Clues

All clues should be recorded in a **Clue Log** with respect to:

- Time/date of detection.
- Description.
- Where they were found.
- Who found them.

Track Identification

The cost of ignoring a possible track, or "identifying" the wrong track, is enormous. If available, use a picture catalog of the shoe or boot prints. Go to a store and find identical footwear if possible. The time used in this endeavor can be insignificant compared to the time spent on the wrong track. Accept no "estimates" on the size of a track found in the field. Accuracy here is crucial! Carry a small tape measure or other measuring device. If necessary, break a small stick to match the size of the track found. Protect the track and

identify its location so that it can be easily found again. If possible, take a photograph of the track and include a familiar object in the picture for scale.

Terrain Analysis – Where to look for Clues

It is best to look for terrain clues in two parts. The first is how the terrain would affect the subject in becoming lost. Do not just accept that the person is missing from the LKP, and start looking some distance away for distinguishing features. Put yourself in the subject's shoes, analyze where he/she was, what he/she was doing.

Mazes - Areas riddled with so many intersections that the subject would likely take the wrong one. This area needs to be accurately mapped.

Confusion factors - Factors such as multiple routes, forks in trails, dead ends, changes in terrain, sights or sounds that could attract the subject, possible short-cuts or switch backs, and parts of trails that may be hard to find because of lack of use.

Natural boundaries These can serve to confine the subject:

Routes of least resistance: Look for routes that would provide the "easiest way out" for the category of subject.

Plan for the unexpected: Plan for all possibilities and not just your favorite. In which direction could they disappear in the shortest time?

Certainly, on some searches it will be difficult to determine the likely routes of travel. We can still assess terrain assuming the subject went in a particular direction. This also applies to when there are likely routes from the subject's last known position. If you suspect a particular direction of travel, then look for terrain lures that would draw a lost subject into continuing along a route.

Limiting the Search Area

The search area can often be limited by major barriers, minor barriers and binary search techniques:

a) Major barriers such as rivers, highways, cliffs, some trails, slippery banks, lava fields, and railroads. These are features that would likely stop the subject's direction of travel and lead to a new direction (for example, walking along a power line that veers off to one side).

b) Minor barriers can also help limit and define the search area. These include small streams, dense brush, forest downfall, etc. But if the subject has reason to cross them, then they are passable. Look for minor barriers in areas where the subject is not cut off by main roads or other major barriers.

Natural routes, for example, a large steep drainage, offer less resistance to movement or may eventually confine the subject. Other examples are old road grades, game trails, and drainages, or clearings. (You should establish definitions in your unit for words that are similar, for example, borders, boundaries, and barriers).

A good classroom exercise for a unit is to show maps of varying terrain for the sake of identifying, labeling, and discussing the effect terrain features may have on limiting the search area.

c) Binary search techniques seek to eliminate large portions of the search area by determining **where the subject has not been**. Binary refers to a situation in which only one of two mutually exclusive states is allowed, much like "on or off" switches which are designated as a "1" for "on" or "0" for "off." Consider the search area in Figure 7.3 composed of three regions.

Imagine a team of sign cutters moving along a trail, indicated by the dashed line, which neatly divides the search area in half. To simplify the example, we will assume that the ground is covered by a sheet of encrusted snow, and that the subject became lost by wandering off the central trail.

Figure 7.3

Binary Sign Cutting

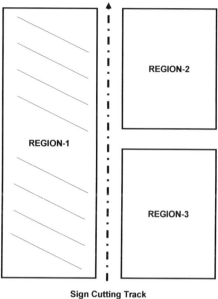

Sign Cutting Track

The hasty team sign cutters notice that there are no boot prints in the snow along the edge of Region 1, but that many boot prints, one of which may be the subject's, diverge off the trail into Regions 2 and 3. In this idealized situation, the sign cutters have eliminated half of the entire search area, effectively assigning a near zero probability of finding the subject in Region 1. Using a binary technique like this, to conclusively establish where the subject has not been, is a kind of reverse or "negative" clue (the "no-clue clue") that can be enormously helpful in limiting the search area.

General Principles of Clue-Seeking

Clue seeking is an on-going process that starts with preplanning, continues through a mission and does not end until the critique and after action report is filed. Good clue seeking is a learned skill, and must be practiced to develop a sense of what minimum information is needed to work with.

Avoid forming an opinion and then gathering information to support that opinion. Do not immediately form an opinion about the value of a clue!

Gather information from everyone, as no one person can adequately provide all the facts. Assemble a complete profile of the missing subject and the situation and let it offer direction.

Summary

We defined a clue as a <u>signal</u> or <u>message</u> that <u>reduces uncertainty</u> regarding the subject's location. Because there are many more clues than subjects, search theory is based on clue detection. We described four categories of clues: <u>physical</u> (an item or event detectable by searchers), <u>documentary</u> (a written record), <u>testimonial</u> (a statement provided by a witness or other individual), and <u>analytical</u> (the results of reasoning).

We also pointed out that the <u>absence</u> of clues can also be a clue (the "no-clue clue"), a principle that provides the basis for the <u>binary search technique</u> for ruling out large parts of the search area through <u>sign-cutting.</u> Finally, we described some general principles of clue seeking, including (1) that it is an ongoing process that does not stop until the subject is found, (2) that clue seeking is a learned skill requiring practice and training, (3) that it must be <u>unbiased</u> by opinions and hastily formed decisions, (4) that no one person can gather all the clues, and (5) that a complete profile of the subject and situation should be developed from available clues.

Questions for Discussion:

1. Why is a consideration of clue orientation critical for search planning?

2. How does the <u>absence</u> of clues provide important information? When a search resource does not find any clues, what is important to know about that resource?

3. How can you use natural and man-made features to limit the search area?

CHAPTER 8

INITIATING THE SEARCH

"Getting off on the right foot" is probably the single most important step towards successfully resolving the lost person incident. **Actions taken during the initial report, the callout of resources, and the first hour or two of on-scene activities will often determine the ultimate outcome of the search**. In this chapter, we will discuss the manner in which the initial report may be received, the types of information that should be obtained, the methods of assessing the urgency of the situation, and the appropriate responses that should be made early in the incident.

CHAPTER OBJECTIVES:

When you finish studying this chapter, you should be able to:

1. Describe how it is determined that someone is missing.

2. Discuss the types of information about the missing person that are important to SAR personnel.

3. Determine the relative urgency of a lost person incident.

4. Describe the process of calling out resources, and identify the information that must be provided to them.

When A Person Is Lost:
The Initial Contact

A call comes into a 911 dispatcher, a ranger station, a park warden or similar agency. A missing person report may be transferred to a SAR deputy, a park warden, or another designated person depending on the local protocol. This initial phase generally begins with a hasty search where the command post may be the hood of a truck.

The impression that the report-taker gives the reporting party and the initial actions taken sets the tone for the rest of the incident. The task must be done in a thorough and organized manner without wasting time or resources. The report-taker must immediately consider the following:

a) <u>Proper Attitude:</u> The right attitude regarding the incident is important from the very beginning. The initial contact with the reporting party (whether by phone, radio, or in person) should be calm, professional, inquisitive, and with a definite tone of concern and a willingness to help. The report-taker cannot let personal problems (for example, being awakened from sleep or called away from Christmas dinner) interfere with the obligations as report-taker.

b) <u>Name, Call-Back Number, and Location</u>: Whichever agency (Sheriff's Office, Forest Service, RCMP, etc.) receives the intial report, the report-taker must realize that the top priority is to record the name, phone number (where they can be reached now), and location of the reporting party. The party should be told to stay there until they are contacted to do otherwise. It is extremely important that the reporting party be discouraged from returning to the search before an in-person interview is completed. If the report is made in person, then keep the reporting party at hand until all crucial information is obtained.

c) <u>Search Is An Emergency</u>: From now until the subject is found, time is precious and it must not be wasted. This does not mean, however, blasting full speed ahead without direction. It does mean making every minute count through careful, efficient planning, and organization.

A Major Consideration:
How Does The Report Come In?

Is this . . .

1. An overdue report by relatives or friends?
2. A report by member of party?
3. A discovery of:
   - An abandoned vehicle.
   - A name on a register that has not been signed out.

- A deserted camp or equipment.
4. A distress signal?
5. An Emergency Locator Transmitter (Aircraft ELT)?
6. A Personal Locator Beacon (PLB)?
7. A call from the lost person by cellular telephone?
8. Other indicators?

Important Points About
Initiating a Search

1. Get all the information necessary to determine:
   - Is there a problem?
   - How serious is it or could it become?
   - . Where is it?
   - Who is involved?
   - How did it happen?
   - When did it happen?

2. Get all the information necessary to decide what to do next. It is better to get more information now than later.

3. Referring to a Lost Person Questionnaire (LPQ):
   - What information do you need immediately to determine whether or not you have a problem?
   - What information do you need to take initial action?
   - What information could be gathered a little later?

Initial Information

Initial information on the situation may be very complete or very sketchy. There are certain things that are important to know immediately, but now is not the time for recording a complete life history of the subject or even filling out the entire lost person questionnaire. **One must quickly sort out the pertinent information that is needed for immediate decision making**. As Search Manager, you need to be able to evaluate the following information from the report-taker or the reporting party.

The initial inquiry should help you:
- Determine the search urgency.
- Provide searching data to initial action personnel.
- Provide basic planning data for subsequent actions.

Determine Search Urgency

The following factors directly influence the well-being of the subject:
- Subject profile.
- Weather profile.
- Equipment available to subject (and the knowledge of how to use it).
- Subject's experience.
- Terrain hazards.
- The subject's health.

In addition, the following factors, while having no direct influence on the subject, do influence the decision-making process concerning the urgency of the situation.

   a) History of incidents in area: the frequency of past incidents in the area and their outcomes can be a key in decision-making.

   b) Time: the time elapsed from the moment the subject actually went missing is important in three respects:
   - time frame for survival.
   - effect of time on clues.
   - size of the search area.

   c) Political sensitivity: influences that can affect decision-making:
   - VIP involved?
   - Interest of politicians.
   - Pressure from relatives.
   - Pressure from media.
   - Adverse publicity.
   - Pressure from administrators higher in your organization.

Evaluating Search Urgency

Search managers need some method for evaluating the relative urgency of each search. A lost toddler would typically rate a higher urgency than a lost hunter. Figure 8.1 provides a set of urgency factors that can be used for assessing urgency. **The lower the numerical rating of the factor, the higher the relative urgency becomes.** The chart is intended as a guide. It is a tool for the manager to use in evaluating individual incidents.

Figure 8.1

SEARCH URGENCY RATING FACTORS	
Subject Age Profile	Rating
Very Young	1
Very Old	1
Other	2-3
Medical Condition	
Known/Suspected injured, ill, or mental problem	1-2
Healthy	3
Known Fatality	3
Number of Subjects	
One Alone	1
More Than One (Unless Separation is Suspected)	2-3
Subject Experience Profile	
Not experienced, does not know area	1
Not experienced, knows area	1-2
Experienced, does not know area	2
Experienced, knows area	3
Weather Profile	
Past and/or existing Hazardous Weather	1
Predicted Hazardous Weather (less than 8 hours away)	1-2
Predicted Hazardous Weather (more than 8 hours away)	2
No Hazardous Weather Predicted	3
Equipment Profile	
Inadequate for Environment & Weather	1
Questionable for Environment & Weather	1-2
Adequate for Environment & Weather	3
Terrain/Hazards Profile	
Known Hazardous Terrain or other dangers	1
Few or No Unusual Hazards	2-3
TOTAL RANGE	**7-21**

TOTAL URGENCY FACTOR:	7	14	21
URGENCY RATING:	**HIGH**	**MEDIUM**	**LOW**

Note that all of the ratings in Figure 8.1 are relative and the total derived from the chart only indicates the potential relative urgency. **THE LOWER THE TOTAL, THE HIGHER THE URGENCY!** All other factors bearing on the incident need to be evaluated. These factors help ensure that a potentially crucial influence to the well-being of the subject will not be overlooked. Viewed collectively, the factors indicate the relative urgency for initiating a response, and how extensive the response should be. Generally speaking, the more serious the previous incidents were, the more time that has elapsed since the subject became missing and the more "politically" sensitive, then the greater the urgency becomes.

Over-reaction is justifiable . . .
Under-reaction is inexcusable!

It is extremely critical that an early determination be made by law enforcement personnel as to whether the person being sought is "missing" or "lost." A missing person could be abducted, particularly young people and most particularly, young girls. Parallel investigations may be very prudent. Pursue both "lost" and "missing" scenarios.

The combination of the factors affecting urgency will help determine not only how quickly to respond, but also the nature and level of response. Some kind of escalating response should always begin immediately —

even if it is only an increase in the event that the problem becomes more serious. Note that urgency factors may go up or down as clues are found and the investigation uncovers new information.

Searching Data

Searching data is the information that must be given to your searchers and should include:
- Name to call.
- Shoe print description, to include tread, length, and width. Provide a drawing, if possible.
- Clothing worn, types, brands, colors, described from outside in.
- Equipment description, especially items that could be easily discarded.
- Brands of cigarettes, gum, candy, other possible clues.
- Location of a valid scent article.

Initial Planning Data

The initial planning data is information that assists the IC to make decisions about the place to look for the lost person and the search tactics to employ:

Category of the Subject. Subject information, knowing whether the subject is a hiker, a hunter, a child, a walkaway, etc., provides clues and other indicators to help determine potential behavior of the lost person. These include:

- The detectability of the subject.

- The potential travel aids
- The possible total distance traveled
- The potential for the subject's survivability (including clothing, equipment, and experience).

For example, consider a **hunter versus a hiker:**

Detectability: Hunters usually wear bright clothing (except for bow-hunters), while hikers tend to wear "earthy" colors that blend in with the environment.

Travel aids: Hunters travel cross-country or follow game trails, while hikers normally travel on defined trail systems. Identify "paths of least resistance" for the subject type.

Distance traveled: Hikers on trail systems usually travel farther than hunters who are "beating the bush."

Survivability: A hiker with all necessary equipment and clothing for extended backcountry living would have a higher potential for survival than hunters who may carry little more than the clothes they wear.

Type of Activity: It is important to know specifically the type of activity the subject intended doing, whether it be hiking versus rock climbing, or cross country skiing versus snowmobiling. This is helpful not only in judging the danger of the activity but also in considering the amount of terrain that might have been traveled by the subject (which impacts the initial size of the search area and whether confinement might be practical).

Place Last Seen (PLS) or Last Known Position (LKP): The more precise the better. If the reporting party cannot pin it down to more than a region, then you may have to enlist the help of another agency, such as the Highway Patrol or Sheriff's Office, to try to find the car the person was driving and then use that location as the starting point.

The PLS and the LKP are critical for search planning purposes, because either one can be:

a) The starting point for the median distances traveled by subjects in the same category. (The term "median" is defined in Chapter 12.)

b) A starting point to look for clues or for some indication of the subject's direction of travel.

The PLS or LKP becomes the Initial Planning Point unless subsequent investigation later reveals different points (Chapter 10).

Missing How Long? The seriousness and the urgency of the incident increases with the time elapsed from an intended return or meeting time. Make sure there was not a mistake or misunderstanding between the subject and the reporting party (or you and the reporting party) regarding times or even dates and days of the week.

Trip Plans. Be sure to talk with friends and relatives who knew the subject's trip plans. Were any alternate trip plans discussed or considered?

Circumstances of Loss: Pay attention to detail. Exactly when and where was the subject missing? Possibilities include:

Missing from a known location.

Missing en route.

Missing in wilderness (off trail).

Equipment: This information is often directly related to the activity, such as camping trip verses a day hike. We are especially interested in knowing whether the subject was equipped to cope with the terrain and weather. Clothing and equipment will also be important to know about because:

- They are clues to survivability.
- The type of footwear will be relevant for tracking.
- Color will affect the subject's detectability by searchers.
- Types and brand names are important for verifying relevance of clues.
- Equipment could influence the route, direction, or distance traveled.
- Equipment determines the subject's signaling capabilities (for example, whistles, flares, fires, mirrors, firearms).

- Equipment may provide a clue about the subject's capabilities and expertise.

Number Of Persons Missing: Generally speaking, there is safety in numbers. The more people there are in a lost party the better their chances of being found in good condition as long as they stay together. The following data should then be obtained on each individual who is missing.

Age: The younger (below 15) or older (above 50) a person is, the more serious the problem may be. Young people often do not have the experience or presence of mind to take care of themselves, while older people may have increased possibility of complications from medical problems. (However, do not assume that old age per se indicates frailty or senility. Many older people are physically fit and capable of traveling long distances.)

Physical and Medical Condition: The primary thing you want to know is whether there are any medical problems, physical or mental handicaps, or, in the case of children, behavioral problems for which the child is receiving medication. In some circumstances, an accurate evaluation of the subject's medical condition may be difficult to obtain from the family. They may exaggerate minor problems in order to stress the urgency of the situation, or, for reasons of their own, they may downplay or even hide medical or mental conditions that could impact on the search. When there is time, you may want to speak with a family doctor or some other person who can provide an accurate account of the subject's health. Health information privacy requirements may make this more difficult.

Experience/Ability: This is usually even more subjective than physical condition, but it is helpful to know general levels such as rank beginner verses experienced mountaineer.

Personality traits: Is the subject the type of person who could be described as persevering, self-reliant, or determined? Or, conversely, are they inclined to give up easily under adverse conditions? These factors could affect both survivability and the distance the subject will travel in an effort to walk to safety. (However, remember that many so-called "weak" subjects have traveled many miles and survived much longer than either searchers or family had expected.)

Previous Action: Determine exactly where and when any previous "searchers" (family members, neighbors, law enforcement officers, local firefighters) looked before you were called out. Were there any clues detected?

Terrain: Knowing the potential search area should give you an idea of the type and degree of difficulty of the terrain. This will affect your evaluation of the situation, both in terms of the subject and the searchers. Consider:

- Is the terrain level or sloping?
- Are there terrain barriers?
- Are there routes by which the subject could have left the area?
- Do any confusion factors exist?
- Can sights or sounds of civilization be seen or heard?
- What were the possible short cuts?
- What are the paths of least resistance?

Weather: This is another consideration that is determined by knowing the general area of search and that also affects your evaluation for the subject and searchers alike. Weather is also one of the most critical factors to be used in your evaluation of the problem. You should always investigate the weather at the time the party was lost as well as the current weather and the forecast for the specific area. Weather conditions may indicate the potential for:

- Hypothermia (loss of body heat).
- Hyperthermia (overheated).
- Restricted travel (due to snow, mud, or rising water conditions).
- Keeping the subject stationary.
- Causing the subject to seek shelter (such as caves or remote camps).

<u>Names, addresses, and phone numbers</u> for all family, friends, co-workers, schoolmates, teachers, doctors, or other potential witnesses need to be gathered.

Evaluation of the Problem

The information you receive from the first notice regarding a lost person can come from many different sources and in various degrees of reliability. The reporting party may have their own ideas about what you should do, but it is important for you to evaluate all of this initial information in a calm, intelligent manner.

<u>Talk to the reporting party in-person</u>. Some search managers prefer to talk in person with the reporting party. You know better than anyone what questions you want answered and how to evaluate the answers. There may be no substitute for direct contact, but further delay until such contact can be carried out may not be warranted.

<u>Evaluate the initial information</u>. The first reports on a lost person usually consist of three general types of information. Each type is a perfectly valid source but each has its own relative level of reliability. It must be stressed, however, that no information should be totally discarded regardless of your initial evaluation. Types of information include:

Circumstantial: This is information that is generally not substantiated (at least not yet) by the report of some person. Examples of this might be a car left at a trail head but with no persons reported missing, or a register at the trail head and where the person had not signed back out.

Second hand: This information comes from a person who heard it from someone else. Generally speaking for oral information, the more people it has traveled through, the more distorted it has become. In any case, it is usually better than circumstantial information. This category would also include the person who is reporting a subject as simply overdue from a removed location such as a distant town.

Eye witness: This is usually the best information and comes from an individual who was actually on the scene and is possibly a member of the party from which the subject is missing. This person should be able to confirm that someone is definitely missing and give you specific "last seen" information. Take eye witnesses back to the PLS and ask them to recall details and affirm the direction in which the events occurred.

<u>Evaluate The Source Of The Information</u>. Consider the background knowledge and the state of mind of those persons who are giving

you information. Do they understand your questions and do they have the background to answer them accurately or are they merely guessing? Are they distraught and frantic or calm and thinking clearly?

Consider The Facts. Look at the information that you are reasonably certain of. This might include the weather and terrain of the area as well as the subject's age, gender, and known medical problems. These facts can now form a foundation upon which to build the evaluation process.

Consider the probabilities. Consider those items that are not as definite as the "facts" but that are highly likely, such as the "probable" activity and the "probable" experience level of the subject. These may be items on which you should gather more reliable information if it is available without too much delay.

Consider the possibilities. Now look at the information that is questionable but still usable. Maybe you have had various reports on the equipment carried and similar uncertainty as to the general physical condition of the subject. More investigation might be indicated while remembering that time is also critical at this point.

Combine information objectively. Combine all of the information you have into an evaluation of the problem while keeping in mind the reliability of your sources and the relative accuracy of each item. From your

"facts" regarding the terrain and weather conditions in the general search area you can assess some potential hazards as they relate to the subject's "probable" activity, type and level of experience. Then by taking into account his/her age, gender, and "possible" physical condition, as well as evaluating the adequacy of the subject's "possible" equipment list, you can begin to get an objective evaluation of the situation.

Getting More Information

Once the search has begun and initial actions have been taken, you must now move into the next phase of the incident. However, the information you have gathered so far is probably sketchy and certainly incomplete. While you make decisions and begin coordination of the operation, the information gathering process should continue so that when you arrive on the scene you will have more information on which to base your planning and strategy decisions.

Appoint Investigators and/or Interviewers. Their primary job is to gather, sort, and evaluate information on the subject, the search area, and the situation in general. During the operation they never go into the field as active searchers. An investigator may operate by phone or may be the first person on the scene to interview the reporting party personally. If the Lost Person Questionnaire has not been started, then this person should do it. If it has, then this is the person to follow through on all the information. (Planning Data is discussed further in Chapters 9 & 10).

Protect Scent Articles. Do not run the risk that usable scent articles will be washed, contaminated, or unavailable if they should be needed later by search dogs. The best scent articles are articles of clothing recently worn next to the subject's skin and which have not been washed, worn or handled by others. They should be carefully picked up with a stick or tongs, placed in a previously unused paper bag or clean lock-top "food-grade" plastic bag and sealed. Do not use treated or scented bags of any sort. Many K9 handlers prefer to "harvest" their own scent articles because of mistakes made in previous missions.

Call Out Initial Resources. Many jurisdictions have developed trained teams that are ready to respond on a moment's notice. This may include a Type 4 Incident Commander, a hasty team, a trailing dog crew, and/or a helicopter. These resources are often successful in finding initial clues such as footprints, direction of travel, or the lost subject in person. These highly trained, preplanned resources can be taking initial action as the search begins to develop.

Initiate Confinement. Sheriff's deputies on patrol, or other agency personnel may be in a position to help to confine the lost person to the most probable area based on your

preliminary information. It makes sense to use these available resources to reduce the chance of your lost person getting farther and farther away with each passing minute.

Figure 8.2 summarizes the major actions that should be taken as an initial response to a lost person incident.

Figure 8.2

THE INITIAL RESPONSE

- Investigate.
- Determine the PLS or LKP.
- Determine the subject's direction of travel (using trackers and K9's).
- Confine the subject to an area as small as possible.
- Hasty search the high probability and high hazard trails and locations.
- Document with the ICS-201 incident briefing form.

Calling Out Additional Resources

Once the IC has assessed the situation, he/she should decide whether there are sufficient search resources on the scene to deal with the problem. The decision should be made early in the incident whether to extend the scope of the callout, or to request additional resources from other agencies or organizations.

Information to Provide to Resources When
You Call:
When requesting assistance from outside resources, you must provide them with certain information. Information may vary with each resource, but generally will include:

- Incident number (if applicable).
- When you want them.
- Where they should report.
- Include address, building name
  or number and phone number
  to call if delayed.
- Situation description (who, what,
  when, where, how).
- Special skills needed from them.
- Who else is responding.
- Number of persons (and/or
  teams) required. Request that
  they call you back and confirm
  numbers actually responding
  before they depart.
- Current weather and forecast at
  the search area:
  — Road conditions.
  — Flying conditions.
- Terrain description.
- Elevation range.
- Personal equipment needed by
  searchers.
- Specialized equipment needed.
- Communications procedures and
  frequencies.

- Maps being used and datum.
- Check-in information: signs,
  markers, suggested route.
- Who to report to upon arrival at
  the search area.
- Callback number.
- An indication of how long they
  might be needed.
- Cancellation procedures (in case
  subject is found while they are
  enroute):
  a) License plate numbers,
    vehicle descriptions.
  b) Check-in periodically
    while enroute.
  c) Monitored radio
    frequencies.
  d) Cellular phone
    numbers.

Actions taken during the first two hours will often determine the outcome of the incident.

Some kind of response should <u>always</u> happen immediately . . .

**SEARCH IS AN
EMERGENCY!**

DO SOMETHING!

Summary

We began this chapter by describing the manner in which the initial missing person's report may be received by the responding agency. We listed various sources of a report, including family or friends of the missing person, a member of the person's party, discovery of an abandoned vehicle, an entry on a park register that has not been signed out, and distress signals or other communications coming directly from the lost subject. We also discussed methods for determining the relative urgency of the response, while reminding you that search is always an emergency — regardless of the perceived urgency — and that some sort of response should therefore always occur.

The kinds of information that should be collected about the missing person, such as name, age, subject category, activity, experience, and PLS, were also discussed, as well as the necessity for obtaining information about terrain and weather conditions. We concluded the chapter with a discussion of the initial actions that should be taken during the incident — once the critical planning and searching data are acquired — and procedures for calling in search resources.

In the next chapter we will continue the discussion of the search planning process, from the initial response to the completion of the first operational period.

Questions for Discussion:

1. Think of a lost person incident that you might consider to be relatively low in urgency. How would this judgment impact on your callout of resources and the search tactics employed?

2. Many SAR groups will respond to practically any lost person report by calling out all available resources immediately, regardless of perceived urgency. What are some of the pros and cons of this approach?

3. When an apparent lost person report first comes in, under what circumstances might it be appropriate to conduct a further investigation before calling in search resources?

4. Why is it important to estimate or predict the distance a subject might travel from the place where they were last seen? How might this affect the perceived urgency of the incident? How would you go about making such an estimate?

CHAPTER 9

PLANNING THE SEARCH

In the last chapter we discussed the initial response to the lost person incident. Important decisions and actions are made by the responding incident commander with respect to the urgency and scope of the search. These include gathering sufficient search and planning information to start the search, taking steps to confine the subject to as small an area as possible, protecting the place last seen (PLS) as well as any scent articles, and considering whether to call in additional search resources. In this chapter, we will describe **the search planning process subsequent to the initial response**.

CHAPTER OBJECTIVES:

When you finish studying this chapter, you should be able to:

1. Describe the importance of planning as a means of ensuring efficient search tactics.
2. Discuss the necessity for measuring and quantifying search efforts.
3. Describe the importance and components of SMART incident objectives.
4. Describe the difference between objectives, strategy, and tactics.
5. Describe the components of the Incident Action Plan (IAP).

The Importance of Search Planning

Planning ensures effective and efficient use of resources applied to the problem, reducing redundancy and confusion, evaluating success, and focusing efforts directly into resolving the emergency. Most importantly, it ensures that all actions taken follow a logical, systematic course designed to locate the lost person in the least amount of time.

Planning for the First Operational Period

This critical phase of the search incident includes the actions taken during the initial response and is generally:

-Aimed at high probability areas that have been determined by the initial response.

-Approached with both speed and efficiency as priorities.

-Considered the first day's search effort. It usually ends at either 6 pm (1800 hrs) or 6 am (0600 hrs), depending on when the initial response took place, or can be any time-frame selected by the incident managers.

Identifying Possible Scenarios

There will never be sufficient resources available to immediately respond to all possibilities. Further, while the urgency chart described in Chapter 8 is useful in providing direction as to the level of initial response, it alone is not adequate for determining exactly how these resources should be employed.

The efficient use of resources can be maximized by identifying and prioritizing possible scenarios, as follows. First, consider the four "Subject Condition Assumptions," described later. Then build scenarios on each of these assumptions. Select those scenarios which put the subject at greatest risk, and dispatch resources to resolve each of these risks.

For example, consider a hypothetical incident in which a toddler is reported missing from a campground. The campground is located in a remote forested area. Environmental and geologic hazards are present. A number of scenarios are identified, depending on whether the child is able to move around (mobile) and whether the child will be responsive to searchers:

The Four Subject Condition Assumptions

1. **Mobile/Responsive**

- The child is with another family member.

- The child has been found wandering by some well-meaning stranger.
- A person is caring for the child while attempting to locate the parents.
- The child is lost and is wandering nearby in the forest.
- The child is lost and in a high risk area (cliffs, highway, water, etc.).
- The child has been abducted by a family member.
- The child has been abducted by a stranger.

2. **Immobile/Responsive**
- The child is lost, and is waiting to be found.
- The child is stranded in the forest in a dangerous location.
- The child has been abducted, but is still in the campground.
- The child is injured in the forest, but responsive.

3. **Mobile/Unresponsive**
- The child is hiding.
- The child is in good condition, but is scared and will not answer calls from strangers (very common with young children).

4. **Immobile/Unresponsive**
- The child is asleep, unconscious or dead.

The reality of having limited search resources does not allow full investigation of all scenarios immediately. Some are obviously of higher urgency then others. The key is to assign available resources to address the more urgent scenarios. In this example, IC might decide to record all license plates of vehicles at the campground, to interview campers, to broadcast a "be on the lookout for" alert to law enforcement agencies, to conduct a hasty search of likely spots or hazardous areas, and to establish confinement. Searchers might be instructed not only to call for the child, but also to focus on identifying and searching locations where the child could be hidden. The objective in this initial period is to locate the child should he or she be injured or in immediate jeopardy. Less emphasis is placed on locating the child who is not at risk, or is already deceased.

Establishing possible scenarios can help search managers to identify the types and numbers of resources needed. As the high risk scenarios are eliminated, the urgency chart score (from Figure 8.1) should be recalculated. Changes in the urgency score might justify changes in level of response. Simply stated, the use of this procedure can increase the efficiency of the response.

Planning Data

Planning data refers to that information required for adequate search planning. Some examples of planning data include the Place Last Seen (PLS) and the Last Known Position (LKP), concepts discussed in more detail in Chapter 12, as well as any information

concerning the trip plans or intentions of the missing subject. During the initial phase (as discussed in Chapter 8), some data was gathered and an investigator was assigned to continue gathering information for the lost person questionnaire. As the Planning Section is organized, the investigator may become a part of the Situation Unit if one is established, or may work directly for the Planning Section Chief.

The Investigation Unit and Clue Analysis Unit, as subordinate units of the Situation Unit, should be especially persistent in efforts to corroborate reports regarding the exact location of the PLS or LKP.

You should now be able to begin segmenting your map (described in detail in Chapter 13). You are beginning to prioritize the search area so that more extensive field search activities can begin. The value of using "subjective" data in the early phases of a search cannot be overstated. Historical records, witness reports, and lost person behavior play an important role.

Searching Data

Searching data refers to that information that will be provided to searchers and investigators who are looking for clues as to the subject's location. Some examples include the subject's name, description, equipment, and any articles the subject could be carrying. As with planning data, an effort should also be made to verify the accuracy of the searching data. Often, the clothing and footwear described initially by the reporting party is discovered to be incorrect. Also, it may be discovered that the subject had additional equipment or food which may indicate the nature of clues available. In any case, never assume that the searching data provided at the start of the incident is accurate or complete. Investigation is a continuous process of collecting new information and verifying data that you already possess (see list at p.79).

Introduction to Search Theory

Modern search theory emphasizes mathematics — especially probability theory— which is often employed in computer programs designed to assist with search management.

Regardless of the mathematical skills or inclinations of the search planner, you cannot avoid the use of probability. In modern search theory, probabilities are used both for <u>prioritizing the search area</u> (picking which places have the best chance of containing the lost subject), and for <u>estimating search coverage</u> of the places that have been searched (the chance that the subject would have been detected if present in the area).

Search planners often assign some type of non-quantitative measure of success to their search effort. For example, "The subject has

most likely gone down Cold Water Creek. If I assign a team to check out that drainage, they have a good chance of finding him there. If I'm right, we can start packing up, because we should have him back in about an hour."

Without being aware of it, the search planner is using probabilities. Indeed, this example above could be reworded to: "There is an 80% probability that the subject has gone down Cold Water Creek (Probability Of Area), a 90% probability that the team will spot him (Probability Of Detection), and therefore a 72% probability (80% times 90%) that we will be successful if the subject is there, since POA times POD = POS, the Probability Of Success."

Probability Theory

Probability theory is a branch of mathematics that is used for estimating the likelihood of uncertain events. Appropriate use of probabilities is an important tool for the search planner. In its simplest definition, the probability of any possible event (E) of a given sample space (the set of all possible outcomes from an experiment) is a number, $P(E)$, that satisfies:

$$0 \leq P(E) \leq 1$$

This means that the probability, P, of the event (E), has to be between 0 and 1, inclusive. Probabilities can be expressed in decimal form (for example, 0.46) or, by changing units, as a percentage (46%). Thus, for example, the probability of drawing a spade from a deck of cards (13 chances in 52) is 0.25 or 25%.

Applying probabilities to search management means that a search planner must consider all possible outcomes to an action or decision and then select the outcome that has the highest probability of occurring. For example, in any given defined portion (segment) of an entire search area, the lost subject, is in fact, either in that segment (probability =1), or not in that segment (probability = 0). However, when the probability that the subject is in any one segment is compared with the multiple probabilities of the subject being in any of several other segments, these probabilities lie somewhere between 0 and 1 (or expressed as a percentage, between 0% and 100%).

Therefore, **the search planner should first divide up or segment the entire search area into manageable units**. Then he or she must make an first-cut estimate of the probability that the lost subject is in each of the segments, a process normally done as a "consensus" with others. (This process will be described in detail in Chapter 13.) Ideally, planners should never plan alone.

Assuming that the lost subject is in a given segment, when any particular method of searching that segment is completed (considering the type of resource doing the searching, the way they search, or how many times they search), there is some probability (between 0 and 1) that this method will detect the lost person. A number of factors will affect whether any clues will be detected or missed. Considerations about how well a segment is searched will be addressed in Chapter 15.

Calculating POS – Probability Of Success

The basic equation for search probability is:
$$POA \times POD = POS.$$

$$POA \times POD = POS$$

POA represents <u>Probability of Area</u>, which is the probability that the subject is in a particular search segment or location. **POD** represents <u>Probability of Detection</u>, which is the conditional probability that the subject, or clues, will be detected by a particular search activity, if either is in the segment searched. **POS** represents <u>Probability of Success</u>, that is, the probability of finding the subject or clue in a particular segment (POA), given the efficiency of a particular search tactic (POD). POS is computed as the product of POA and POD. The sum of all of these interactions between POA and POD (adding up each calculated POS) is called the Overall Probability of Success or OPOS for short.

The derivation of POD, as a function of search "coverage" will be developed in Chapter 15. **POD** is an extremely important value that is derived from coverage, a physical measure of actual search effort. As such, POD provides our best indicator of resource effectiveness. The derivation of an initial POA is covered in Chapter 13. How POA shifts for each segment over the course of the search will be demonstrated in Chapter 16.

Figure 9.1 provides an exercise in the use of this terminology and shows how the interaction of POA with POD forms the basis for maximizing OPOS, one indicator of how the search is proceeding.

Figure 9.1

Maximizing the Overall Probability of Success

Imagine the search area contains just two segments, called Segment 1 and Segment 2. It is known that the chance of the subject being in Segment 1 is 50% and in Segment 2 it is 40%. You have one resource available and this resource can search both segments with the same efficiency of 60%, which means that the resource has a 60% chance of finding the subject, if the subject is in the segment being searched. However, there is only enough time to search one of the two segments. Do you put the resource in Segment 1 or Segment 2? Intuition suggests that our chances of success are greater if we put the resource in the segment with the highest probability, which is Segment 1, at 50%. In fact, intuition is correct, but to confirm this we need to introduce some terminology and some calculations.

The chances of the subject being in Segment 1 is called the Probability of Area (POA), of Segment 1, usually written POA(1), which in this case is 50%. However, probabilities are numbers between 0 and 1 and since 50%=0.5, that means POA(1)=0.5. In the same way, the Probability of Area of Segment 2 is POA(2)=0.4 The efficiency of a resource in Segment 1, assuming the subject is in Segment 1 is called the Probability of Detection (POD), usually written POD(1), which in this case is 60%, or 0.6, so we have POD(1)=0.6, if we use this resource in Segment 1. However, if we do not use this resource to search Segment 1, we have POD(1)=0%

Putting this together we have POD(1)=0.6 if this resource is used to search Segment 1 and 0.0% if no resource is used to search Segment 1. In the same way, we have POD(2)=0.6 if this resource is used to search Segment 2 and 0.0% POD if no resource is used to search Segment 2.

A measure that combines how well and how much of the search area has been searched is called the Overall Probability of Success (OPOS). For a search with two segments OPOS is calculated as:
OPOS= [POA(1) times POD(1) + POA(2) times POD(2)]

If we calculate OPOS after the single resource searches only Segment 1, we have OPOS=[(0.5 times 0.6) + (0.4 times 0.0)]=0.3. This yields a 30% chance of success. If we calculate OPOS after the single resource only searches Segment 2, we have OPOS=[(0.5 times 0.0) + (0.4 times 0.6)]=0.24, which is a 24% chance of success. Thus, putting the resource in Segment 1 gives us a higher overall probability of success. Finding the interactions of POA and POD which yield the highest POS for each search assignment is called "maximizing OPOS."

Why Do We Need Probabilities?

We need to know how effective search resources have been, or can be, in order to:

    a) Distribute or redistribute resources. For example, to search or re-search a search area segment, to increase or decrease the size of a search area segment, or to expand the search area.

    b) Decide if or when to suspend an unsuccessful search.

    c) Rationalize your actions to the family, media, or higher authority.

    d) Defend yourself against possible litigation.

The Case for Quantification

By using numbers to express <u>relative</u> indications of probabilities, we can manipulate combinations of variables and calculate results of alternatives. This is usually not possible by using words alone. Quantifying probabilities with numbers allows us to compare them in relative terms (40% is twice as likely as 20%) and to manipulate them in interactions like multiplying POA times POD to compute POS. In one way or another we always evaluate our chances or our efforts. In many cases this has been done subjectively — using abstract words to state our evaluation. In SAR calculations we can either use numbers directly or convert verbal cues to usable numbers, a topic discussed in Chapter 13.

Table 9.2 illustrates some examples of probability estimates used in everyday language.

Figure 9.2

PROBABILITIES
In Everyday Language

I'LL BET MY LIFE

I'M POSITIVE

I'M SURE

I'M CONVINCED

A GOOD CHANCE

IT'S 50-50

I THINK SO

COULD BE

MAYBE

PERHAPS

I DON'T KNOW

Information Management

A good deal of search planning involves the management of information. Properly managed information can reveal guideposts to logical actions (that is, a <u>plan</u>). As the above categories of information, statistics, probabilities, and equations indicate, there is much information to be processed, and it can easily become overwhelming. But if organized and processed correctly, information provides direction for search planning and facilitates the effective use of resources. What follows are some ideas on how to collect and manage this information.

The Situation Unit

To manage the flood of information the Planning Section Chief should either assume or assign someone the responsibilities of Situation Unit Leader, to oversee the "situation status" of the search. This person manages all data through the use of maps, displays, assignment summaries, and other tools discussed in detail later. Situation Unit responsibilities include keeping track of what resources have been deployed and debriefed, and what effect the reported PODs have on changing search priorities based on shifting segment POAs. Delay in establishing a Situation Unit Leader can result in loss of data caused by poor documentation. For this reason, the job is normally a full time responsibility. When the initial response effort does not locate the lost person, the IC should be prepared to escalate the incident response and mobilize the various section chiefs, including the Planning Section Chief.

When the initial Planning Section Chief arrives on scene and receives a briefing, the planning function must be brought up to date. He/she should perform the following actions:

1. Draw the search area on a map.
2. Segment the search area into manageable sizes (to be described in more detail at Chapter 13).

3. Prioritize each segment in the search area by assigning probabilities of area by way of a consensus of experts (also to be described in more detail at Chapter 13).

Establishing Incident Objectives

The incident objectives represent the single most important planning document, as it guides all decision-making with respect to the allocation of search resources. As such, it should represent a concise statement of the search strategy for finding the lost subject. As described later, it will have direct implications on which priorities are set and how resources are ordered and applied. Use ICS Form 202 to document incident objectives.

Another method for developing good objectives is to use the acronym "SMART." SMART objectives are Specific, Measurable, Assignable, Reasonable and Time Referenced.

SMART Objectives

S: Specific
M: Measurable
A: Assignable
R: Reasonable
T: Time-Referenced

SMART objectives are SPECIFIC. The objective is designed to be task oriented and includes enough detail to be clear yet concise.

SMART objectives are MEASURABLE. They make specific reference to the quality or thoroughness of a search activity, usually by stating a desired probability of detection (described in Chapter 15). Being measurable, there can be agreement as to whether an objective has been successfully reached.

SMART objectives are ASSIGNABLE. The objectives are action-oriented tasks that can be assigned to a resource on ICS From 204.

SMART objectives are REASONABLE (REALISTIC). Objectives are doable by the available resources in the time allotted.

SMART objectives are TIME - REFERENCED. The objectives are **time-referenced**. That is, they specify a time at which each objective should be accomplished.

Normally, the objectives are formulated by the IC, in concert with the Planning Section Chief, who is responsible for developing strategies and tracking search progress, and the Operations Section Chief, who tasks resources in accordance with those strategies. There is no component of search management where the principle of **"Never Plan Alone!"** is more important than in the development of the incident objectives.

Generally, the incident objectives should address the following questions:

- How much time do you have to find the subject alive? (Consider weather, subject profile, statistics, and any other survivability factors.)
- What locations or areas are most likely to contain the subject?
- Where are the best places to look for clues?
- How large an area will you search during this operational period?
- What probability of detection can you accept for each of the segments in the area? (That is, how <u>thoroughly</u> will you search them?)

Figure 9.3 contains a fictional example of incident objectives formulated at the beginning of a fictitious search incident. Please review them carefully, and decide whether they meet the SMART criteria of being Specific, Measurable, Assignable, Realistic and Time Referenced. Many experienced search planners may want to add or revise the list of objectives in Figure 9.3, which is fine. However, in order to ensure that the objectives are **attainable**, an important characteristic of a list of useful objective is the KISS principle, "Keep It Simple, Searcher." A long, shopping-list of objectives is likely to be unreasonable and unattainable, setting the management team up for failure. In practice, the list of incident objectives should rarely exceed 10 items.

Figure 9.3

Examples of Incident Objectives

In this fictional example, the subject was reported missing at 2200 hrs on New Years's Eve (yes, these things do happen!). Assume that the search team arrived on the scene within an hour and that the objectives are formulated at 2300 hrs.

Incident Objectives

1. Find John Doe by 0600, Jan 1.

2. Obtain reliable searching and planning data (clothing, trip plans equipment, circumstances of loss) by 2400 hrs, Dec. 31.

3. Establish his direction of travel by 2400 hrs, Dec. 31.

4. Confine him to an area within 3 mi of the PLS, by 0200 hrs, Jan. 1.

5. Obtain POD's of 50% for all trails, drainages, and water edges in the search area, by 0300 hrs, Jan. 1.

6. Identify and obtain POD's of 90% for all cabins, camps, and other likely spots, by 0300 hrs, Jan. 1.

7. Obtain POD's of 50% in segments 1, 2, 3, and 4, by 0500 hrs, Jan. 1.

There is virtually no reference to search tactics or specific types of resources in the incident objectives. For example, the Operations Section Chief could decide to determine the direction of travel by sending to the LKP a tracking team, a trailing dog, or a psychic (although we would not recommend the latter option). Similarly, tactical decisions regarding confinement could entail trail blocks, string lines, trap tracks, or any number of possibilities, depending on available resources, terrain, or weather conditions. The point is that **the Operations Section Chief should have the flexibility to make these tactical decisions and to allocate resources in a manner that best meets the objectives**.

In addition to being reasonable, the objectives must also be **flexible**. As conditions change — or new information comes in — objectives may be revised or new ones may be added to the list. For example, tracks discovered by a sign-cutting team may indicate that an area not listed in the objectives may be "hot," thus requiring a higher priority. Other causes for revising objectives include worsened weather conditions, or unexpected difficulties in obtaining sufficient resources to meet the current objectives.

Because the objectives drive all tactical decisions during the incident, it is important to remember that any search activity must be justifiable in terms of a specific objective it is intended to meet. Otherwise, search managers run the risk of conducting an ad hoc search in which there is no effective plan for organizing search efforts.

The Incident Action Plan (IAP)

The Incident Action Plan (contained within ICS Form 202), which includes the incident objectives and all other planning documents, provides a systematic plan for successfully resolving the search. Although the content of the plan will vary from incident to incident, it will always have three characteristics:

- It must be dynamic and flexible.
- It must be updated for each operational period.
- There must be only one plan for the operational period.

The role of the Incident Action Plan in incident management is extremely important to the overall search effort. It should provide all incident personnel with the following:

1. Defined operational periods.
2. Written search objectives reflecting the policy and needs of all jurisdictions.
3. Assignment lists (tactical assignments.)
4. Organizational chart.
5. Search maps delineating assignment areas.
6. Communications plan.
7. Resource status and availability.
8. Mission situation/status reports.
9. Weather information.
10. Situation predictions.
11. Medical plan.

12. Transportation plan.
13. Safety considerations for weather, hazards, etc.
14. Air operations summary (ICS-220), if appropriate.
15. Subject profile.
16. Trip plans; backcountry permit, route, etc.
17. The name of the incident, which should be determined from a geographic identity in the area, rather than using the subject's name. This is very important where the identity of a minor may be restricted by law.

All major functional areas are responsible for preparing portions of the Incident Action Plan, and includes:

Incident Commander

- Provides overall objectives
- Establishes off-incident resource ordering procedures.
- Approves the Incident Action Plan.

Planning Section Chief

- Determines search strategies, and proposes alternative strategies.
- Collects, documents and disseminates all necessary information for planning.
- Typically conducts the planning meeting and briefings.
- Coordinates the preparation of the Incident Action Plan.

- Responsible for ICS Forms 202, 203 & 204.
- Prepares all maps.

Operations Section Chief

- Determines resource requirements in light of pre-determined objectives.
- Ensures segment boundaries are realistic for tactical assignments.
- Determines tactics.
- Determines work assignments.

Logistics Section Chief

- Ensures that the resource ordering procedure is known.
- Ensures that the Logistics Section can support the action plan.
- Develops the Transportation Plan to get searchers to and from their assignments.

Finance/Admin Section Chief

- Provides cost implications of incident objectives.
- Determines financial implications of the Incident Action Plan.

Components of the Incident Action Plan

A major objective of the Planning Section is to produce an effective Incident Action Plan as early in the incident as possible. Most components of the plan have a designated ICS form. A non-exhaustive list includes:

I. Incident Objectives (described previously)
- Form ICS-202.

II. Organizational Assignment List
- Lists all individuals assigned to incident management positions.
- Form ICS-203.

III. Assignment Lists
- Describes tactical assignments for each search activity.
- Form ICS-204.

IV. Communications Plan
- Identifies radio frequencies and assigns them to specific functions.
- Form ICS-205.

V. Medical Plan
- Describes procedures for treating injured searchers.
- From ICS-206.

VI. Other forms as required, such as
- Air Operations.
- Briefing and debriefing forms.
- Subject profile and LPQ.
- Footprint diagram.
- Vehicle traffic pattern.

VII. A Map of the search area

Resource Unit

The other critical Planning Section position is the Resources Unit Leader. This person maintains current records on the status of all resources. The position may be staffed full time, or the Resources Unit Leader might have other duties such running the Check-In or Situation Unit.

A Logical Sequence of Planning Actions

What follows is a recommended sequence of actions which will normally ensure the development of an efficient search plan. Keep in mind, however, that there will often be alterations in this sequence, and that many of the "steps" may be conducted simultaneously. (See also the planning checklist in Chapter 5.)

Actions for developing a Search Plan:

1. Develop a subject profile.
2. Locate the PLS or LKP.
3. Define the search area and identify its boundaries. Consider theoretical, statistical, deductive and subjective methods, search objectives, subject profile, and lost person behavior data.
4. Confine the subject. That is, search the edges of the search area and take steps to ensure that the subject does not cross the boundaries.
5. Segment the search area into manageable units.

6. Establish incident objectives, as described earlier.
7. Determine POA for each segment.
8. Determine the approximate size of each segment. This information will assist with estimating the time necessary for resources to complete assignments.
9. Determine Probability Density. Probability density (PDEN) is the probability that the lost person is in a given segment, divided by the size of that segment: (PDEN = POA/Size). The higher the probability density, the greater the chance of finding the subject sooner because there is a relatively higher POA per square foot. With all other factors equal (e.g., terrain, segment accessibility, etc.), higher priority should be given to segments with the highest PDEN.
10. Evaluate resources.
11. Estimate the total resources needed to achieve the incident objectives. Consider: The types of resources needed or available; how long each is available; Time available versus area to be covered; estimated POD for each resource.
12. Hold a planning meeting to assess and modify the plan as necessary.
13. Outline and review the Incident Action Plan.
14. Allocate resources and brief searchers.
15. Debrief searchers as tasks are completed.
16. Calculate changing probabilities as segments are searched.
17. Calculate cumulative POD for each segment.
18. Calculate shifting POA for each segment.

19. Brief General Staff personnel for the next operational period.

The Planning Clock

Plan for whole operational periods, not just for the next task assignment. Outline a general plan for the next shift, subject to revision as further information is received. Meet with Operations and Logistics and lay the groundwork for the following phases:

The Second Operational Period

- Aimed at new high probability areas as well as secondary search areas that have been previously covered.
- Approached with both efficiency <u>and</u> thoroughness as priorities.
- Terminated at either 6 pm or 6 am, depending on when the initial response was started, and continues for 12 hours.

Subsequent Operational Periods

This phase of the search incident will probably follow the planning process started during the first full operational period regardless of when it started. These phases are generally:

- Aimed at high and low probability areas simultaneously.
- Approached with both efficiency and thoroughness in mind.
- Involve 12-hour periods of time throughout the rest of the search mission.

Review and — if necessary— revise the search objectives, resource needs, subject profile, and search urgency.

Additional Suggestions:

1. Don't make anything worse!
2. Don't let the management of the search generate its own special problems.
3. Troubleshoot early, and encourage everyone to keep sight of the search objectives.
4. There seems to be an inverse relationship between level of responsibility and workload; the higher the responsibility, the less the workload. Managers are paid to think, not staff the production line.
5. The IC, and to a lesser extent, the Planning Section, Operations, and other Chiefs should save themselves for the main events and refuse to be drawn into trivia. As managers they need to be available to their subordinates, and have time to evaluate and think ahead. Good managers delegate as much as possible so they are prepared to handle the additional problems that are sure to appear.
6. The only thing worse than a bad decision is indecision. There is no such thing as a "bad" decision if it is made in good judgment based on available information.

7. Searches are great opportunities to receive on-the-job training in managing large incidents. Take advantage of this by assigning inexperienced personnel to shadow the more experienced to learn from them.

8. A common problem on many search incidents is down time for search teams as they wait for additional assignments. Unfortunately, briefing teams by radio — one common "solution" to getting people in the woods earlier — tends to congest communications, and presents the risk that significant information will not be conveyed. These problems can be minimized by providing each team with secondary and alternative assignments during the initial briefing.

9. Encourage input. Don't plan in a vacuum. Searchers, family, and locals will have good ideas, some of which you may not have considered. Obtain their input by methods such as:

- Direct agency and family liaisons to solicit suggestions and forward these ideas to the Planning Section.

- Organize a brainstorming session and invite key people to participate, including the IC, the Operations Chief, selected family members, representatives of participating organizations, individuals with special knowledge of the search area, and persons well

skilled in search strategy and tactics.

- Provide a briefing.

- Allow each person two to five minutes to make and justify recommendations. List each of these on a flip chart or blackboard.

- After everyone has made recommendations, provide a certain amount of time for discussion.

- Prioritize the recommendations and conclude the session.

- Direct the Planning Section to implement strategies to address the recommendations.

10. A prudent Planning Section Chief will always have more tasks prepared than can be done with available resources, and will always have something for staff and resources to "do next."

These ten techniques allow everyone the opportunity to provide input, to draw the freelance locals into the operation in a constructive manner, to allow the family to participate, and to identify original ideas while still allowing decisions to be made in an orderly manner. This will also save time.

Figure 9.4 provides a list of suggested items for a assembling a basic planning kit for missing person incidents .

Figure 9.4

Items for a Basic Planning Kit

- Computer, Projector & Printer
- Miscellaneous stationery and supplies: Ruler, pens and pencils, pad of paper, tape, scissors and/or Exacto knife, glue sticks, paper clips, stapler, tags (for evidence or clues), expandable file folders.
- Map template to find segment sizes
- T-card organizer, or 3 x 5 index cards
- Lost subject behavior statistics.
- Search management and mapping software.
- Laminated or plasticized large-scale maps of the search area.

  Forms:
  - Lost Person Questionnaire
  - ICS 201 (Incident Briefing)
  - ICS 202 (Incident Objectives)
  - ICS 203 (Organizational Assignment Sheet)
  - ICS 204 (Assignment List)
  - ICS 205 (Incident Radio Communications Plan)
  - ICS 207 (Organization Chart) Large
  - ICS 213 (General Messages)
  - ICS 214 (Activity Log)
  - ICS 215 (Operational Planning Worksheet)
  - ICS 219 Resource Status Cards
  - ICS 220 (Air Operations Summary)
  - SAR Briefing/Debriefing forms

Summary

This chapter stressed the importance of search planning toward successful resolution of the lost person incident. While the emphasis has been on planning for the first few hours of the search, we have described the necessity for preparing for an extended incident by considering the requirements of later operational periods. Initially, the responding IC will attempt to acquire sufficient search and planning data necessary for starting the search, as well as identifying a specific location where the subject was last known to be. A lot of information gathering must be conducted very quickly, so the IC would be wise to appoint someone to assist with the planning function. Immediate tactical activities (as described in the previous chapter) will usually involve searching any hazardous areas where the subject may be injured and require rescue or medical treatment, to take steps to confine the subject to as small an area as possible, to protect the PLS, and, if sufficient resources are available, to begin searching high-probability locations and trails.

Once these actions are initiated, the IC will begin the formal planning process, usually indicated by the appointment of a Planning Section Chief (who may, in turn, recruit others to assist with the planning function, such as appointing investigators and interviewers).

The most important component of this early planning phase is to establish written incident objectives, which provide the strategy that will drive all tactical activities taken on the subject's behalf. A critical requirement of useful objectives is the prioritization of areas or segments in the search locale. This prioritization is performed through the systematic application of probability theory, often with the assistance of computer software. These incident objectives will be part of a collection of documents and forms called the Incident Action Plan, which in total constitutes the organizational framework for all aspects of the incident, from communications to searcher safety, as well as providing incident documentation.

In the next chapter (and the remainder of Part II), we will begin taking a closer look at the planning activities described in this chapter.

Questions for Discussion:

1. Why are the planning decisions that are made during the first two or three hours of the incident so critical for determining the outcome of the search, regardless of how long the incident lasts? Which types of decisions are especially important?

2. Why is it important for the Operations Section Chief — who is responsible for search <u>tactics</u> and the deployment of resources — to participate in the Planning Section Chief's development of a search <u>strategy</u>? Who else should participate in search planning, and why?

3. Considering the three ways that probability is applied during search planning, how are they applied to specific kinds of planning decisions?

CHAPTER 10

GATHERING INFORMATION

The lost person incident is a classic mystery. As with any mystery, all the clues needed to solve it are available. Thus, we need to uncover the clues and then interpret them correctly. However, too often, good investigative techniques are not employed in lost person incidents, or are initiated too late in the incident to have a significant impact on its outcome. In this chapter, we'll describe how **good investigative techniques** can contribute to a successful resolution of the "mystery" of the lost person.

CHAPTER OBJECTIVES:

When you finish studying this chapter, you should be able to:

> Describe the importance of investigation during the lost person incident.
>
> 2. Describe the types of information that must be obtained.
>
> Identify possible sources of information to be gathered.
>
> 3. Describe four types of evidence relevant to the lost person incident.
>
> 4. Describe the fundamentals of interviewing.

The Importance of Investigation

Search incident reports often contain examples of critical information that was discovered several days after the search began. Often, this information — had it been available to the incident management team — could have had a significant bearing on early decisions, thereby possibly saving time, effort, money, and even lives. Figure 10.1 shows the five "W's" of investigation—the essential information for developing a strategic search plan.

Figure 10.1

The Five W'S of Information Gathering

1. **What?**
2. **Where?**
3. **When?**
4. **Who?**
5. **Why?**

What happened? What was the intended activity and goal? What went wrong? Overdue, cries for help, crime, slipping, stuck, cold, thirsty, fallen, injured, dead, symptoms, walking wounded, equipment/personnel on- scene, instructions by/to the subjects, reason for overdue?

Where? Show maps or photos to witness. On ground, how far up/down, what climb, what pitch, in water, on bank, what trail, where last seen, headed in which direction, landmarks, mileage, type of terrain, route taken before accident, afterwards, washed downstream, how long did witness take to get out, car parked, was he/she staying here? Etc., etc.

When? Last seen, supposed to return, injured, ran out of water, symptoms appeared, fresh tracks or old, did storm hit (match itinerary to the weather)?

Who? Name, age, gender, weight, etc., address, phone, parents, friends, condition (mental/physical), vehicle, skills, experience, personnel with subject, back country personnel in area, kind and size of shoes (sole), clothing types and equivalent and colors, complete list of equipment?

Why? Family problems, drugs, avalanche, rock-fall, chronic (heart problems) or induced illness (hypothermia, hyperthermia, heat stroke)?

Embedded in these questions area a series of "hows" which need to be answered. How many subjects are missing? How was it determined that the subject was lost or missing? How will the subject react when the sun goes down? How much water, if any, did the subject carry? How has work and family life been going lately for the missing subject?

The Priority for Investigation

Investigation should begin immediately. From the initiation of the search until the location of the subject or a decision to suspend, investigation should be ongoing. It is easier to dismiss information that you have when it is not needed, than to find out too late that you needed information, or to receive information after the need has become critical.

The investigation process starts with the first call to 911 and continues up to and after the subject was found. The information gathered from the missing subject, if found alive, can reconstruct where they went, what they did, and what they did if they heard their name called. This information can be used to update statistical and historical information to update the preplan and improve training. For example, if the missing subject saw the searchers but did not hear his name called, then training may need to be adjusted to include the effective use of sound.

Typically, some type of lost person report is taken as an immediate action. The qualities of a good lost person report are:

a) Data critical to making immediate decisions are obtained first and quickly.

b) Detailed planning data and searching data are obtained (Chapters 8 and 9).

c) The lost person report serves as a checklist or reminder of even remotely possible considerations, reducing the chances of overlooking anything.

Organizationally, the investigative function is usually the responsibility of the Planning Section. However, early in the incident, when there may not be a separate Planning Section, it will still be important to designate someone to assist with the investigation. As with all important search functions, the investigation should be performed by people who are appropriately trained.

The Goal of Investigation: Evidence

The objective of investigation is to develop evidence relating to the lost person that will establish clues to be used in determining his or her location. In its simplest form, **evidence is information**. It is obtained through four distinct processes:

1. **Observing and recording** the actions of people, occurrence of events, description of conditions, or physical condition of things related to the lost person or the incident.

2. **Interviewing people** who might have specific knowledge of the lost person or the incident.

3. **Examining documents** that contain information relevant to the lost person or physical clues left by the lost person.

4. **Analyzing statistical data**, computations, or reasoning that shed light on the lost person's behavior, intent, or location.

Evidence helps to establish whether something is true or false. It provides the search planners with a factual basis for forming opinions, judgments, conclusions, or recommendations about the possible location of the lost person and the methods needed to find him/ her. In short, evidence provides clues to help solve the mystery.

Types of Evidence

There are four types of evidence or "clues" gathered in the course of any search incident: **physical**, **documentary**, **analytical**, and **testimonial** evidence. Each piece of evidence should be viewed by the investigator and the incident management team as a potential clue to the location of the lost person. Often, the most useful clues are comprised of several pieces of evidence of various types from various sources, which, when considered together, form a coherent clue the way that pieces of a jigsaw puzzle make a picture. Indeed, there is seldom one single bit of evidence that unravels the mystery and leads to the successful conclusion of the incident. Thus, there is a need for an ongoing investigation and the continuous evaluation and reevaluation of the available evidence.

Physical evidence: On a search, physical evidence generally produces the most reliable clues and is often the least subject to misinterpretation. As such, it is generally the most useful. Most physical evidence on a search is left by the subject and found in the field, either through investigation or as the direct result of the search. It is generally obtained by the direct observation of people's activities or behavior (for example, the subject's companions or, in some instances, the subject himself/herself), things or the condition of things (for example, the subject's car or discarded equipment) or events (for example, smoke, noises, or other possible signals).

Physical evidence can be gathered and recorded in many ways. It is most often generated as a written record of

someone's first-hand observations or the examination of a particular item. However, recording physical evidence by taking photographs or videos is also common and increasingly used. Charts, logs, maps and graphs that relate search results or the location of particular clues can also be considered related physical evidence.

Physical evidence is often used to corroborate other types of evidence. For example, a witness from the area may report that he thinks he saw the subject hiking on a particular trail. Finding a discarded candy wrapper of the same brand known to be carried by the subject on that trail would tend to corroborate the witness' report.

Documentary evidence: Written records that establish the occurrence of an event or relate a sequence or order in which things may have happened represent the most common forms of documentary evidence in lost person incidents. Examples include trail logs, summit registers or any other document that the subject may have signed or written in that would indicate his or her presence in a specific area, at a point in time. Camping permits, credit card charge slips, or store receipts are documents that serve similar purposes. The subject may also have generated notes, letters, or other types of correspondence that provide documentary evidence of his or her intentions. Determine if any cameras were in use prior to the subject's disappearance. Get color prints as soon as possible. You may have images of how the lost person appeared on the day of the loss.

Documentary evidence is the next most reliable, after physical evidence. The actual documents, or photocopies of them, are preferred to a record of someone's review or observation of them and, of course, they must be unaltered to be considered reliable.

Analytical evidence: The results of computations generated by the Planning Section during the search effort or reasoning about the subject's behavior produce analytical evidence. When we conclude that the subject is probably not in a specific area because of the measured thoroughness of the search coverage we have engaged in inductive, or scientific, reasoning. When we conclude, based on consideration of all available alternatives, that the subject must have taken the one remaining course of action, we have engaged in deductive reasoning. In either case, the conclusions we reach constitute analytical evidence. Separating events or sequences into their component parts for closer investigation may also produce analytical evidence. Similarly, benchmarking, comparing the incident or the subject to prescribed standards, past

operations, or similar incidents, is also an analytical process.

Analytical evidence must be cross-checked to be considered reliable. Computations should be independently verified as a check for accuracy. The source of any information used in the reasoning process must be checked and verified and the source itself must be found to be reliable. Moreover, it is generally wise to obtain possible different, knowledgeable interpretations of an analysis before accepting the conclusion from the analysis as a valid clue.

Testimonial evidence: In most search incidents the most available source of information is other people. The information received from others, either through interviews or as letters or statements received in response to inquiries, is termed testimonial evidence. While companions, family members, on-lookers, or others with information about the incident or the subject are often readily available, the information obtained through interviews with them is also the least reliable type of evidence. Questioners and interviewees alike may misinterpret or misunderstand what has to be discussed in an interview and care must be taken throughout the interview process to ensure the credibility of both the interviewee and his or her information.

Notwithstanding the care that must be taken with testimonial evidence, interviewing is the primary source of search information and trained interviewers can be a resource critical to the success of the search. Accordingly, interviewing is discussed in detail in this chapter.

Interview or Interrogation? Figure 10.2 discusses the difference between an interview and an interrogation.

Figure 10.2

Investigation and Interviewing
Techniques for Search and Rescue Responders
Christopher S. Young
Contra Costa County CA Sheriff's Search and Rescue Team

Interview and Interrogation

It is helpful to understand the difference between interview and interrogation. Law enforcement agencies are tasked with investigating incidents to determine whether crimes have been committed and, if they have, to arrest the perpetrators. Established rules and techniques have been developed to complete these tasks, which include interview and interrogation. For law enforcement, these are defined as:

Interview – A structured non-accusatory process to obtain useful information from someone who may or may not have knowledge of events or circumstances of the incident. Specific techniques may be used to aid recall or elicit behavior useful in determining the veracity or involvement of the interviewee. It should be noted that the interviewee might not have any knowledge of the crime or the perpetrators. Interviews may also evoke lies and themes to use against the uncooperative. In some instances there will come a point in an interview where the interviewee may become a suspect of a crime. The interview will then become an interrogation.

Interrogation – A structured accusatory process during which a suspect of a crime is confronted in a confident manner and then convinced that the best decision would be to admit responsibility. The techniques used in obtaining useful information are designed to apply pressure to or intentionally trip up the interviewee.

In law enforcement interview and interrogation, laws and codes protect the interviewee and define when a person is considered free to walk away from the questioning at any time, if they are being detained or in a custodial environment. It may be necessary to read the person their Miranda rights. An attorney may need to be present before any questioning occurs.

In law enforcement interviews and interrogations much of the time is spent preparing for the actual interview session. Questions are carefully crafted and well thought out in order to induce a specific response. During the interview sessions, the first hours are devoted to general conversation, which the investigator uses to develop a rapport with the interviewee and observe the person's behavior as the topics change.

In lost or missing person incidents involving law enforcement and/or search and rescue personnel there is a more specific definition:

> Search Interview – A structured but informal questioning process to obtain useful information from someone who has first hand and/or pertinent knowledge of the missing person. The tone of the interview is such that there is no condoning or condemning the action of the missing person, the interviewee or the circumstances surrounding the missing person's disappearance. Questions are structured to aid the interviewee in recalling specific details and events leading up to the disappearance of the missing person. The information gathered is used to develop a missing person profile, collect lists of other persons to interview and aid in the planning of where to look for the missing person.

In this type of missing person interview, the questions are nearly the same for all types of searches. A rapport is developed almost immediately because of the common goal of the interviewer and interviewee: to find the missing person and bring them home safely. In most circumstances the interviewee is free to walk away from the questioning at anytime but is encouraged to stay and help.

Techniques used in search interviewing and investigation are designed to elicit full and accurate information about the missing person. Questions may even be designed to trip up the interviewee so the answers can be corroborated with other interviews in order to find out who has the most credible information.

Excerpted from Young, C. & Wehbring J. (2007) *Urban Search - Managing Missing Person Searches in the Urban Environment:* Charlottesville, VA: dbS Productions.

Reprinted with Permission of the Authors.

Guidelines for Gathering Clue Information

Did you ever go out the door or leave on a trip and know there was something you forgot? What was your first clue? In general, to discover what it was, you must mentally go backward through your activities or down a list in a step-by-step fashion. It is much easier and more efficient to organize in the initial stages of a search, or even before it begins. To prevent oversights and disorganization, each clue seeker should write down what information he/she has received. In addition, the source of the clue and an estimate of its accuracy should be noted.

As the first sketchy information comes in, the process of gathering, recording and planning must begin. Eventually, information must be gathered under several topics, and should be arranged in chronological order. Since we begin with limited information when the subject is first reported missing, we can begin our search for clues from limited topics. The calls reporting someone missing are generally brief. The first bits of data are usually gender and activity, such as, a male hunter, or a grandmother who was berry picking. Clues from a statistical basis can offer the responsible agency a start. An agency's first response can be conditioned by several areas of study.

Figure 10.3 summarizes the four main types of clues and provides some examples of each type.

Figure 10.3

Four Categories of Clues and Examples

1. **Physical** (an item or event)
    - Footprints.
    - Candy wrappers.
    - Flashing light.
    - Whistle or gunshot.

2. **Documentary** (a written clue)
    - Summit log.
    - Trail register.
    - Suicide note.

3. **Testimonial** (statements by others)
    - Family member.
    - Witness.
    - Persons contacted in the search area.

4. **Analytical** (the results of reasoning)
    - If the subject wanted to get from 'a' to 'c' then he would have to go through 'b'.

The following is a list of information categories that can provide many hidden clues. In each category there are a series of questions or points that may prove helpful in the quest for all pertinent facts:

Category of Subject

> Child?
>
> Hiker?
>
> Hunter?
>
> Berry Picker?
>
> Fisherman?
>
> Climber?
>
> Walkaway?

<u>Detectability</u>: By convention, we define "high detectability" as being visible from a distance of 50 feet. Consider, for example, the deer hunter. Because he's usually wearing bright clothing (e.g., hunter orange) he can easily be spotted in the densest of foliage (even from a helicopter). Unfortunately, other lost subjects are not usually so visible. Berry pickers, for example, are significantly harder to detect, as are Alzheimer's patients and young children. Assumptions about detectability will necessarily impact search tactics.

<u>Travel Aids</u>: These include trails, drainages, switchbacks, dry river beds, or any terrain feature that facilitates the subject's travel away from PLS. It is important to remember that some types of subjects, such as hikers, tend to rely on travel aids for movement through the environment, while others, such as hunters or despondent "walkaways," are just as inclined to bushwhack (travel directly through) the densest vegetation.

<u>Distances Traveled</u>: Estimates on how far the subject could have traveled will determine the size of the search area.

<u>Survivability</u>: Here the elderly berry picker will be more susceptible than the male hunter in any type of weather.

These initial clues can help the agency determine priority of the mission and what type of first response is preferable from one mission to another.

Place Last Seen (PLS) or
Last Known Position (LKP) as
The Initial Planning Point (IPP)

Where exactly was the subject last seen by someone? Where is the subject's last known position? Recreate the scene. Take the witness to scene and have them re-create the event. Many more details may result. The PLS or the LKP (discussed again in Chapter 12) becomes the Initial Planning Point (IPP) unless subsequent investigation later reveals different points. Don't change the IPP, but update the LKP or PLS as clues give evidence of the subject's movement. The first PLS or LKP is designated as the **Initial Planning Point (IPP)** which remains important for determining the statistical search area. Pinpoint its location on a map. Physically go to the spot and investigate it thoroughly.

Initial information maybe something like this: "A 13 year-old hiker is missing on the return trip from High Rock Lake. Last seen approximately 3 miles from the trailhead." The IPP must be determined accurately "in the field," because it provides the starting point to the median (mid-point) and other distances traveled, while acting as a focus for an area survey of clues such as tracks, confusion factors on trail, or possible short-cuts.

What are the Circumstances of Loss?

- Known location?
- En route?
- Wilderness or inaccessible location?
- Recreate to the best of your ability.

This should be investigated with detail in mind. Here is where the witnesses and others in the area can add surety to when and where the subject was (or was not, as this is just as valuable). In the preliminary stages, the reported lost subject can be placed in one of these categories:

Missing from a known location: That is, a known or some familiar location such as a picnic area, home, or car. This information frequently involves children and elderly people. Many times, the subject could have wandered off, unnoticed, in any direction, making it difficult to limit the search area. Under this classification, it may well be best to keep the scene secured to allow visual trackers or tracking dogs to work on direction of travel.

En route: A category where the subject is traveling a trail, ridge, or logging road, to a known objective. If en route to the objective then the subject may be confused due to poor maps, poorly marked or maintained trails or intersections. When returning from the objective, the subject may, partly due to fatigue, choose short-cuts or pursue straight line routes or wander from obliterated trails. Information of this nature should lead us to send people into the field that are trained to look for these types of clues.

Wilderness: Such activities take people off the main trails or paths. This classification is generally composed of hunters and pickers who frequently are preoccupied with their activities and do not pay attention to changing terrain, weather or location of the remainder of their party. Once again, we need searchers trained to seek these clues by "walking in the subject's shoes" to fill in the grey areas concerning circumstances of loss.

To be complete, we must **get the timing of the events up to and after the loss,** including the **weather <u>then</u>, not now!**

Some key points:

- How thoroughly did the subject prepare for the trip?

- Have the witnesses reenact the events where they happened. This will assure you as to when or where the subject was last seen. Also work with other people who were witnesses or just in the area to "balance" the likelihood that the information is accurate. Example: If possible, talk with everyone who you know was on the trail or in the campground at the time.

- Determine as well as you can, exactly when and where the witnesses and initial responders looked for the subject. This can help dramatically when we assess what the subject did at the time of loss and shortly thereafter.

Example: The entire family shouted for Grandpa in the vicinity of where he was picking mushrooms. Judging from his doctor's report, the man was in good condition. So although he could have had a problem in the immediate area and was not able to respond, it was more likely he was farther away. When Grandpa was found, 1.5 miles away "resting under a nice shade tree" it proved the search effort had made a suitable reaction to a very subtle clue.

- Be sure to ask about the weather as it occurred that day. Knowledge of the condition can be crucial in determining its effect: impaired vision from fog, low clouds or night time; impaired judgment from hypo/hyperthermia; exertion from deep snow or a slippery side hill.

What is the Subject's Physical and Mental Health Condition?

- General capabilities? Reported from two or more sources, based on a relative or friend's assessment or an informed third party.
- State of health and condition at time of loss?
- Diabetic?
- Alcoholic?

- Drug user?
- Medications – effects, and how
    often taken?
- Heart problems?
- Mental condition?

This information can be gathered in two parts. First, find out how the subject was feeling on this particular trip. It is important to get a detailed description and not just a brief answer like "she was feeling pretty good." Test it by asking what she had been eating, or look for other clues that may indicate whether the subject was working above or below their norm.

Second, get a feel for the usual day to day conditioning of the subject. A good example was a search for an elderly lady, who, due to the terrain, was not expected to have traveled out of the immediate area. However, opinions changed when the family mentioned she had just purchased a new bicycle for herself!

Get answers from at least two sources to compare accuracy. Preferably, one person should be outside the family such as a friend or fellow worker. This may require having the person brought to the command post. Note that

- Many witnesses will not
    recognize signs of fatigue,
    hypothermia, or hunger.
- Family may not offer

information about physical or mental problems.

- Family may be reluctant to
    mention, or be unaware of,
    senility or Alzheimer's disease.
- Family may also be reluctant to
    mention mental illness (for
    example., psychosis or
    depression) or even mental
    retardation.

Family members should be interviewed separately and watched for uneasiness as they try to avoid referring to a "problem." Reassure them that their answers will help in finding their loved one. The family doctor may offer insight into the subject's health. In any case, remember that the family is desperate to understand just what has happened to a loved one and may under or over emphasize a mental or health problem. This can result in . . .

Over emphasis: heart attack, stroke, arthritis.

Under emphasis: senility or mental health.

What is the Subject's Dominant Personality?

Aggressive?

Stubborn?

Brooder?

Loner?

Self-sufficient?

Upset easily or irritable?

Despondent?

Once again we should gather information from several sources, such as hunting partner, co-worker, initial witness or family members. Not all will be present at the search site. Don't fall into the trap of seeking these individuals only after the initial plan did not go well.

Figure 10.4 below shows an example of three different personality groupings that might be encountered. Differences in personality traits can translate into different chances of survival.

Figure 10.4

Three Personality Groupings

1	2	3
Independent	Aggressive	Dependent
Persevering	Anxious	Reserved
Realistic	Neglectful	Composed

From these three simple groupings, which is most likely to overexert or take risks? Which has the best chance at surviving in poor conditions? Which would seek shelter? Which is most likely to be a moving target? Which one is high risk, high priority search subject?

What was the Subject's Equipment?

Size?

Color?

Brand names?

Extra gear?

Shoe size and description?

Candy, soft drinks, or cigarettes, with labels and variety?

Witnesses vary greatly in the type of details they may recall. Gender can affect what is recalled. Female witnesses may have better recall of color, fabric, physical profile, hair style, etc. Male witnesses may notice equipment by brand, kind of accessories carried. When getting descriptions of the subject's equipment and clothing we can assess their capability or expertise at their activity. It is easy to predict who is at high risk between two hunters, one wearing rubber boots and blue jeans while the other is in pack boots with felt liners and wool pants.

A list of equipment, clothes and colors for the searchers give them something to tune their eyes for, but it must be accurate, because when an article is found, it frequently becomes the most important clue causing a major shift in search planning. That is a high cost if it is incorrect due to a faulty equipment list compiled on a casual, aimless basis.

Note-Taking and Note-Making

How you **keep track of all the information** you gather is as important as getting it. Plan to be successful at note-taking and note-making. Note-taking is the jotting down of key facts and details you observe or get from a witness or interviewee. Note-making is capturing those key thoughts that you felt were important, that you have questions about, or that came to you while you were jotting down other person's thoughts. Make sure you use a system of symbols or methods to differentiate the witness's facts from your thoughts. An audio recorder may also be helpful for verbal notes to oneself. However, be sure to get the interviewee's permission before attempting to tape them with audio or video equipment.

There are at least five different styles of note-taking, each of which may have a place in information gathering. The *sentence method* is the construction of a series of complete sentences that capture the essence and priority of the witness's information. This is perhaps the most difficult to master but the easiest to use after the fact. The *Cornell method* uses the left third of a page for key words and the right two-thirds of the page for the running stream of facts. After the interview, you may review your facts and mark the key words, follow-up ideas and

your ideas on the left side. The *outline method* uses a series of progressive indentations to sort major facts from minor ones or details. The *mapping method* uses groups of words or sketches distributed all over the page to capture information. Circle like concepts and draw connecting lines where appropriate to emphasize the relationships. The *charting method* combines some of each of the above by jotting down the grouped facts in different columns and highlighting the most important facts with underlining or color highlighting. Whichever system you use, prepare yourself by having a method of abbreviations and symbols to use to speed your writing and the later recognition of what you wrote. Have a primary and backup writing instrument, adequate paper, and a firm surface to write on so you are dependent on no one else for your notes. Use only one side of the paper and leave it connected to the pad or book. Spiral bound pads work very well and pages turn easily. Have a standard page titling process to include time and date, interviewee's full name and relationship to the situation. There are many available lists of prepared questions that can be included in a preplan.

Listen actively concentrating for a few moments to understand how the person speaking uses timing, emphasis, and emotion to prioritize facts and transition to new thoughts. Then do your listen-think-write process over and over. When the interview is completed, quickly review what you wrote to see if you missed anything and check that you can read what you wrote. Expand abbreviations, get correct spelling particularly of names and places, and make sure that you have all time-sequenced information in the right order. Include the names of any others who were involved with the interview. If possible, make a copy of your notes, and turn over the copy to the appropriate Plans Section function. Then you will have your database to build on and reference as you gather additional information from others.

Interviewing as an Investigative Tool

Interviewing is a face to face conversation with a purpose — to get information to save a life, recover a body, or protect searchers. The interview is a critical element in the investigative processes. It is not a cross examination, nor is it testimony for a court case.

Interviewing is a primary means of data gathering, whether obtaining testimonial evidence or gaining access to some form of physical, analytical, or documentary information, the interview process is the vehicle that is relied upon most during the search investigation. The interview is one of the primary tools of a skilled investigator and one of the key indicators of a successful investigation. The quality and quantity of data collected in the investigation is directly related to the interviewer's ability to ask appropriate questions, gain an understanding of interviewee's perspective, and to determine the appropriate action based on information obtained from an interview. Good interviewing is an art that is acquired through training and experience. Preplanning is the means to assuring that trained people capable of good interviewing are available when they are needed. Law enforcement agencies deal extensively with techniques of interviewing and often are a good source of resources to fulfill this function. However, interviewing is not interrogation in the law enforcement context and, while in some instances interrogation may need to be employed, the IC must be alert to the proper use of each.

Interviewing, it must be emphasized, is a data gathering tool, rather than a data analysis tool. However, interviewers need to think and listen to determine the significance of the information. Clue interpretation is the job of the Planning Section Chief and, ultimately, the IC, but the interviewer's insights can provide essential keys for turning information into actionable knowledge. Generally, an interview can yield some combination of three possible outcomes:

1. <u>The interviewee's perspective</u>. The individual being interviewed can provide his/her opinion or observations regarding the incident or the subject.

2. <u>Referrals to other people</u>. An interviewee can provide the names of other individuals who may be able to provide additional information regarding the incident or the subject. Whenever possible, the interviewer should ask for referrals to continue the investigation.

3. <u>Documents</u>. The interviewee, in addition to his/her opinion or observations, can provide documentary evidence or data.

The key to effective interviewing is that the interviewer should pursue all three outcomes. Further, the effective interviewer does not engage in challenging or questioning the answers provided by an interviewee. If an interviewer suspects that the person being interviewed is hedging or giving misleading information, then the interviewer puts less emphasis on that person's perspective or opinions, and more emphasis on documents or referrals.

General Principles of Interviewing

Interviewing people who have first-hand knowledge of the incident or the subject should take place as soon as possible,

while the information is still fresh, and before collaboration with others colors the interviewee's interpretation of the information that he/she possesses. The following guidelines may be helpful to prospective interviewers:

a) Always assume that everyone will have something to contribute if asked the right question in the right way.

b) Let the information lead to conclusions. The greater the amount of information, the stronger the validity of the conclusion. Conclusions sometimes must be made based on incomplete information. Good managers will be flexible and able to change conclusions and actions as information improves. Beware of the trap of forming your own conclusion, then gathering or interpreting information to support it. Be aware that witnesses will have different interests, conclusions, biases and past experiences. These may influence their answers. For example, one person may be much more "tuned into" geographical features than into clothing and, thus may emphasize that aspect during the interview.

c) Be aware of cultural differences between yourself and the interviewee (see the later discussion regarding cultural diversity). Do not assume that one person can give you all the information. And do not be too concerned about conflicting information. There will always be conflict. The differences must be evaluated and, whenever possible, the information verified.

d) Always interview witnesses separately. Do not automatically assume that anyone is telling the truth or cooperating to the fullest extent:

—The witness may not understand the complexity or seriousness of the situation, or the relevance of particular information requested. If the witness is a relative of the subject, they will be under tremendous stress, so much so that they may not even hear the questions.

— There is a natural tendency for family and friends to make the subject or themselves look as good as possible, by minimizing or ignoring faults, deficiencies, etc.

— Relatives especially may be embarrassed about the subject's condition or behavior.

— A person may be suspicious or afraid of the interviewer.

— Rivalry, jealousy, or animosity may exist between the lost subject

and the witness.

— There may be a crime involved. Be aware that some people are looking for publicity or are motivated to become the center of attention.

Techniques for the Interviewer

The interview should be in an informal, relaxed, comfortable setting, which should be private and free from interruptions. At minimum, try to find a location away from bystanders and other interviewees.

If possible, interviewers should work in pairs while interviewing. This provides for two interpretations and evaluations of the information presented by the interviewee. It also reduces the chances of overlooking something. Use an audio recorder if at all possible, particularly if working alone. Inform the witness of your intention to record the interview and ask if they have any objections. Some people react negatively to recording, or "clam up". If this becomes apparent, or the interviewee objects to use of the recorder, then discontinue its use. In note-taking, be especially careful when writing down the interviewee's responses. Your writing may detract from what the witness says or you may be writing when you should be listening.

Begin the interview by introducing yourselves. Explain, in detail, your purpose and the importance of the information you are trying to obtain. Try to set the person at ease, relax them. You might start off with general conversation. Try to establish a good interpersonal relationship with the interviewee. You may be dealing with a panicky person who may not be able to control his or her frame of mind. Statements such as "calm down" or "try to get control of yourself" rarely work. Start with general questions, or enlist the person's aid. You may need to ask him or her to go to a designated place, write down statements and come back later once they have calmed down.

You must convey a sense of controlled urgency and concern, but not excitement, particularly if the witness is a relative, close friend, etc. Even if you feel the situation is not urgent, you must convey that you are taking action—doing the best possible.

Confirm identifying information about the witness for the record, and to enable future contact for follow-up or clarifying questions.

Try to understand the person and the mentality you are dealing with so that your questions will be appropriate. If you need to interview a child and you do not "relate" to kids, then find someone who

does. When interviewing children, position yourself lower than them, and face the same way they are facing. You will be less imposing and more inclined to elicit cooperation in a bid to help others.

We all have biases that we must recognize when interviewing. **Be especially aware of cultural differences.** In an excellent discussion of the impact of cultural diversity on the interviewing process, Judith Moore (1996) has described some of the many subtle but significant mistakes that a white interviewer can make when speaking to witnesses of a different cultural background, such as African Americans, Asian Americans, Latinos, and American Indians (also termed Natives or First Nations Citizens). The potential interviewer who can expect to interact with people of different cultural backgrounds should make the effort to develop the appropriate cultural sensitivity.

Also be wary of expressing any disapproval of the witnesses' actions. For example, it is easy to communicate disdain for a parent who let a small child wander away from a campsite. You must try to control your biases or have someone else do the interviews.

Structure your questions to obtain the type of answer you need. Open-ended questions are best when seeking explanatory information from the interviewee.

Closed-ended questions should be used when seeking confirmation of a specific fact. Probing questions may be necessary to gain additional information following a response. Use a field tested **Lost Person Questionnaire (LPQ)** to help you structure your interview questions to get the information you need, but don't just read from it. Be spontaneous and genuinely concerned.

You can "program" people to give erroneous responses by the way you ask the question. The question can contain information that reinforces the interviewee's conclusions, biases, or hearsay information.

Your questions should reinforce, not distort the interviewee's memory. People will want to appear knowledgeable and helpful. They can often sense the direction you are going and may tend to go along, even if they have few facts. You might ask the interviewee what he/she thinks happened or what he/she thinks the subject did or will do. But this must be considered an opinion and carefully separated from more objective facts.

Be a good listener. Ask the question, and then listen to the answer. Do not interrupt or begin to think ahead to the next

question you want to ask. Wait until the answer is complete to clear up confusing points or to decide what you want to ask next.

Active Listening

The most crucial aspect of conducting an interview is to practice active listening. Active listening occurs when the listener provides feedback (verbal and non-verbal) to the speaker regarding the extent to which the message has been understood. The purpose of active listening is to ensure that the message received by the listener is the same message that was sent by the speaker.

Overcoming Barriers to Active Listening

1. Suppress disruptive habits (finger drumming, pencil tapping, etc.)
2. Don't begin reading documents provided by the interviewee.
3. Don't let your biases interfere with interviewee's message; keep an open mind.
4. Don't jump to conclusions; hear out the interviewee.
5. Don't interrupt or debate.
6. Don't assume what the interviewee meant; request clarification (especially

regarding the meaning of key words)

7. Don't monopolize the conversation or try to have the last word.

8. Allow the answers to lead to other questions. If told that the subject smokes, follow up by asking what brand they smoke.

Some Verbal Active Listening Techniques

1. Reassuring sounds (for example: "uh huh," "I see," "yes?" "ok," "you don't say," "that's interesting," etc.)

2. Mirror statements (repeating back to the interviewee a statement he/she just finished making).

3. Probing the interviewee's initial responses in order to expand and/or clarify the information given.

4. On key points, restating in your own words what the interviewee has said.

5. Summarizing the main points of the discussion.

Some Non-Verbal Active Listening Techniques

1. Good body attention through such practice as maintaining continuous eye contact with interviewee and leaning forward. However, be aware that this is not advisable when interviewing people from cultures that find direct eye contact intimidating. Know your audience!

2. Occasional affirmative nods to show understanding and interest

3. Note-taking as appropriate.

4. An expectant pause to indicate to the interviewee that more is expected.

Do not be afraid to pause after an answer. This gives you a chance to think, to digest the answer, and the "awkward silence" may prompt the interviewee to volunteer more information.

As necessary, paraphrase or summarize the answer to make sure you understand the interviewee's intent. You might also check validity by asking a question differently later, or ask a question you know the answer to.

Avoid jumping around in the chronology of the incident. Generally follow the continuum of events, even if the witness may not know certain parts. However, one technique is to let the witness tell his or her entire story first, even if this involves jumping around. Then when you begin to ask questions, following the actual sequence of events, voids can be filled in, and some verification accomplished.

When you have run out of questions, ask, "Is there anything else that you think might help?" This may bring out something you have not thought of or give the person a chance to add something that they think is important.

You will probably want to reduce the interview to a written statement, particularly if a recording was not possible. If so, inform the interviewee that you may need to re-contact him/ her for further information or clarification. Be sure to inform the interviewee of any specific further action needed on his or her part.

At the conclusion, thank the interviewee. Reassure them that you are concerned and that the information has been helpful. This leaves the person with a good feeling. If the person felt "on the hot seat" at all, then this may further break down some reluctance and generate some helpful off the cuff remarks. Always provide the interviewee with a call back number. Ask that they use it if they think of something else or

If you have used more than one interviewer, then they must get together and compare information, reactions, "gut feelings," discrepancies, and missing

information as soon after the interview as possible.

QUESTIONING TECHNIQUES

Ways of Asking Open-ended Questions

1. **Ask questions that cannot be answered yes or no.**
Ask questions that require an explanatory answer. In order to answer your question, the other person must explain what he or she means rather than merely provide a yes or no answer.

2. **Preface key words with "what about" or "how about."** This is another way of requesting the person to start at some relevant point and explain from there.

3. **Repeat back the key words.** Here you are merely repeating back some of the key words, implying that you would like to know more about it.

4. **Summarize back.** Summarize back to the interviewee your understanding of what they meant. If the interviewee agrees, then it becomes a closed-ended question to which he or she responds "yes." But if the interviewee disagrees, then he/she is faced with an open-ended question which requires another

explanation of just what was meants. Often, the interviewee will add new information.

Probing as a Questioning Technique

1. Probing is a technique used by the interviewer to stimulate discussion and obtain more information without biasing responses.

2. Probes motivate the respondent to communicate more fully.

3. Probes focus the discussion on the specific interview content

4. Inadequate answers make probes necessary.

Times When Probes Are Necessary

1. To enlarge on, clarify, or explain reasons for what an interviewee has said.

2. To omit irrelevant information.

3. When inadequate answers are given.

4. When an interviewee responds: "I don't know."

Common Interviewing Pitfalls

1. Asking multiple questions at once – the interviewee is not sure which one to answer.

2. Asking yes/no questions when there may be more than two possible answers.

3. Asking leading questions that hint at an expected answer or by using emotionally loaded words that inappropriately "lead" the interviewee.

Possible Reasons for "I Don't Know" Responses:

• The respondent does not understand the question and says "I don't know" to fill the silence and give himself/herself time to think.

• The respondent is thinking the questions over and says "I don't know" to fill the silence and give themselves time to think.

• The respondent may be trying to evade the issue because he/she feels he/she is uninformed, may give the wrong answer, or because the question strikes him/her as too personal.

• The respondent may really not know or he may have no opinion on the subject.

• The respondent may be too overstressed to respond coherently.

A closed question requires a specific answer. Figure 10.5 compares the advantages and limitations of open-ended, closed and probing questioning styles.

Figure 10.5

QUESTIONING TECHNIQUES

Technique	Advantages	Limitations
Open-Ended: Ask for general information. Example: What did Tom have with him? Would you describe what he was wearing when you last saw him?	1. Give interviewee freedom to structure answer. 2. Useful when not sure of information desired. 3. Learn how interviewee feels: angry, excited, etc.	1. Can take more time. 2. Difficult to control. 3. Note-taking can be more difficult. 4. Interviewees may digress into providing irrelevant information.
Closed: Restrict answers — multiple choice, Yes/No, specific answers required. Example: How old is Tom? When did you last see him? Were you with him when he left the trailhead?	1. Saves time. 2. Maximizes control. 3. Easier for note-taking. 4. Useful when answers require no further explanation. 5. Can ask many questions in a short time. 6. Useful when it is necessary to tabulate or compare results.	1. Limits amount of information that can be obtained. 2. Easy to lie. 3. If not used properly, can make interviewee feel like they are on a witness stand.
Probes: Following up on a response to gain additional information. Example: Tell me more about this. I am not sure I understand the route you said you took. Could you elaborate?	1. Focuses on exactly what you need to know. 2. Clarifies response. 3. Can resolve apparent inconsistencies. 4. Can determine when the interviewee is evading questions.	1. Used only in follow-up questions.

Additional Reminders for Conducting Interviews

1. Control your attitude.
2. Control the interview.
3. Get acronyms defined.
4. Be ready for off-the-record comments.
5. Obtain supporting documentation.
6. Try to get needed information in one hour, or less.
7. Respect interviewee's environment.
8. Special care needs to be taken when interviewing children to avoid psychological trauma.

Children should be interviewed by professionals trained in the techniques of child interviewing unless the circumstances dictate that the immediate interview of the child is necessary for the safety and well-being of the lost person.

CRIMINAL POSSIBILITIES

Every lost person incident must be treated as if it has criminal possibilities until absolutely proven otherwise. Three possibilities stand out:

1. <u>Staged Incident</u> - Social, economic, and moral influences contribute to the potential that, at any given time, a person may stage an incident to make it appear as if he/she is lost, but in fact, he/she has purposely staged a disappearance.

2. <u>Homicide</u> - Cases are known where deranged persons have preyed upon unsuspecting victims in remote areas, assaulting or killing them. In addition, you must always consider: what better place is there to carry out a planned homicide (made to look like an accident, such as a fall) than in a remote or wilderness location — then report the victim as being lost?

3. <u>Abduction</u> - Abduction for ransom (kidnapping) is very rare. More likely are cases of custody related abductions by parents or other family members. Abduction by strangers, though relatively rare, are the most dangerous. These can be either a well planned or spur of the moment action on the part of a person with criminal intent. Children are particularly vulnerable. Cult activity and sexual assault should also be considered.

Whenever the investigation begins to show a possibility of criminal action, specialized resources for criminal investigation should be used. In the event the subject is found dead or badly injured, searchers must **take steps to protect what may possibly be a crime scene**. In situations where children are lost and potentially victims of abduction, additional resources should be used. Law enforcement should maintain jurisdiction as the lead agency and the National Center for Missing & Exploited Children® (NCMEC) needs to be contacted to activate a variety of resources that assist in this type of case (Figure 10.6).

Figure 10.6

NCMEC
The National Center for Missing and Exploited Children®

NCMEC's mission is to help prevent child abduction and sexual exploitation; help find missing children; and assist victims of child abduction and sexual exploitation, their families, and the professionals who serve them. NCMEC was established in 1984 as a private, nonprofit 501(c)(3) organization to provide services nationwide for families and professionals in the prevention of abducted, endangered, and sexually exploited children. Pursuant to its mission and its congressional mandates (see 42 U.S.C. §§ 5771 et seq.; 42 U.S.C. § 11606; 22 C.F.R. § 94.6), NCMEC offers the following services: technical assistance, informational databases, and detailed maps of the entire United States are available to law enforcement agencies involved in the search for missing, abducted, or lost children.

NCMEC also serves the nation in the following capacities:
• Serves as a clearinghouse of information about missing and exploited children.
• Operates a CyberTipline® the public may use to report Internet-related child sexual exploitation.
• Provides technical assistance to individuals and law-enforcement agencies in the prevention, investigation, prosecution, and treatment of cases involving missing and exploited children.
• Assists the U.S. Department of State in certain cases of international child abduction in accordance with the Hague Convention on the Civil Aspects of International Child Abduction.
• Offers training programs to law-enforcement and social-service professionals.
• Distributes photographs and descriptions of missing children worldwide.
• Coordinates child-protection efforts with the private sector.
• Networks with nonprofit service providers and clearinghouses about missing-persons cases.
• Provides information about effective legislation to help ensure the protection of children.

Planning data and tactics in abducted-child cases will be different from that in typical lost- person searches. NCMEC can provide a rapid-response team (Team Adam) staffed with experienced, retired law-enforcement officers when a request is made by the investigating law-enforcement agency.

These individuals, who have investigated multiple cases of lost and abducted children, are among the most seasoned child abduction experts in the country. NCMEC contact information is listed below.

National Center for Missing & Exploited Children®
Charles B. Wang International Children's Building
699 Prince Street
Alexandria, Virginia 22314-3175 USA
Phone: 703-274-3900
Fax: 703-274-2200

IN AN EMERGENCY, CONTACT THE NCMEC HOTLINE:

1-800-THE-LOST (1-800-843-5678)

Summary

In this chapter, we discussed the role of investigation in solving the "mystery" of the lost person. We began by describing the "5 W's" of information gathering (What, Where, When, Who, and Why), emphasizing the importance of acquiring this information as early as possible in the incident. Initially, investigation (a function of the Planning Section) should uncover the necessary search and planning data required to start the search. Subsequently, investigators should continue to collect and corroborate.

The four types of evidence sought by investigators include physical evidence (perceivable traces left by the missing person), documentary evidence (notes, letters, or other or other "paper trails"), analytical evidence (inferences or conclusions made by search planners, based on the analysis of clues), and testimonial evidence (verbal statements by witnesses and other informants). With respect to the latter, we described interviewing as a critical investigative tool, and suggested some general principles of interviewing as applied to the lost person incident. We described the value of active listening by the investigator during the interview, which facilitates communication and increases the accuracy of the information obtained. We discuss methods of note-taking and their differences from note-making. Finally, we described three major questioning techniques, including asking open-ended questions (when the informant can elaborate or structure an answer), closed questions (which must be answered by specific replies, such as "yes" or "no"), and probes (in which the interviewer asks the informant to elaborate on something they've said). The skilled interviewer will apply each of these techniques appropriately during the interview, as the situation dictates.

Questions for Discussion:

1. Do you agree with this chapter's contention that testimonial evidence is the least reliable of the four types of evidence? Why or why not?

2. How would you handle a critical witness who was too emotionally upset to be interviewed (for example, the mother of a missing toddler)?

3. What information about the missing person would you want to obtain before tasking search resources?

4. Would you handle the interviewing of adults and children differently? Why?

CHAPTER 11

PREDICTING LOST PERSON BEHAVIOR

While every person who becomes the subject of a land search is unique, **lost people have much in common**. Indeed, the search planner can often predict how a specific lost person may behave, by knowing how similar subjects have behaved in past incidents. In this chapter, and the one following, we will discuss the characteristics of the lost person that are crucial to the development of a useful search strategy. We will see how **"getting inside the subject's shoes"** can be the single most important step toward solving the classic mystery.

CHAPTER OBJECTIVES:

When you finish studying this chapter, you should be able to:

1. Explain the relevance of lost person behavior to search planning.

2. Identify those lost person behavior factors that should be considered in search planning.

3. Describe common reactions to the experience of being lost.

4. Describe some common types or categories of lost persons.

Syrotuck's Legacy: Analyzing Lost Person Behavior

While searchers have long appreciated the importance of predicting how a lost person might behave, the scientific approach to the topic began with the publication of William Syrotuck's classic monograph, "Analysis of Lost Person Behavior: An Aid to Search Planning" (1976). In his study, Syrotuck analyzed case reports of 229 search incidents occurring mostly in Washington and New York States, in the US. The key variable of interest to Syrotuck was the "crow's flight" or straight-line distance between the place where the subject was last seen and the location where the subject was found (regardless of how long it took the subject to get there). He also recorded other significant behaviors of lost persons, such as the circumstances under which they became lost, whether they traveled up or down in hilly terrain, and features of the environment that contributed to their disorientation. Although the areas providing the case reports varied widely in terrain and forest density, Syrotuck found a remarkable similarity in findings. Because of this similarity, he proposed that his results could be reasonably applied to "any part of the country that contains forested wilderness areas." Syrotuck found it useful to divide his sample up into six "lost person categories," including **small children** (1 to 6 years),

children (6 to 12), **hunters**, **hikers**, and **elderly** individuals (over 65 years), and "**miscellaneous**" adults (such as fruit gatherers, bird watchers, nature photographers, and other outdoor enthusiasts). He also described two "special categories," for which he had little data, including **mentally retarded** persons and **despondents** (depressed people contemplating suicide). He provided "profiles" describing behavioral characteristics of the "typical" member of each category, and computed (excluding the special categories) what he called "probability zones" with respect to distances traveled.

In the next chapter we'll discuss how important the concept of distance traveled is for search planning purposes, especially for establishing and prioritizing the search area. In this introductory chapter, we'll describe more generally how the analysis of records of lost person incidents (called **archival** reports) contributes important information for planning future incidents. In addition to Syrotuck's work, this discussion benefits from research reported by Kelly (1973), Mitchell (1985), Koester and Stooksbury (1992), and Hill (1992, 1996).

Common Search Planning Questions Related to Lost Person Behavior

The analysis of lost person behavior is a critical planning tool. It provides important information pertaining to the incident objectives, such as determining the size of the search area, deciding upon which areas or locations to search first, and estimating desired probabilities of detection for each segment in the area. Careful analysis of past cases of similar lost person can help answer numerous questions pertaining to search strategy and tactics, such as:

- **"How far can someone like this travel?"**

  The ability to predict the approximate distance a subject will travel from the PLS allows planners to start the search an optimal distance away, in areas where the subject <u>is</u> or soon <u>will be</u>, rather than <u>was</u> some time earlier. Predicting distance traveled also helps the planner to <u>prioritize the search area</u> by considering the average distance and probability zones for past lost persons of a similar type. (In Chapter 12, we will discuss methods for predicting how far lost persons are likely to travel, and how this information is used for search area prioritization.)

- **"How large an area should we search?"**

  Subjects who typically travel farther distances will require a larger area to be searched, usually at the cost of decreased thoroughness. In such cases, confinement becomes an especially high priority.

• **"Where should we try to confine the subject"**

Confinement is an important component in modern land search strategy. However, it is not always easy to decide where confinement lines should be established. Confinement too close or too far away from the PLS can be equally hazardous to the lost person's health. Analysis of lost person categories allows searchers to determine a probable distance the subject may travel, with optimal placement of confinement teams. While confinement is especially important for some lost person categories (for example, hunters, hikers, and school-aged children), it may be less of a priority for other types (for example, walkaways and despondents) when search resources are limited.

• **"How thoroughly should we search?"**

Types of lost persons who are difficult to detect require a relatively thorough search, with a greater expenditure of resources. Fortunately, these same types do not usually travel as far as subjects who are more detectable.

• **"What kind of clues should we be looking for?"**

Clues are the direct result of behavior, whether it is something discarded by the subject or a pattern of "sign" left behind as the lost person tries to reorient himself. Unlike the proverbial needle in the haystack, the lost subject will normally move around some period of time before becoming stationary. The searcher's task is to locate this moving target by assessing the information provided by the many traces of the subject's behavior.

• **"How difficult will it be to detect this person?"**

Some lost persons tend to stay on trails and in open areas, while others, such as small children and walkaways, often end up in dense foliage, which makes them difficult to detect. Moreover, some types of lost persons are less inclined (or able) to answer searchers' calls or respond to signals, which further reduces their detectability. Low-detectable subjects normally require much more thorough search tactics than do highly detectable subjects.

- **"Is it time to suspend the search?"**

   The decision to suspend a search should be based largely on consideration of lost person behavior. For example, is the subject the aggressive type who might be able to survive several days of bad weather? Have you extended the search far enough, considering the distances this type of subject usually travels? Have you searched thoroughly enough, considering the detectability of this type of subject? These questions require both an assessment of your current subject (through interviews with friends and family members) and an analysis of previous cases of lost person behavior.

Lost Person Behavior Factors Related to Lost Person Behavior

Apart from the specific type or category of lost person, there are a number of factors pertaining to the subject and the environment that will affect the search plan, including the perceived urgency of the search. These include:

- **General state of health**

   The subject's health may determine the distance and rate they may travel, as well as their expected survivability.

- **Past experience**

   Outdoors experience, survival training, woodsmanship, and related skills may indicate the subject will take positive steps to protect himself/herself.

- **Effects of the environment**

   Terrain, vegetation, and weather may all contribute to how the lost person behaves. Steep contours, ravines, and "blue lines" (edges of lakes and rivers) may channel the subject into natural cachement areas, while dense trees or undergrowth may affect the direction or route the subject will travel. Cold weather may lead to hypothermia, which affects the subject's ability to make sound judgments or engage in rational problem solving. Map and terrain analysis is especially useful in predicting subject behavior. "Confusion factors" on a trail, mazes, barriers, attractions, and natural routes or travel aids should be identified and factored into the search plan.

- **Circumstances under which the person became missing**

   What, exactly, was the person doing just before they became a missing person? Were they involved in some recreational activity, such as hunting or fishing? Were they on route to some specific location, such as a cabin, a fishing hole, a patch of berries, or a trail head? Was there an interpersonal dispute just before the incident, or anything that might have caused emotional turmoil in the subject? Had they recently received any bad news? Had they recently taken — or missed taking — a medication? Often, the events occurring in the few minutes just before the subject became missing will be important to the task of finding him/her.

How People React to Becoming Lost

The discussion that follows is based on interviews with rescued subjects of lost person incidents as well as surveys of numerous outdoorsmen asked to describe their experiences of being lost. The results are of more than academic interest, as they have important implications on search planning, such as where to look for clues, and deciding on the appropriate search tactics. Generally, knowing how people react to becoming lost — and what steps they may take to get "un-lost" — can help us with the important but difficult problem of "getting inside the subject's shoes."

The Initial Reaction

The mental impact of being lost or disoriented varies among individuals, but is typically characterized by shock and disbelief. Some subjects, especially school-age children, may experience a flood of irrational or fearful thoughts, while others, such as hunters and other outdoorsmen, may dread the embarrassment of being the target of a search. There is often a feeling of great urgency to "hurry up" and find some familiar place, especially if darkness is approaching. Usually, the person will eventually overcome this panicky state and become more purposeful in their attempts to become oriented. They may then apply some sort of plan or strategy to find their way out of trouble.

Behavior While Lost

Syrotuck described what he termed "notable behaviors" of the lost subjects he studied, including:

> **Failure to make a shelter or a fire.** Very few individuals in his sample took steps to protect themselves against the environment. A possible exception to this general trend seems to be the overdue hunter who has been overtaken by darkness. Often, they may improvise a lean-to and/or build a fire for warmth, intending to

walk out of the woods at first light.

Discarding equipment. Stories abound describing the lost person who died with a full pack of food and shelter at hand. Whether through shock, hypothermia, or forgetfulness, many subjects have discarded or abandoned the very equipment they needed to survive.

Disrobing. People new to search and rescue are often incredulous that a lost person would discard his clothing in freezing weather. Nevertheless, it does happen, usually from the effects of advanced hypothermia. The body reacts paradoxically by making the person feel as if they're overheated. Being irrational, the person disrobes (paradoxical disrobing), usually starting with the shoes and pants. Indeed, it is not uncommon for such victims to empty their pockets and stack them neatly nearby, as if preparing for bed.

Failure to respond to searchers. Subjects of all ages and types have failed to signal helicopters hovering overhead, or even to answer searchers calling their name. Syrotuck described this behavior as a "sense of abandonment," in which the lost person has given up hope and no longer believes that people are looking

for him/her. While this may describe some cases, it is equally likely that the person may simply be non-responsive from shock, or — especially children — may not believe that they could be the subject of an organized search or, more recently, have been taught to fear strangers and hide from them. In any case, regardless of the age and category of the subject, it cannot be assumed that the person will necessarily be responsive.

Travel aids. Lost persons frequently travel the path of least resistance, which includes such "travel aids" as trails, stream edges, dry stream beds, drainages, survey lines, power lines, and roadways. However, as Syrotuck noted, not all lost persons are inclined to use such travel aids, as some types (such as hunters) may be more inclined to "bushwhack" to some distant location, rather than use a trail which may be going in the wrong direction. In any case, the identification of travel aids is an important component in the search plan.

Common Lost Person Strategies for Getting "Un-lost"

Trail running. The disoriented person realizes he's "turned around," then moves down the nearest trail or travel aid very quickly in order to reestablish his bearings as soon as possible. The farther they go on the trail, the less likely they are to reverse their direction. Adults — but rarely children — eventually abandon this tactic in favor of a more "rational" strategy.

Following a straight line. Many outdoorsmen believe that if they follow a straight line far enough, then they will eventually come out on a road or highway. The futility of this strategy is soon realized when they come to the first impassable stream, cliff, or thicket.

Direction sampling. Starting with a clearly identifiable "base," such as a large boulder or unusual tree, the lost person travels short distances, holding the base in view behind them. When they do not see something familiar, they return to the base to "sample" another direction. Their pattern of movement resembles the spokes of a wheel, with the base at the "hub."

View enhancement. The lost person climbs a hill or a tree in order to improve or enhance their view of the area. Children will be looking for some recognizable landmark, especially a house or other building, while adults are usually trying to improve their mental map of the surrounding terrain.

Employing folk wisdom. Many bits of folk wisdom about how to get "un-lost" are commonly shared around the campfire. For example, following streams to civilization is one such popular myth, which is more likely to lead the lost person to a remote swamp than to people.

Staying put. The "strategy" of staying in one place and waiting for searchers is unfortunately uncommon. It is most evidenced by older outdoorsmen as well as by people with previous experience of being lost.

> **Lost people — even children — usually have some plan to reorient themselves, however ineffective the plan may be. They rarely wander aimlessly unless they are hypothermic or in shock. The particular strategies they employ will directly affect the pattern and location of clues available to searchers.**

Categories of Lost Persons

The following are common types or "categories" of lost persons. There tend to be certain trends and characteristics of persons within each group, but exceptions are common and no particular subject should be expected to behave exactly as described for his/her category. Nevertheless, category descriptions are often quite useful for purposes of search planning, especially in the absence of specific information pertaining to a particular lost subject. These descriptions are based on a relatively small sample set and should be used only for general guidance. Agencies and organizations involved in SAR missions are encouraged to develop their own profiles.

Children (1 to 3 years)

They are unaware of the concept of being "lost." Navigational skills and sense of direction are almost nonexistent. They tend to wander aimlessly. They often seek out the most convenient location to lie down and go to sleep:

- **Inside a log.**
- **Under a thick bush.**
- **Under an overhanging rock.**
- **Under a picnic table.**
- **Inside an automobile trunk.**
- **Inside an abandoned appliance.**

They are almost always very difficult to detect, as they are frequently out of sight and will rarely answer searchers' calls. Because they tend to seek shelter in poor weather, their chances of survival are often quite good. However, their temperature coping

mechanisms are not as strong as older children so their urgency factor rating is high.

CHILDREN 1-3 yrs - Implications for search planning: a highly thorough search may be necessary. **As small children rarely travel far, confinement is not usually a high priority when search resources are scarce.**

Children (4 to 6 years)

They are capable of traveling farther than younger children.

They have a concept of being lost and will generally try to return home or go back to someplace familiar.

They are frequently drawn away from homes or campsites by animals, following older children, or just exploring.

Similar to younger children, they will usually seek shelter when tired, at nightfall, or when the weather becomes bad.

Having been taught to avoid strangers, few children of this age will answer searchers calling their name, nor will they show themselves when searchers are near.

CHILDREN 4-6 yrs - Implications for search planning: a highly thorough search may be required, with searchers focusing on visual clues.

Children (7 to 12 years)

Their navigational and directional skills are much more developed than those of the younger child, and they are learning to construct primitive "mental maps" of their environments, which may be highly inaccurate. They frequently become lost while attempting a short cut to a familiar location. They may become extremely upset and confused when lost, seeming to react very irrationally. Lost children of this age frequently resort to **trail running**, which may take them some distance from the PLS. Subjects of this age may respond more maturely if accompanied by a friend or sibling.

> **Children (of all ages) are rarely able to find their own way out of the woods.**

Statistical data: an analysis of 9 cases of missing children (7-12 yrs) by Hill (1996) revealed that:
— 89% (8 out of 9) survived.
— 55% (5 out of 9) of the cases involved 2 or more subjects.
— No child of this category found his/her own way out of the woods.

CHILDREN 7-12 yrs -Implications for search planning: because of the distance they tend to travel, combined with their panicky state, **the search for a child of this age can be particularly difficult. Confinement of trails, roadways, and other travel aids is a top priority**.

Youth (13-15 years)

Frequently become lost in groups of two or more people, while engaged in exploring or some other "adventuring" activity.
When in groups, they will rarely travel very far. They will usually respond to searchers' calls. They often resort to **direction sampling**, looking for some familiar place or landmark.
Statistical data: an analysis of 20 cases of missing youths by Hill (1996) revealed that:
— 60% of the cases involved 2 or more missing subjects.
— All subjects survived, But only 10% found their own way out of the woods.

YOUTH 13-15yrs - Implications for search planning: confinement is not usually a high priority unless the subject is alone.

Hunters

Their concentration on game often distracts them from navigation. Hunters frequently become disoriented while chasing wounded game into thick areas of trees or brush. They tend to overextend themselves in darkness and push beyond their physical abilities. When game laws prescribe the wearing of "hunter orange", these subjects can be easily detected from a distance or from a helicopter. Many hunters will fire shots if they believe searchers are looking for them, and will respond to sounds if they are able. Due to ego or game laws, many hunters will go to great lengths to walk out unassisted by search teams. The "typical" hunter will attempt to build a shelter at night, then walk out of the woods at daybreak. On average, about one in three lost hunters will manage to find their own way out.

Statistical data: an analysis of 167 cases of lost or overdue hunters by Mitchell (1985) revealed the following characteristics:

— One in three missing hunters was overtaken by nightfall.
— 39% followed a natural drainage.
— Between 45% and 80% traveled at night.
— 90% did not travel after the first 24 hours.
— Between 25% and 45% found their own way out of the woods.

An analysis of 100 cases of lost or overdue hunters by Hill (1996) revealed:

— 16% of the cases involved 2 or more subjects.
— 93% survived.
— 24% found their own way out of the woods.

HUNTERS - Implications for search planning: confinement is a priority, as some hunters travel long distances on trails or woods roads. Attraction methods (sirens, whistles, gunshots) may also be effective. Also look for clues off the trails, such as in drainages or along river banks.

Fishermen

Shore fishermen often become lost while traveling on a trail to or from their fishing site. **Boat fishermen** sometimes become disoriented while trying to find the spot from which they launched their boat. They may become overcome by darkness and forced to land in some unfamiliar location. There is a somewhat higher possibility of drowning for boat fishermen than for shore fishermen, especially if there is alcohol involved.

Statistical data: an analysis of 25 cases of missing fishermen by Hill (1996) revealed that:

— 88% of subjects survived (the remainder died of drowning or exposure).

— 25% found their own way back to safety.

— 32% of the cases involved 2 or more subjects.

FISHERMEN - Implications for search planning: a thorough investigation is imperative. For shore fishermen, identify the subject's favorite fishing sites, and whether he/she liked to move around a lot. Direction of wind and current may be important for locating the landing sites of lost boaters.

Hikers

Hikers are trail-oriented and often become lost when their trail is obscured for some reason, or when they encounter a confusing junction of intersecting paths. Because of their reliance on trails, hikers tend to travel farther than other lost person categories, although extreme distances are less frequent than for hunters. They are often less prepared and "woods-wise" than hunters and

fishermen.

Statistical data: an analysis of 501 cases of lost or overdue hikers (Mitchell, 1985) revealed the following characteristics:

— Only about 40% were considered to be adequately equipped.

— 92% did not travel after the first 24 hours.

— Between 30% and 40% traveled at night.

— About 40% were located by a "hasty search".

An analysis of 24 cases of missing hikers (adults only) by Hill (1996) revealed :

— 29% found their own way back to safety.

— 92% survived.

— 42% of the cases involved two or more subjects.

HIKERS - Implications for search planning: confinement is a top priority, especially trail blocks. Clue-aware searchers should be tasked to run all likely trails, paths, roads, and similar travel aids.

Skiers

Most are young and in fairly good physical condition. They are usually well equipped and dressed for the weather. Most become lost because they took the wrong route, or misjudged time and/or distance. Some skiers are made immobile by injury and may be vulnerable to hypothermia. They are usually wearing brightly colored clothing, which makes them highly detectable against the snow. With the advent of ski areas charging the lost person for search and rescue services, more skiers may use searchers as "offset aiming points" so they may find their own way out and avoid costs.

Statistical data: an analysis of 87 cases of lost or overdue skiers (Mitchell, 1985) revealed the following characteristics:

— 50% found their own way back to safety.

— When found by search teams, only 50% were mobile.

— 83% stopped moving within the first 24 hours.

— Between 30% and 45% traveled at night.

SKIERS- Implications for search planning: visual trackers should be especially effective for locating missing skiers.

Climbers

They are usually well equipped and self sufficient. They tend to remain on or near designated routes.

A common factor for missing climbers is weather or hazardous conditions which limit their capabilities. Other important factors are falling debris and avalanches.

CLIMBERS - Implications for search planning: technical expertise is usually needed for both search and rescue (or recovery) of climbers.

Miscellaneous

This category includes gatherers (for example, mushrooms, berries, other fruit), nature photographers, rock hounds, and people engaged in some outdoor occupational activity, such as surveyors, forestry employees, conservation officers, and park rangers. Many are inadequately equipped or clothed for an extended duration outdoors. Many subjects in this category are found away from trails, depending on the nature of the activity in which they had been involved. They are frequently located near natural boundaries, such as rivers and lake shores.

Statistical data: an analysis of 26 cases of lost persons engaging in miscellaneous outdoor activity by Hill (1996) revealed:

— 96% survived.

— 23% of the cases involved two or more subjects.

— 31% of subjects found their own way back to safety.

MISCELLANEOUS - Implications for search planning: investigation is especially important for a subject of this "mixed bag" category. Effort should be made to identify the relevant locations which may have attracted the person, as these may be the most likely to contain clues.

Despondents

These are individuals with a history of depression or suicide attempts, or who are explicitly described by family or friends as having been severely depressed or suicidal just before the incident. It is not usually their intention to travel very far, but to find a place where they can be alone and possibly contemplate suicide. Despondent individuals are frequently located at the interface between two types of terrain (for example, forest and meadow), and sometimes in a "scenic location" where they can sit and meditate, such as on a hill overlooking a lake or city. Despondents will rarely answer searchers' calls, and will sometimes avoid or even hide from search teams. There is an extremely high fatality rate for this category, as despondents rarely take steps to protect themselves

from the weather, and, in addition, drugs or alcohol may be involved.

Statistical data: an analysis of 16 cases of missing despondents by Hill (1996) revealed:

— None walked out to safety on their own.

— None of the cases involved two or more subjects.

— Only 35% survived (the remainder died from exposure or suicide).

DESPONDENTS - Implications for search planning: the search for a despondent individual, even in moderate weather, should be considered highly urgent, likely requiring medical treatment and rescue. Confinement is not normally a high priority. While the search area may not be particularly large, the search should be thorough, as these subjects are often hard to detect and may not respond to sounds. Focus on likely spots and visual search methods.

Walkaways

These are individuals who "walk away" from a constant-care situation, whether a hospital or a residence. This includes people with senile dementia (for example, Alzheimer's disease), mentally retarded individuals, as well as person suffering from some debilitating form of mental illness (for example, psychosis). They rarely understand they are lost, and their wanderings may seem non-purposeful or at least non-predictable. They are almost never dressed appropriately for wet or severe weather conditions. They rarely respond to callers, and in some instances, such as with mentally retarded subjects, they may hide or even run from searchers. Persons suffering from Alzheimer's disease (or related illnesses) may be attempting to return to some former home or place where they once enjoyed being (however far away that place may be). They often walk in a straight line until running into a barrier, then turn and continue in another directions (the so-called "pinball effect"). Eventually, they become entangled in brush or mired in mud, unable to continue. Some have even walked straight into a lake and drowned. Walkaways who are allowed some independence by an institution (or a person managing home care) with respect to going outside unsupervised, may travel farther than persons requiring more supervision. The fatality rate for subjects in this category is extremely high.

Statistical data on Walkaways. An analysis of 22 cases of missing walkaways (general category) by Hill (1996) revealed:

— 45% were found dead (from exposure or drowning).
— None walked out to safety on their own.
— None called for help or answered searchers' calls.

Statistical data on Alzheimer's patients in particular: An analysis of 25 incidents involving missing Alzheimer's patients (Koester & Stooksbury, 1992) revealed the following characteristics:
— Average age was 73 years (59% male).
— Not one Alzheimer's subject called for help from searchers.
— 28% were found dead.
— They were found a median distance of 1/2 mile from the PLS.

WALKAWAYS - Implications for search planning: the search for a walkaway should be considered highly urgent. Man-trackers and trailing dogs may be especially effective, with air scent dog teams employed in high probability areas with dense vegetation. Because walkaways are usually very difficult to detect, often hidden under brush or in thickly treed areas, a highly thorough search may be necessary. Alzheimer's patients, mentally retarded individuals, and other institutionalized walkaways are often found somewhere on the grounds of their respective institutions, so a thorough search should begin there. Confinement of Alzheimer's patients is not normally a high priority, compared to other lost person categories, as these walkaways seldom travel great distances. However, be warned that some allegedly "frail" Alzheimer's patients have traveled much farther than their caretakers had expected. As well, mentally retarded subjects have been known to hide from searchers and to flee when spotted. Recurring discrete patrols focusing on visual searching may be helpful.

Other Lost Person Considerations

Gender Differences

Approximately one in five cases involves a female subject. Comparisons suggest few significant gender differences in lost person behavior, although there appears to be a slight difference in survival rates, favoring women. Females should not necessarily be expected to travel shorter distances than males.

Multiple-Subject Searches

Between 25% (Hill, 1996) and 49% (Kelley, 1973) of searches involve two or more subjects. Comparisons suggest few behavioral differences between single-subject and multiple-subject searches when the lost persons are adults. However, children over the age of approximately five will usually respond more maturely and less panicky when

accompanied by another child. Children under five frequently separate during their ordeal, while older children and youths are usually highly motivated to stay together.

The Elderly Lost Person

It is important not to underestimate the older subject merely because he or she is over the age of 65. Studies of elderly outdoor sportsmen, such as hunters, hikers, and fishermen, reveal that they are capable of traveling just as far when lost as younger subjects (Hill, 1992). More importantly, the elderly subject often behaves more rationally when lost than does his/ her younger counterpart. The elderly subject may be more willing to build a shelter and prepare to be rescued by searchers. However, if the older person has Alzheimer's disease or some other form of dementia, then the incident should be treated as a walkaway situation.

> For adult subjects, it is the
> ## Lost Person's Category —
> not his or her age as such — that is
> significant for search planning.

The Bogus Search[2]

Nothing is more frustrating than to initiate a full-scale search for a subject who is not there

---

[2] We use the word "bogus" here out of deference for the sensitive reader who dislikes profanity. Actually, searchers commonly use another "b-word" to describe the subjects of such searches — a rather derogatory term that tends to cast doubt on the legitimacy of a person's lineage.

to be found. Unfortunately, false searches are common. Kelley (1973), in his review of 167 cases in Southern California, described 26% of searches as "false alarms" (including cases were the subject found their own way out to safety, as well as bogus searches where the subject had not been in the woods in the first place). In the Nova Scotia sample, Hill (1996) found a similar rate of false alarms, with about one search in ten involving bogus (no-subject) searches. It was also noted that the single most "typical" bogus search involved two teenage girls missing together, usually after one had recently had a fight with her mother. In one such example, the girls watched the search covertly from the forest, just yards away from the command post.

Searchers will usually suspect a bogus search when the incident has been proceeding for several or more hours without the discovery of clues. Such suspicions will impact negatively on the efforts they apply to their search efforts. For this reason, it is extremely important to maintain a thorough investigation in order to ensure searchers in the field that there is indeed a subject out there to be found.

Overview of Lost Person Behavior

Lost Adults:

- Will usually search primarily for paths and routes rather than for places.

- Will bushwhack when they're "positive" they know the right direction.
- Will usually stay on a trail if not absolutely certain of the correct direction.
- May climb a hill to improve their view.
- Rarely move around randomly.
- Rarely attempt to travel in an arbitrary straight line.
- Will rarely reverse direction on a trail unless absolutely certain they've been going the wrong way.
- May attempt to apply "woods wisdom," such as traveling downstream.
- May "regress" to less effective methods when panicky.

Lost Children:

- Have relatively poor "mental maps" of their environment.
- Will usually search for familiar places rather than for routes (travel aids).
- Are rarely good at judging direction or distance.
- Often become lost when taking a "short cut" (ages 7 to 12).
- Will often try "trail running" (ages 7 to 12).
- May move randomly or unsystematically (ages 1 to 6).
- May be extremely panicky.
- Are rarely able to find their own way out of the woods.

- Rarely answer searchers calling their name.

The behavior of the perpetrators of missing or exploited children has recently attracted a lot of discrete analysis. Investigation should be retained by law enforcement to avoid exposing criminal techniques. To be better prepared to implement urgent search tactics for a suspected abduction, seek special classes within the law enforcement community. In cases where child abduction is suspected, do not hesitate to reach out to specialized investigators and agencies like NCMEC for assistance.

Preventive SAR (PSAR)

Knowing what we do about lost person behavior, we can accomplish much by providing preventive SAR (PSAR) programs to make our job easier. For example, children can be taught to stay in one place and protect themselves from hypothermia, rather than running recklessly down a trail. Indeed, a few months after the Andy Warburton search (Chapter 2), a children's "woods-proofing" program was initiated in the area. Among the hundreds of school-aged children exposed to the program during the first year was one boy of Andy's age who became lost on a school outing. He was found, not far from the PLS, hugging a tree — a behavior highly uncharacteristic of children who have not

been exposed to a woods safety program. The best known of the children's PSAR is the "Hug-a-Tree" program used widely throughout North America, with literally hundreds of presenters trained and willing to provide the program for free.

Regarding other lost person categories, many states and Canadian provinces include the use of map and compass as part of hunter safety programs, and some outdoor groups, such as snowmobile associations, provide relevant PSAR information to their members. Nevertheless, PSAR has a long way to go, as witnessed by the increasing numbers of people who are becoming the subjects of land searches. We suggest that an important part of any SAR group's activities be the identification of high-risk groups in their jurisdiction, and the implementation of appropriate PSAR programs.

> Remember . . .
>
> **The most successful lost person incident is the one you don't have to conduct!**

Summary

In this chapter we discussed the importance of "getting inside the subject's shoes." We described the early work of Bill Syrotuck, who analyzed case reports from various U.S.

States, and stressed the significance of recording the **straight-line distance** between the PLS and the point where the subject was eventually found. Syrotuck also divided his sample into various **lost person categories**, each demonstrating different behaviors of interest to the search planner. We further described how such information would be useful toward **search planning**, such as estimating the distance a subject may travel, determining the size of the search area, deciding where to confine the subject, deciding how thoroughly to search for the subject, suggesting what clues should be searched for (and where to search for them), estimating the probable difficulty in detecting the subject, and making decisions regarding the suspension of the incident. Additional factors to consider were listed as the subject's health, his/her past experience, the effects of the environment on the subject's behavior, and the circumstances under which the subject went missing.

Toward furthering understanding lost person behavior, we described how people react when they become lost. First, there is the **initial reaction**, which may involve the experience of shock, denial, or disbelief. There is often an urgent motive to "hurry up" and find some familiar location, followed eventually by a more rational, problem-solving approach to becoming "un-lost." We described various **notable behaviors** which lost people show, including a failure to make a shelter or build a fire, the discarding of

equipment and clothing, the failure to respond to searchers, and the use of travel aids. We also described some **lost person strategies** which subjects employ, including trail running, following a straight line, direction sampling, view enhancement, employing folk wisdom, and staying put. With respect to categories of lost subjects, we described various types which would be common to many areas, but added the caveat that search planners may want to add additional categories that are relevant to their area, such as mountain bikers, canoeists, or cross country skiers. We also discussed other lost person considerations, such as gender differences, multiple-subject searches, the elderly lost person (who should not be underestimated), and the so-called "bogus" search. We ended the chapter with a discussion of the usefulness of **preventive SAR** (PSAR) programs directed at children and various outdoor recreational groups.

In the next chapter, we will describe how a consideration of lost person behavior — especially distances traveled by subject category — may be applied directly to the establishment of the search area during the planning process. Because access to, and sharing of, search related data is essential to developing practical strategies for managing lost person incidents, we've included a suggested sample of items to record after each search in Figure 11.1. SAR databases are under continual development. We should all work toward the day when we routinely upload our data to a central database for downloading by the next person in the worldwide SAR community who needs it. A free web-based data collection system is available at http://sarstatistics.org.

Figure 11.1

<u>Some Suggested Items for a Lost Person Behavior Database</u>

1. Name, age, and gender of subject; plus a brief medical history.

2. Category: deer, bird, rabbit, or other hunter (specify), shore or boat fisherman, hiker, canoeist, skier, snowshoer, ATV/snowmobiler, despondent, walkaway, small child (1 - 6), child (7-12), youth (13-15), occupational activity (for example, surveying, woodcutting: specify), miscellaneous recreational activity (leisure, sport, hobby, gathering: specify).

3. Location: nearest town and/or geographical feature.

4. Terrain: mountainous, hilly, fairly level.

5. Vegetation: dense (heavily forested), medium (low vegetation or lightly forested), little or none.

6. Straight-line distance between the initial planning point (IPP) and the place where the subject was located, to the nearest yard/meter.

7. Outcome of search: Subject found alive by searchers; Subject found alive by non-searchers; Subject found deceased; Subject walked out before being found; Subject not found; False search; Other (specify).

8. Method of finding subject: Helicopter, Fixed Wing Aircraft, Dog team (air scent or trailing), Tracking team, Hasty team, Confinement team, Open grid (50 feet/15 meters spacing or more), Close grid (under 50 feet/15 meters), Attraction, Other (specify).

9. When found, was subject visible from the ground at a distance of 50 feet/15 meters?

10. When found, was subject under brush or otherwise hidden from view or in open space?

11. When found, was subject: Standing, Walking; Sitting; Lying down. If lying down, was subject conscious?

12. Did subject respond to callers?

13. From the subject's location, what was the distance to the nearest trail or road?

14. From the subject's location, what was the distance to the nearest barrier (lake, river, stream, cliff)?

15. First aid administered by searchers: None, CPR, hypothermia, hemorrhage, broken bones, shock, prescribed medication, other (specify).

16. Did subject require rescue/evacuation by stretcher or other device?

17. Prevailing weather conditions: Dry/normal, Cold temperature (Zero and below), Rain, Snow.

Questions for Discussion:

1. Why should searchers in the field also be informed about lost person behavior? What kind of information is especially important for them to know?

2. Why should both searchers and search planners be informed about common lost person strategies?

3. Why are lost people reluctant to reverse their direction on a trail? What implication does this have for search planning?

4. What kinds of questions might you ask the mother of a missing 9-yr-old boy in order to improve your chances of finding him? How about the wife of an elderly fisherman?

CHAPTER 12

ESTABLISHING THE SEARCH AREA

In the last chapter, we introduced the topic of lost person behavior and described its significance to search planning. In this chapter, we will extend that discussion to show how **understanding lost person behavior can help us to establish the search area, to calculate the optimal size of that area and to determine search priorities**.

CHAPTER OBJECTIVES:

When you finish studying this chapter, you should be able to:

1. Describe the methods of establishing the search area in a lost person incident.
2. Define a "median distance" and explain its importance for search planning.
3. Understand the concept of "probability zones," and calculate the rank position of the median, the 75th percentile and a range for the 75% Plus probability range.
4. Explain the importance of considering "probability density."
5. Describe the benefits of collecting data on lost person behavior for future search incidents.

The Need to Establish a Search Area

The first step in developing an effective search strategy is to identify those areas that should receive priority. This important step has three general components: (1) determining a reliable last known position, (2) estimating how far the subject has likely traveled from that position, and (3) identifying areas or places on a map where the subject is most likely to be located.

The Initial Planning Point (IPP)

Syrotuck introduced the advantages of recording, for every lost person incident, the straight line distance between the PLS and the point where the subject was found. Such information allows for the compilation of data for the purpose of computing median distances traveled and probability zones for various categories of lost persons (described later). For purposes of establishing the statistical search area, this initial Place Last Seen (or Last Known Position) should remain constant regardless of further sightings or the discovery of clues. Otherwise, probability zones would remain a constant distance from each new LKP and, in theory, you could never catch up to the subject. To distinguish this unique starting point from other LKP's, Lavalla, Stoffel, and Jones (1996) introduced the concept of the Initial Planning Point (IPP). The IPP is the last logical locale where the subject was known to be (through definitive clues or sightings) or expected to be (through investigation) at the time the search starts. For purposes of determining the statistical search area, the IPP will rarely change. To help clarify the differences among the significant locations, consider these examples:

> **IPP**: the location where the subject was seen leaving his car at daybreak. This will become the basis of the statistical search area, regardless of new clues. The first PLS or LKP.
>
> **PLS**: the location where the subject was seen hiking in the woods that morning.
>
> **LKP**: Initially, this was the car. However, since then, remnants of the subject's lunch were found, so that location is now the current LKP.

The Importance Of
The Last Known Position (LKP)

The last known position is an important starting point for search strategy, and will change as clues are discovered throughout the incident. The LKP can be any one of the following:

> **The Place Last Seen (PLS)**. The point where some person last saw the lost subject. The PLS, if directly associated with the area the subject is logically assumed to be in, can be a critical point in determining the search area.

A Departure Point. This is the location, corroborated by evidence, from which the subject is assumed to have departed, en route to some destination.

Examples of Departure Points:
— the subject's automobile
— a trailhead
— a campsite
— the top of a ski lift.

Most Recent Clue. The location of a clue that can be reliably associated with the subject and is more recent than other clues, is a third way to determine the LKP. As clues are discovered and the LKP is updated, the search area should become progressively smaller — indicating that the search effort is getting closer to the subject.[3]

---

[3] However, keep in mind that the Initial Planning Point (IPP), which is used for estimating the theoretical and statistical search areas, will usually remain the same throughout the incident.

Methods Of Establishing The Search Area

1. **THEORETICAL** * Distance that the subject could have traveled in the time elapsed.

2. **STATISTICAL** * Data which reflects the distances other subjects have traveled under similar conditions.

3. **SUBJECTIVE** * Evaluation of the limiting factors that exist for the specific incident and geographic location.

4. **REASONING** * Systematic analysis of circumstances surrounding the disappearance of the subject.

The Theoretical Search Area

The theoretical search area is a circle plotted on the map indicating the estimated maximum distance the subject could have traveled from the IPP during the elapsed time.

When considering the probable actions of a lost subject, it is important to realize that **an individual theoretically can travel in any direction from the IPP**. The search planner initially must consider the total area (that of a circle) in which the subject may be located. **The area of a circle equals π times r^2** (where π [pronounced "pie"] = 3.14, and **r** = the radius of the circle, the straight line distance the subject is estimated to have

traveled from the IPP). For example, if a subject was capable of traveling 1 mile in any direction from the last known position, the total area to be searched would encompass approximately 3.14 square miles, as shown in Figure 12.1, which shows the formula for the area of a circle. A subject who traveled 3 miles from the IPP would create a search area of over 28 square miles. A three to one ratio in the distance traveled translates into nine to one in terms of area (3.14 sq mi vs. 28 sq mi)! It is clear from this relationship that it is important to utilize confinement and a quick response to keep the search area from growing geometrically with each step that the subject takes away from the IPP.

Figure 12.1

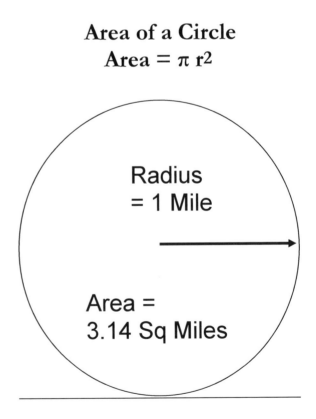

Area of a Circle
Area = π r^2

Radius = 1 Mile

Area = 3.14 Sq Miles

If a subject was capable of traveling 2 or more miles from the IPP, then:

for 2 miles: $(3.14 * 2^2)$ or $3.14 * 4$
Area = 12.6 square miles

for 3 miles: $(3.14 * 3^2)$ or $3.14 * 9$
Area = 28.3 square miles

Notice that the size of the search area does not merely double when the distance traveled is doubled. For example, when the radius of a 1-mile circle is increased to 2 miles, the size of the area is quadrupled. Increasing the radius to 3 miles increases the area by 9 times that of the 1-mile circle. This fact illustrates the importance of confining the subject to as small a "circle" as possible.

Growth of the Theoretical Search Area

As was noted, the theoretical search area is a circle plotted on the map indicating the estimated maximum distance the subject could have traveled from the IPP during the elapsed time. When considering the probable actions of a lost subject, it is important to realize that **an individual theoretically can travel in any direction from the IPP**. The search planner initially must consider the total area of a defined circle in which the subject may be located, **given the amount of time the subject** has been missing. The area is circular because no direction of travel has yet been established, so the subject could have gone in any direction. Given that the formula

for a circular search area "A" is $A = \pi r^2$ where $\pi = 3.14$, for a quick estimate, π can be rounded to just 3. For the theoretical search area, "r" (the radius) is the maximum straight line distance that the subject could travel from the IPP. In this case the radius "r" is determined from this formula:

r = (amount of time missing) times (the speed at which the subject traveled). The amount of time the subject has been missing is known from the initial investigation. The search manager must estimate the subject's travel speed based on the initial investigation. Some travel speeds for adults and children are shown in figures 12.2 and 12.3. For example, the subject has been gone for one hour and he/she traveled at one mile per hour. The theoretical search area "A" is:

$A = \pi \times [(1\ hour) \times (1\ mile/hour)]^2 = 3.1$ square miles But if the subject has been gone two hours, the theoretical search area is calculated as:

$A = \pi \times [(2\ hours) \times (1\ mile/hour)]^2 = 12.6$ square miles. Note that though the subject was missing only an hour longer, the theoretical search area went up by a factor of four. If the subject has been missing 3 hours, the theoretical search area becomes 28.3 square miles. **It is this rapid growth in the theoretical search area with time that is a major factor in why search is an emergency**. It also shows why containment is an important initial search tactic. The theoretical search area may be used initially, but it is generally replaced by a smaller statistical search area (based on known data) or a subjective search area.

___

How fast do subjects travel?

___

In order to estimate the theoretical search area, it is useful to know something about the rate of travel for the type of person you are searching for. Figure 12.2 presents travel speeds for various adult categories, while Figure 12.3 (based on research conducted by Cornell & Heth, 1996) presents measures of walking speed for children 3 to 12 years of age, traveling through a suburban neighborhood. Keep in mind that these are only averages for adults and median values for children. Many subjects are capable of traveling faster than the tables indicate.

___

Figure 12.2

Travel Speeds for Six Categories of Adults
(average experience, level terrain)

	Mi per Hour	Km per Hour
Hiker		
No pack:	2 - 2.5	3.2 - 4
With pack:	1.5 - 2	2.4 - 3.2
Bicyclist	10	16
Canoeist		
No wind:	2	3.2
Head wind:	1 - 1.5	1.6 - 2.4
Tail wind:	3	4.8

(Fig. 12.2 cont.)

	Mi per Hour	Km per Hour
Cross-country Skier		
On trail:		
No pack	2.5	4
With pack	1.5	2.4
Off trail:		
No pack	1.25	2
With pack	0.75	1.2
Snowshoer		
On trail:		
No pack	2	3.2
With pack	1	1.6
Off trail:		
No pack	1	1.6
With pack	0.75	1.2

___

Figure 12.3 provides data from one suburban study on the median walking speeds for children between three and twelve years old.

___

Figure 12.3

Median walking speeds for five age groups of children 3 - 12 years (suburban streets)

Age (yrs)	Mi/Hr	Km/Hr
3 - 4	2.0	3.2
5 - 6	2.4	3.9
7 - 8	2.7	4.3
9 - 10	2.9	4.4
11 - 12	3.0	4.8

Source: Cornell & Heth (1996). Note: these data are computed from the 50th percentile group for each age.

___

While the numbers in Figure 12.3 are not reflective of a wilderness environment, they do **demonstrate expected variations across the age groups**.

With regard to walking speed, a useful rule of thumb (in the absence of indications to the contrary), is that **walking subjects will average about one mile per hour** away from the LKP. They may well walk faster than this, but not necessarily in a straight line (see Figure 12.4). For example, two hours after becoming lost, a subject may be approximately two miles away from the point where he entered the woods, although actually walking perhaps five miles or more to get there. However, if there are many trails or other travel aids available, and the person is panicky and motivated to "hurry up" and find their way out, they may well travel farther than that predicted by the one-mile-per-hour rule of thumb.

Figure 12.4

Lost Subject vs. Hiker Possible Travel Patterns

LOST:

HIKER:

A lost subject may have walked a total of 5 miles but ends up only 2 miles from the Last Known Position (see Figure 12.4).

Statistical Search Areas

Descriptive statistics like the median and maximum distance traveled, collected by subject type and region, can be helpful in limiting the search area to something more practical than the theoretical search area. This is supported by an observation of distances traveled over the time missing, which reveals that lost persons rarely, if ever, walk in a straight line at the same speed for the duration of time that they are lost.

The largest statistical (data-based) search area would be calculated by using the maximum distance traveled in the available data as the radius. However, the maximum distance may be an extreme value out to which few lost subjects can be expected to travel. Like the theoretical search area, a statistical search area based on the maximum distance traveled is likely to be unmanageable and impractical; unmanageable due to its size, and impractical due to the fact that there is a low probability of finding subjects out at distances where resources are spread thin and where subjects rarely venture. Clearly, land search planners need techniques for establishing a search area which strike a balance between the likelihood of finding the subject and the ability to deploy limited resources for a limited time over a limited amount of terrain. One solution is to use the median to divide the data in half, and another is to use the 75th percentile as the radius for defining the circle containing the initial search area. In the absence of clues to the contrary, this last technique eliminates outliers in the most distant 25% of cases, and describes an area within which 75% of subjects lost under similar circumstances were found. Consider the "raw" hypothetical data in Figure 12.5 for lost hikers. Each incident is logged with an identifier that ends with the last digit of the year, the date of occurrence and the distance found in miles from the IPP.

In order to compute the median and the 75th percentile for the distance traveled, the data in Figure 12.5 needs to be sorted by distance in ascending order, with no regard for its sequence of occurrence in time. Figure 12.6 provides the lost hiker data sorted by distance.

Figure 12.6

"Sorted" Lost Hiker Distance Traveled Data For 17 Hypothetical Incidents

Rank	ID	Miles
1	F6	2.9
2	D6	3.4
3	E5	3.5
4	B4	3.6
5	B5	3.7
6	C5	3.8
7	F5	3.9
8	A4	4.2
9	A5	4.4
10	A6	4.6
11	C4	4.8
12	D5	5.1
13	G6	5.3
14	D4	5.7
15	B6	5.9
16	E6	6.1
17	C6	7.3

Figure 12.5

"Raw" Lost Hiker Data

ID	Date	Miles
A4	11-Jun-04	4.2
B4	28-Jun-04	3.6
C4	5-Jul-04	4.8
D4	17-Aug-04	5.7
A5	28-May-05	4.4
B5	7-Jun-05	3.7
C5	13-Jul-05	3.8
D5	8-Aug-05	5.1
E5	10-Aug-05	3.5
F5	5-Sep-05	3.9
A6	25-May-06	4.6
B6	3-Jun-06	5.9
C6	9-Jun-06	7.3
D6	12-Jul-06	3.4
E6	19-Jul-06	6.1
F6	23-Aug-06	2.9
G6	3-Sep-06	5.3

Finding the Median

Since the Median is defined as the value of the data point in the "middle" position of a dataset (not the average), it is easy to find in Figure 12.6. The value at Rank 9, 4.4 miles, is the Median of the dataset because eight values lie above Rank 9 and eight below. For any sorted dataset use the following formula to find the rank position of the Median: **[0.5 * (n + 1)]** where "n" equals the number of observations in the dataset.

Rank Position of the Median:

$$[0.5 * (n + 1)]$$

Where "n" is the number of observations in the dataset.

The hypothetical example of lost hikers in Figure 12.6 has an odd number (17) of sorted observations. The rank position of the Median is calculated as:

$[0.5 * (17+1)] = [0.5 * 18] = 9$. The value at Rank 9 gives a median of 4.4 miles, the same value we get from eyeballing the data. Using the median distance traveled as the radius, a circle will be defined with an area that contains the distances where half of all subjects were found closest to the IPP (inside the 50th percentile). That would be one example of a statistically determined portion

of a search area. The area of a circle with a radius of 4.4 miles would be calculated as $[\pi * 4.4^2] = 3.14 * 19.36 = 61$ Square Miles.

As is apparent from the formula for the position of the median, the median is also defined mathematically as the value in the data at the 50th percentile. If there were 18 observations in the dataset (an even number), then the position of the median would be at $[0.5 * (18 + 1)] = 9.5$. In this case the median is calculated as the average of the values at Rank 9 and Rank 10. For any dataset with an even number of observations, the median is computed as the average of the values at the two "middle" rank positions, the whole numbers found on either side of the "integer+0.5" fraction that results from the $[0.5 * (n + 1)]$ formula when "n" is an even number.

Finding the 75th Percentile

To find the rank position of 75th percentile, simply modify the formula for the position of the median as follows: **[0.75 * (n + 1)]**.

Rank Position of the 75th Percentile:

$$[0.75 * (n + 1)]$$

Where "n" is the number of observations in the dataset.

For the data in Figure 12.6, the rank position of the 75th percentile would be [0.75 * (17 + 1)] = 0.75 * 18 = 13.5. When the result is halfway between two rank positions (in this case 13.5), take the average of the two values from the rank on either side. Since Rank 13 is at 5.3 miles and Rank 14 is at 5.7 miles, the value of the 75th percentile in miles would be calculated as (5.3 + 5.7)/2 = 5.5 miles. When the rank position of the 75th (or any other) percentile is some fraction other than half, use interpolation to find its value. For example, the rank position of the 90th Percentile in the data listed in Figure 12.6 would be computed as [0.90 * (n + 1)] or [0.9 * 18] = 16.2. To find the value of the 90th Percentile through interpolation, take 20% (the additional fraction of 0.2 in 16.2) of the difference between the values at Rank 16 (6.1 mi) and Rank 17 (7.3 mi), and add that to the value at the starting rank in the percentile formula (in this case Rank 16). For this data, the value of the 90th Percentile would be calculated as:

[(0.2 * (7.3 - 6.1)] + 6.1 =

[(0.2 * 1.2)] + 6.1 =

[0.24] + 6.1 = 6.34 miles as the lost person distance traveled for this category at the 90th Percentile.

Using the 75th Percentile distance of 5.5 miles as the radius results in a circle with an area of about 95 square miles. If you can provide confinement of major roads and trails along the perimeter of the circle defined by the 75th percentile then you have effectively contained

normal access out of an area where 75% of subjects, under similar circumstances, have been found. Figure 12.7 depicts how the median, 75th and 90th percentiles for distance traveled would look as planning circles based on the hypothetical data in Figure 12.6.

Figure 12.7

Circular Search Areas derived from the Median, 75th & 90th Percentiles of Hypothetical Distance Traveled Data

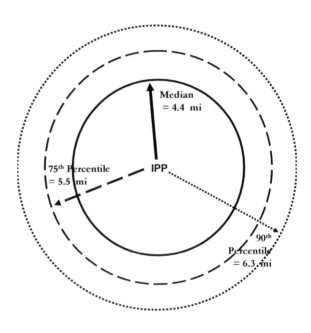

For the data depicted in Figure 12.7, 90% of the subjects in this category could be expected to be found within a distance at or below 6.3 miles from the IPP.

An Alternative to the 75th Percentile

The distance traveled data itself can be readily analyzed to determine actual upper and lower bounds that establish a range of distances where at least 75% of subjects can be expected to be found based on statistical variability. This differs from the 75th percentile which starts at the IPP and works outward. The lower boundary of the range containing at least 75% of the points where subjects can be expected to be found will usually start at some distance out from the IPP, often reducing the total area needed to encompass 75% or more of the cases. Even when the overall area is not reduced, the technique allows planners to focus on the specific range of distances where at least three-fourths of the subjects in a category can be expected to be found. Figure 12.8 is a dot scale diagram depicting the radial distance traveled for the 17 hypothetical incidents in Figure 12.6. Using the 75th Percentile distance as the radius for defining the circular statistical search area, teams would be deployed to search from the IPP out to 5.5 miles, the distance marked by the upward pointing arrow.

Note though that the data, for this hypothetical jurisdiction and subject type, seems to cluster between 3 to 6 miles. In the absence of clues, searching from 0 to 2.8 miles generally does not result in a find for this subject type, and searching only out to the 75th Percentile would exclude the higher probability areas between 5.5 and 6.1 miles. A statistical analysis of the available lost subject distance traveled data can provide planners with a range of distances more focused than the 75th Percentile. By employing "Chebyshev's Theorem," land SAR planners can define the range of distances traveled in which 75% or more of the subjects in a category can expect to be found. We'll call this the **"75% Plus" Probability Range.**

Chebyshev's Theorem

Chebyshev (sometimes spelled "Tchebyshev" like the composer Tchaikovsky) was a 19th Century Russian mathematician whose statistical theorem states that **at least 75% of the data always fall within plus or minus Two Standard Deviations of the data Mean**. The universal availability of computers and spreadsheets makes computing the mean and standard deviation for a dataset quite easy.

Figure 12.8

**Lost Person Distances Traveled
in Miles Found From the IPP
For 17 Hypothetical Subjects**

Finding the "75% Plus" Probability Range

Most spreadsheets have STDEV and AVERAGE or similar functions for computing the Standard Deviation (SD) and Mean (the arithmetic average) of a dataset. Once these two values are known, upper and lower boundaries can be computed defining the range where 75% or more of the subjects will be found. The formulas are:

Lower Bound = [Mean – (2 * SD)]

Upper Bound = [Mean + (2 * SD).

**Formulas for the
"75%Plus" Probability Range**

Lower Bound = [Mean – (2 * SD)]
Upper Bound = [Mean + (2 * SD)]

Using the distance traveled data in miles from either Figure 12.6 or 12.5 (because it need not be sorted), the Mean is 4.6 miles and the Standard Deviation is 1.17 miles. Applying the formulas:

Lower Bound = [4.6 – (2 * 1.17)] = 2.26
Upper Bound = [4.6 + (2 * 1.17)] = 6.94,

we find that the range between 2.26 miles and

6.94 miles can be expected to contain at least 75% of the lost persons in this category. Referring to Figure 12.8, you can see that this "75% Plus" probability range is depicted by the dashed line under the data. This range of distances will contain at least 75% of the cases, but possibly more based on the internal characteristics of the data. In this example, only the last data point is not included in the 75% Plus range, which encompasses 16/17ths or 94% of the incidents.

Note too that the use of the lower boundary does not imply that the first 2.3 miles are to be ignored. Certainly trails and travel aids should be checked in hasty searches along those first 2.3 miles and farther, to ensure that the subject is not simply sitting along the trail with a sprained ankle. However, based on the dispersion of distances within this particular dataset, 75% or more of the subjects can be expected to be found between 2.26 and 6.94 miles. This technique is very robust and can be applied to any dataset, but is especially helpful when planners are restricted by small datasets with skewed values, typical of distances traveled by lost persons. To define a range of distances within which 89% or more of the subjects can be expected to be found, use plus or minus three standard deviations on either side of the mean. Upper and lower bounds based on the formula [Mean +/- (3 * SD)] provide an alternative to using the 90th Percentile for defining a statistical search area.

Putting Numbers into the Preplan

The calculation of the Median, 75th and 90th percentiles and the "75% Plus" probability range of distances traveled for a set of various subject types is something that should be included in the preplan for easy access. Scrambling for lost person data at the start of a search can be frustrating. The best data would be from incidents in your own jurisdiction or region. In the absence of that, borrowed data from other regions, while less representative, provides a starting point for defining the search area. Logging data from each incident and sharing the statistical results with other regions, or in a central database, will help ensure that SAR managers everywhere will have adequate lost person data for search planning.

The Importance of Gathering Data

As more distances are recorded from past cases for similar lost subject types, the statistical measures become increasingly more reliable for predicting where future lost persons are likely to be found. To summarize, in analyzing statistical data, five distances are especially important:

1. **Distance from the initial planning point to where the subject was actually found**, expressed in terms of straight line "crow's flight" distances (as in Figure 12.8).

2. **Median distance** — The median distance within the entire range of case histories is the "middle point" (not the average) where half of the subjects are found at or above that distance, and the other half at or below that distance. In other words, the Median is the distance which divides the number of finds into upper and lower halves.

3. **75th Percentile distance** — The value of the distance traveled data at or below which 75% of the lost persons in a particular category were found.

4. **Upper Bound of the "75% Plus" probability range** — The upper boundary of the distance traveled probability range where at least 75% or more of the subjects in a category can expect to be found.

5. **Lower Bound of the "75% Plus" probability range** — The lower boundary of the distance traveled probability range where at least 75% or more of the subjects in a category can expect to be found.

If none of these statistical measures are available, then the next best thing to do is to use the theoretical search area, based on an estimate of the subject's speed and time lost, to compute a radius for defining the circular search area needed for containment and continued planning.

Even when we cannot determine which direction the subject may have traveled from the IPP, there is still an advantage to putting these statistical measures on the map. When it comes time to segment the map and assign probabilities of area (see POA in Chapter 13), segments lying within the high probability ranges can be more easily recognized as such, and given higher priority accordingly.

Probability Density

For search efficiency, according to John Wartes, it is important to consider the size of an area as well as its likelihood of containing the subject. He proposed using the concept of **Probability Density ("pDen")**, which is defined numerically as the probability that the area contains the subject (POA, as described in Chapter 13), divided by the size of the area. In other words, for high efficiency, areas with high probability density should be searched first (unless circumstances pertaining to terrain or logistics indicate otherwise). The point being made here is not that we should necessarily focus our search efforts close to the areas near the IPP. Rather, search planners should use all of the information available to them in order to increase the efficiency of search efforts, which means getting the job done sooner, more safely, and with the least expenditure of resources. Understanding pDen can be useful when large parts of the search area can be given a lower priority due to factors like the determination of a reliable direction of travel (often from trailing dogs or human trackers) which points the other way, or when there are natural barriers (such as rivers or cliffs) that tend to restrict the subject's movements, increasing pDen in these catchment areas. In Wartes's words, "the task is not as simple as putting circles on maps."

Tables of Distance Traveled by Subject Category

Figure 12.9 was compiled by Ken Hill from the analysis of lost person reports filed in Nova Scotia, Canada. For each category, the figure shows the median straight line (or "crow fly") distance traveled from the IPP to the point at which subjects were located, independent of time and actual distances subjects walked. It also presents the range of distances (minimum and maximum for the number of cases) for each category, the 25th, 75th and 90th percentiles for those distances traveled, and the survival rate.

One warning: the information is presented only as an illustration of how lost person data might be used as a planning tool. Although there is some agreement between this data and Syrotuck's, planners should be wary of relying on someone else's data for search planning, especially for categories with few cases (for example, children). **Planners intending to use distance traveled data should, ideally, compile similar tables from cases in their own locale.**

Figure 12.9

Distances Traveled for Nine Categories of Lost Persons in Nova Scotia, Canada

Category	Cases	25%	Median	75%	90%	Range	Survived
Hunters	127	1.30 km 0.81 mi	2.39 km 1.49 mi	3.83 km 2.38 mi	8.00 km 4.97 mi	0.10 - 19.31 km 0.06 - 12.00 mi	94%
Hikers	53	1.35 km 0.84 mi	2.23 km 1.39 mi	4.80 km 2.98 mi	7.52 km 4.67 mi	0.22 - 24.00 km 0.14 - 14.91 mi	94%
Fishers	38	0.92 km 0.57 mi	1.77 km 1.10 mi	4.15 km 2.58 mi	6.01 km 3.73 mi	0.45 - 17.70 km 0.28 - 11.00 mi	91%
Misc. Adults	49	0.75 km 0.47 mi	1.70 km 1.06 mi	3.57 km 2.22 mi	7.82 km 4.86 mi	0.10 - 19.00 km 0.06 - 11.81 mi	98%
Children (1-6)	16	0.50 km 0.31 mi	1.03 km 0.64 mi	1.81 km 1.12 mi	2.02 km 1.26 mi	0.10 - 2.65 km 0.06 - 1.65 mi	100%
Children (7-12)	15	0.80 km 0.50 mi	1.48 km 0.92 mi	2.50 km 1.55 mi	3.20 km 1.99 mi	0.14 - 8.00 km 0.09 - 4.97 mi	96%
Youths (13-15)	23	0.86 km 0.53 mi	1.49 km 0.93 mi	3.00 km 1.86 mi	4.18 km 2.60 mi	0.40 - 7.00 km 0.25 - 4.35 mi	100%
Despondents	26	0.40 km 0.25 mi	0.81 km 0.50 mi	1.28 km 0.80 mi	1.60 km 0.99 mi	0.10 - 3.38 km 0.06 - 2.10 mi	54%
Dementia	41	0.40 km 0.25 mi	1.00 km 0.62 mi	1.46 km 0.91 mi	2.40 km 1.49 mi	0.10 - 5.43 km 0.06 - 3.37 mi	73%
Total =	388						

Compiled by Ken Hill, Halifax Regional SAR, August, 2006

Sample Search Area Problems

1. As the incident Planning Chief, you have estimated that a particular lost hiker with a backpack was capable of active travel for 12 hours at 2 mph before being reported missing. What is the Theoretical Search Area at the start of the search?

Solution 1: The maximum straight line distance that the lost hiker could be expected to travel is 2 mph times 12 hours, which equals 24 miles, the radius of the Theoretical Search Area at the start of the search. Applying the formula for the area of a circle (Figure 12.1), the Theoretical Search Area would be computed as $[\pi * 24$ squared$]$ = $[3.14 * 24 * 24]$ = 1,809 Square Miles.

2. Based on a compilation of distances traveled by lost hikers in the local area, the value of the distance traveled at the 75th Percentile has been determined to be 8 miles. What is the Statistical Search Area based on the 75th Percentile in this case?

Solution 2: The radius of the circle derived from the 75th Percentile data is 8 miles. Applying the formula for the area of a circle, the Statistical Search Area based on the 75th Percentile is $[\pi * 8 * 8]$ = $[3.14 * 64]$ = 201 Square Miles.

3. Distance traveled data for lost hikers in the local area has been compiled and sorted for 79 incidents. What is the Rank position of the Median and the 75th Percentile?

Solution 3: The formula for the Rank position of the Median is the same as the formula for the 50th Percentile: $[0.5 * (n+1)]$ where "n" equals the number of observations. For 79 observations, the rank position of the Median would be calculated as: $[0.5 * (79+1)]$ = $[0.5 * 80]$ = 40. The Median itself would be the value of the distance at the 40th position in the sorted data. The Rank position of the 75th Percentile would be calculated as $[0.75 * (79+1)]$ = 60. The value of the 75th Percentile would be the value of the distance at the 60th position in the sorted data.

Subjective Considerations Influencing The Establishment Of The Search Area

In addition to the statistical information discussed above, there will also be many subjective factors that will affect decisions on where to search for the subject. Such factors include:

"Likely spots".
Natural barriers and terrain features.
Physical clues left by the subject.
Historical data of the area from case histories.
"Gut feelings" or intuition based on special circumstances.
Physical and mental limitations of the subject.

We describe such factors as "subjective" because their impact on search strategy will vary depending upon circumstances and the perceived importance attributed to them by search planners. Indeed, different search planners dealing with the same subjective factors may easily disagree on their significance.

Likely Spots

These are features or areas that may offer some attraction to the lost person for:

Ease of movement.

Shelter.

Food or water.

Curiosity or companionship.

Some examples of likely spots:

An unmarked path or trail.

A possible "short cut".

Abandoned or unused buildings.

Entrances to mines.

Overheads and caves.

Berry patches and other possible sources of food.

Stream banks.

Any potential natural shelter from the elements.

Whenever possible, searchers should be made aware of the subject's behavior with respect to the identification of likely spots. For example, mushroom pickers, bird watchers, deer hunters, or even despondent individuals, all have preferred locations where clues are most likely to be found. Searchers who have been properly briefed will be able to recognize such likely spots in the field. Search planners should therefore understand the concept and importance of likely spots. Members of each search team should be reminded of the likely spot concept and told to:

- Look for them.

- Mark them on their maps.

- Investigate them whenever possible.

- Discuss them at debriefing sessions.

Whatever type of search tactic is employed, it is important that likely spots be looked for and investigated at the time that they are first identified. The fact that it may be necessary to depart from a predetermined search pattern should not be used as an excuse to bypass, ignore, or forget a possible feature of attraction. Any likely spot identified by any member of a search team should be noted and reported. While it may not be practical to investigate every likely spot immediately, each should be identified and, when necessary, investigated by another search team.

Natural Barriers and Terrain Features

As mentioned earlier, some features of terrain may influence the subject's direction of travel, both positively and negatively. These include cliffs, rivers, dense vegetation, clearcuts, power lines, switchbacks, steep terrain, drainages, old roads, and railroad tracks.

Physical Clues Left by the Subject

Physical clues are evidence that the subject has been in a specific location. Clues are critical for establishing the direction that a subject has traveled, and for narrowing down the search area.

> *Clue examples:*
> Footprints.
> Clothing.
> Equipment.
> Wrappers - cigarette, candy, gum.
> Eyewitness reports.
> Campsites or makeshift shelters.

Historical Data for the Locale

Information from the local case histories often indicates that subjects lost or overdue in a specific area tend to do similar things. For example, in some areas drainages tend to funnel lost subjects into specific locations, such as canyons.

Watercourses and drainages may lead lost subjects into catchment areas where subjects cannot exit without retracing their steps. Such areas should be identified and investigated early in the incident.

Intuition, Hunches, and "Gut Feelings"

Search planning is — and likely always will be — more art than science. With experience from previous incidents, the search planner will develop expertise that is not easily articulated. He or she will often look at a map of the search area and intuitively "feel" that certain locations should receive priority. Alternatively, they may review information about the missing subject or the circumstances of loss, and infer (based on comparisons with similar incidents) new information that is not stated directly. For example, the search planner may suspect that a small child is missing because he followed a deer away from camp (a common occurrence). The planner may then decide to search nearby game trails or deer feeding areas — even though there is no clear evidence that the child did in fact follow a deer.

We are not suggesting that such intuitions are always correct. However, we do recommend that they be given serious consideration, especially when they come from experienced search planners.

Physical and Mental Limitations of the Subject

Subjects with mental and physical limitations (their own or those related to equipment) deserve special consideration.

> *Examples:*
> Handicapped individuals will be restricted in rough terrain.
> Mentally retarded individuals may wander aimlessly.
> Slick-soled, low quarter shoes in rough terrain could limit travel.

It should be noted that friends and relatives of the missing person will often overestimate or underestimate the subject's capabilities. Third party evaluations (such as from physicians or caretakers) are sometimes more reliable as in these two examples:

1. A camp counselor's evaluation of a child's capabilities.
2. A nurse's evaluation of an elderly walkaway from a convalescent home.

Reasoning

Reasoning is the process by which the search planner looks at general facts and evidence and logically infers possibilities that are not obvious or were not known initially. It is distinguishable from intuition (described earlier) because there is a logical link between the facts considered and the conclusion made.

Example Situation:

A car is found parked on a small turnout of a secondary road in Mt. Rainier National Park. It has been parked there for several days.

Known facts:

- There is no trailhead at that location.
- There is no view of the mountain at that location.
- The automobile is registered to an airman at McChord A.F.B.
- Preliminary search of the surrounding area reveals no clues or additional information.

- Terrain is timbered and the turnout is at the base of a small canyon.
- Search of the locked car reveals the following articles:
    - One pair of low quarter shoes
    - An empty film box

More extensive searching in the area revealed no leads or clues. It was deduced that the airman had probably changed shoes (more than likely into boots for climbing). The empty film box was an indication that he had a camera with him. Since there was no view of the mountain from that point, it was suspected that he might have looked for a unique or unusual view to photograph. One of the searchers took this line of reasoning and then tried to project himself into the missing subject's place. "Where would I go if I wanted a unique, unusual, or beautiful photograph, if I were starting from this turnout?" Subsequent searching revealed that the subject had climbed up to a high location

Why Again Prefer the Median to the Mean?

For purposes of predicting how far a lost person is most likely to travel, it is useful to know how far similar lost persons have gone in past search incidents. When we record such distance-traveled data and plot their distribution on a graph, we see that most distances cluster near the bottom end of the scale, with fewer cases recorded for extreme distances. Consider the bar graph in Figure 12.10, which is based on 100 cases of lost hunters (Hill, 1996). Each bar represents a distance category of 1 kilometer width, with the bar's height representing the number of cases for each category. For example, the second bar from the left (the tallest) represents all distances between 1 and 2 kilometers, while the bar's height indicates that 26 lost hunters traveled this distance.

Overall, the shape of this distribution is described by statisticians as a **positively skewed**, because the "tail" of the distribution points toward the right or the positive end of the "curve." **Almost all distance-traveled data, when plotted in this fashion, will have such a positive skew, regardless of the category of the subject or the number of cases added to the sample.** For this reason, the **mean** (numerical average) is not appropriate for use as the radius in defining the circular search area because it is subject to skewing from extreme outliers.

For example, the **mean** for the positively skewed distribution in Figure 12.10 is 3.6 kilometers, while the **median** (the point that divides the distribution exactly in half) is 2.4 kilometers - more than a kilometer difference!

If we added two more data points, one at 2km and one at 100km, the median would stay the same (half the cases above and half the cases below) but the mean would jump to 4.5km, skewing the average value farther to the right.

The median is preferred for search planning because it is a more stable measure than the mean. The mean is most helpful when used in conjunction with standard deviation to provide an estimate of data dispersion when defining probability ranges based on historical experience.

The range of values representing 25% of the cases below the median distance and 25% of the cases above the median distance define the "inter-quartile range" (IQR), which is the most stable 50% of a normally distributed (bell curve shaped) data distribution centered around the median. However, since lost person distance traveled data is typically skewed to the right (long right tail with most data bunched to the left) the inter-quartile range will generally have a lower probability density (less POA per unit of area) than the zone defined from the IPP (zero distance) out to the median (50th percentile). Figure 12.10 depicts this "middle 50%" for a sample of lost hunters in Nova Scotia. Searches in high probabilty density (pDen) areas allow the Oveall Probability Of Success (OPOS) to rise faster than do searches in low pDen areas. In spite of the statistical stability of the IQR, for the same given set of resources, the "bottom 50%" from the IPP to the median offers higher pDen than the IQR.

Figure 12.10

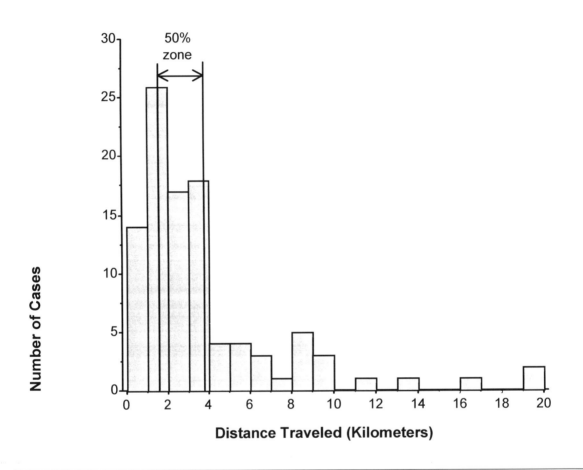

Sample Probability Distribution for Distance Traveled by 100 Lost Hunters in Nova Scotia (Compiled 1996)

The 50% zone represents the distribution of incidents that were recorded for distances where hunters were found between the 25th Percentile and the 75th Percentile. The spread of values within this area is also referred to as the "Inter-Quartile Range" or IQR. Like the distance from the IPP to the median, this defines a range consisting of half of all observations. However, for lost person data which is positively skewed (tail to the right) like that shown above, lost person distance traveled data from the IPP to the median (50th percentile) will have a higher probability density (POA per unit area) than the distances traveled within the IQR.

Returning to our original point, we use the median not merely because our sample sizes tend to be small (which is true), but because of the positively skewed (right-tailed) shape of the distance-traveled distribution. Increasing the size of our sample past 30 observations (by adding new cases) will not usually make significant changes to the shape of the distribution, but will tend to stabilize the median and make it a better indicator for planning. In other words, larger sample sizes are better! As sample sizes of lost person data begin to approach and exceed thirty in number, they become statistically more reliable. For this reason, when using medians from data sets with less than thirty observations, do so with extra caution.

Summary

In this chapter we described four ways of establishing the areas to be searched. The **theoretical search area** is the area defined by the distance that the subject could have traveled in the time since he or she became missing. **Statistical search areas** are based on an analysis of recorded distances that similar subjects have traveled in the past. The **subjective search area** is based on the search planner's judgments of where the subject might have gone, considering likely spots and terrain analysis. Finally, the search planner uses **reasoning** to systematically analyze the circumstances surrounding the disappearance of the subject, in order to identify possible

locations where the subject may be. These methods of determining the area to search are not mutually exclusive, and usually can all be employed simultaneously during the course of an incident.

The theoretical search area may not be particularly useful when the search has been delayed, because few subjects travel more than four or five miles from the initial point last seen. However, as clues are discovered, search planners may be able to use the 1-mile-per-hour estimate for walking subjects, to narrow down the theoretical search area considerably. When useful data are available, the statistical search area will help identify high probability areas as well as optimal locations for confining the subject. Subjective factors such as hunches and intuitions — when based on the search planner's knowledge and experience — can also contribute significantly to the finding of the missing subject, especially when combined with reasoning and logical analysis of the available evidence.

In the next chapter, we will continue this discussion by describing how the search planner can effectively segment the search area into manageable sizes, and to prioritize the segments by applying concepts introduced in this chapter.

Questions for Discussion:

1. Why is the theoretical search area usually less useful than a statistical search area as a tool for search planning?

2. Why is it important to retain the initial planning point (IPP) for search planning, regardless of subsequent known positions?

3. If no lost person distance traveled data exists for your locale or region, how would you establish the search area on the next incident?

CHAPTER 13

SETTING PRIORITIES: THE PROBABILITY OF AREA (POA)

With the primary search area defined, it is time to define segments and set priorities. In this chapter, we will continue the application of probability theory to **decisions about where to search for the subject.**

CHAPTER OBJECTIVES:

When you finish studying this chapter, you should be able to:

1. List the reasons for segmenting the search area.
2. Describe the process of segmenting the area.
3. Define the concept of probability of area (POA).
4. Describe the consensus method of assigning POA.
5. Describe the scenario analysis procedure for assigning POA when alternate lost person scenarios are plausible.

Segmenting The Search Area

An important component of efficient search management is dividing the search area into manageable units or **segments** and assigning priorities to each unit in terms of its likelihood of containing the lost subject (**probability of area**). With the search area divided into segments, the search planner can also keep

track of coverage (or **cumulative probability of detection**) for each segment.

In addition, segments with clearly defined boundaries tend to reduce the possibilities for errors by search teams in the field, including overlapping with adjacent teams and, more critically, gaps in coverage.

Defining Segment Boundaries

The drawing of segment boundaries requires careful thought, good map reading, and ideally, a knowledge of the region. The use of imaginary lines such as latitude and longitude, UTM, or other grid lines is worthless unless completely relying on electronic navigation which is not a good practice for land searches. **The choice of boundaries must be based on what can be seen and readily identified in the field by all searchers.** The following features may provide suitable boundaries:

> **Natural:** Ridge lines, canyon bottoms, rivers, streams, lake edges, cliffs, vegetation breaks.

Artificial: Fences, walls, roads, ditches, power lines, trails, firebreaks, survey or boundary lines, railroad tracks.

Improvised: Compass lines (stringed or flagged). These are necessary when sufficient natural or artificial boundaries are unavailable.

> **Note: any area that will be searched separately should be identified as a unique segment; for example, trails, lake edges, or other high probability areas which will be searched by hasty teams.**

The Size of Segments

Size is dictated by terrain, vegetation, and the type of resource that will be assigned to the segment. A reasonable size is a segment that can be covered by a search resource in 4 to 6 hours. A segment can be large (for example, a square mile or more) if it is a relatively flat, open area that will only be searched by aircraft. More frequently, however, segments will be searched by ground searchers (for example, grid teams, air scent dog teams) working in low visibility conditions. A useful rule of thumb for segment sizes is approximately **0.25 square mile/0.65 square km or 160 acres/65 hectares. A common mistake is to assign ground searchers to segments much larger than this.**

Large segments:
- Are almost impossible to complete in one search period.
- Are bad for morale.
- Cause teams to rush and miss clues.
- Are difficult to continue searching with a new teams in later search periods.

The "typical" search incident may involve many segments, especially when trails and other high-probability areas are assigned their own segment numbers.

Further Considerations When Drawing Segments

Avoid interior barriers. It is not efficient to have teams crossing and re-crossing fences, creeks, highways, ledges, etc.

If grid teams are going to be using **critical separation** (see Chapter 15) as a search tactic, then their task will be easier if the segment is as uniform as possible with respect to visibility (for example, the density of vegetation). This will minimize the need to regroup and alter their spacing when visibility changes.

Don't wait until all segments are drawn on the map before tasking resources. High priority segments and routes can be drawn immediately and assigned to search teams. Lower priority areas can be assigned to relatively "large" segments (regions of similar probability) temporarily and subdivided when the time comes to search them. The task of dividing segments is simplified by search management computer software such as CASIE which was developed to handle the specific needs of land search managers. Also, as the incident proceeds, new information, such as the location of trails, may facilitate the drawing of segment boundaries.

As the boundaries are identified and drawn, the segments should be numbered. Numbering the segments facilitates identification and communications. Team leaders should be given copies of the segmented map and informed of any resources tasked to adjacent segments. **All search resources should be using the same maps or sections of maps with the same scale.** and clearly marked segments. When using **topographic** maps, GPS units should all be set with the same datum as the designated "topos."

Use **biodegradable flagging and string** for improvised boundaries. Non-biodegradable materials, if they must be used, should be removed after completion of the incident. Segmenting a search area can be a time-consuming task, requiring one search planner's full-time attention. As part of the **preplan**, consider segmenting maps of high risk areas **before** people become lost there, deciding exactly where improvised boundaries should be located.

PROBABILITY OF AREA (POA)

Once the area is segmented, each segment should be assigned a value, called Probability Of Area (POA) which represents **the probability that the subject is in that segment**. In effect, this process of assigning POA ranks the segments into the order of priority that each should be searched.

The Concept of ROW Or the "Rest Of the World"

ROW is a traditional land search concept, introduced in the 1970's by John Bownds, that represents everything outside of the defined search area. ROW is seldom if ever used in maritime searches, because it is not usually essential for conducting such a search, especially where a high probability of containment is expected. However, when dealing with the unpredictability of human behavior that can be encountered (faking one's own disappearance, etc.), most land search practitioners and especially those in law enforcement, find the concept of ROW extremely helpful both as a metric for search progress and as a reminder that the subject always has some probability of NOT being in the search area. Typically, ROW is treated as its own segment which is never searched, but whose value goes up as other segments are searched. However, investigation must continue, in both ROW and the search area, throughout the duration of the search.

The issue of shifting segment POA, as resources return from the field and are debriefed, will be addressed in Chapter 16. For now, it is important to know that ROW is usually a part of most land searches, although it is not universally used when creating a consensus or reallocating POA after resources come in from the field with Coverage and POD estimates. For the purposes of most land searches, ROW is treated as a separate segment which is never assigned a POD.

The Consensus Approach to Assigning POA

The most efficient method of assigning probabilities to segments is to use a "consensus" method, that is, to obtain POA estimates from a group of planners, rather than assigning the task to one person. The process of creating a consensus using available expert evaluators familiar with subject

behavior or the local area was developed by retired U.S. Air Force colonel Robert Mattson. **The term "Mattson Consensus" has come to describe any numerical method for estimating the relative likelihood of the subject's presence across a set of segments**. The estimates are "relative" because they are mostly judgmental, not empirically derived from any experimental data, and are based on a comparison between the segments. This type of consensus tries to create a workable hierarchy of search priorities by weighting the hunches, best guesses and experience of a group of local area search experts.

A typical Mattson Consensus would include three to five expert evaluators to rate the likelihood of the subject being in each segment, including the ROW. While one person could certainly create the initial search priorties if necessary, it is better to have multiple inputs to capture the knowledge and experience contained within a selected group of informed individuals. Each evaluator is asked to rate the ROW and each of the probability regions (areas of equal probability) or segments (searchable areas of varying probability) from a total pool of 100%, reflecting the fact that the subject "has to be somewhere." Therefore, the sum of all segment and region probabilities, the POAs, must sum to 100% when including ROW. The consensus, which determines the initial POAs for each segment and the ROW, is obtained by averaging every evaluator's POA for each segment and the ROW.

A region can be thought of as a large area of uniform probability that can eventually be sub-divided into searchable segments. By **averaging the POA** from a small group of experts with varying types of experience and points of view, the consensus method will tend to counter the influence of individual biases and tendencies to underestimate or overestimate probabilities.

Obtaining Consensus POA

Participating planners **individually** and **independently** assign values to each segment, representing the strength of their belief (expressed as a probability) that the lost person is located there.

It is important that all evaluators work from the same information and are equally briefed. When creating a hierarchy of probabilities, **the total of each person's values must add up to exactly 100%, including the ROW "segment." No segment should receive a zero value, as there is always a non-zero probability that the subject could be there.**

After each evaluator has assigned POA, the total values for each segment are averaged. The results represent the initial consensus or planning POA for each segment. (See the example in Figure 13.1).

There is more than one way to create a Mattson Consensus, as the experts could start with a rating of 100 (or 1000) points for the highest probability segment with lower numbers proportionally assigned to lower probability segments. However, the final product, the **INITIAL CONSENSUS**, must conform to a total probability of 100% (or less if ROW is not explicitly used) when all the assigned probabilities are summed.

The values from the Initial Consensus are "relative" in the sense that if Segment 1 is rated at 30% POA and Segment 2 is rated at 10% POA, then this means that the likelihood of the subject being in Segment 1 is perceived to be three times that of Segment 2, based on the averaged opinions of the expert evaluators.

Search management computer software (such as CASIE discussed in more detail in Chapter 24) provides simplified and error-catching methods for creating an initial consensus and for shifting POA based on data from resources returning from the field. Other software and worksheets are also available for helping with these tasks. Some of these use a method that does not directly assign probabilities, rating instead the highest segment POA as 100 and then rating the remaining segments proportional to that. The goal, however, is the same: to create an initial hierarchy of search priorities.

Figure 13.1

A Sample Mattson Consensus
For Developing Initial Planning POA

Evaluator	Jess	Art	Gail	Jack	Total	Average
ROW	7	16	5	4	32	8
Segment 1	15	25	50	30	120	30
Segment 2	5	20	5	10	40	10
Segment 3	20	13	8	35	76	19
Segment 4	10	4	5	5	24	6
Segment 5	5	12	5	6	28	7
Segment 6	25	5	17	5	52	13
Segment 7	13	5	5	5	28	7
Total	100	100	100	100	--	100

Looking at Figure 13.1, based on the averages of the expert evaluators' opinions, the location with highest priority for searching would be Segment 1 with its 30% POA. The results of this initial consensus suggest that the likelihood of the subject being in Segment 1 is considered to be three times that of Segment 2 and over four times that of Segments 4, 5, and 7. At a planning POA of 19%, Segment 3 would have second priority. For an exercise in advanced planning concepts, refer to the discussion of Scenario Analysis in Figure 13.4, after the Summary. Scenario Analysis may be helpful in cases where search planners are unsure about the circumstances surrounding the missing person's disappearance.

Using Verbal Cues To Rate Segment POA

Alternatives to the pure Mattson Consensus, which requires rating initial POA with numbers exactly adding up to 100%, are available. One of these, which is included in the CASIE software, is called the Modified Mattson or O'Connor Consensus method. This system relies on nine verbal cues to rate each segment and lets the computer do the math. One of the main advantages to this system is that it eliminates mathematical errors. However, when using a system like this, care must be taken to ensure that proportionality across the ratings is maintained. For example, a segment rated at 10% POA would be expected to have twice the probability of containing the subject as one rated at 5% POA. In CASIE, the verbal cues are entered based on the appropriate letter and the inputs are converted to numbers which are shown on-screen for review. This ensures that the resulting POAs reflect the intended proportions. Figure 13.2 shows the verbal cues and the nine letters used for input in this consensus method

Figure 13.2

Verbal Cues
for the
Modified Mattson
(O'Connor) Consensus

A – Very Likely
B
C – Likely
D
E – Even Chance
F
G – Unlikely
H
I – Very Unlikely

The verbal cues in Figure 13.2 were originally developed to help avoid math errors when

doing a Mattson Consensus. This rating scheme, using letters to reflect relative differences, has been applied in other SAR applications, including the rating of clues (in CASIE) and in certain aspects of the Sector Ladder, described in the next section and in Chapter 16.

The Sector Ladder Initial Consensus: A Non-Mathematical Approach For Setting Search Priorities

How do you plan and conduct a search without being dependent upon an electrical outlet or charged batteries to run programs and spreadsheets? Perkins and Roberts of the Northumberland National Park Search & Rescue Team in the UK devised a method, called the Sector Ladder, which eliminates dependence on computers for planning a search. Perkins and Roberts also felt that it was important for search planners to have a set of management tools that allowed them flexibility in responding to rapidly changing information from a variety of sources without the false sense of security that sometimes comes from running precise calculations on imprecise data. Using a small workbook of forms, the Sector Ladder methodology allows search planners to create an initial consensus of search priorities, change those priorities as sectors are searched or clues appear, and to expand the search into the ROW. For this chapter we will discuss setting up the initial search priorities using a Sector Ladder Initial

Consensus and save a discussion of how to shift those priorities for later in Chapter 16. The starting requirement is a master map showing search tasks such as likely routes and sectors. These can be arrived at either by developing scenarios or by establishing a Search Area and sectoring it. Up to five participants are then asked to rate each of the defined sectors and routes for the likelihood of containing the lost subject based on a set of nine verbal cues ranging from "Very Likely" (a value of 9) to "Very Unlikely" (a value of 1). These values are then totaled across all participants and ranked. The sector or route with the highest total score is ranked as the Number 1 search priority with the others following in sequence.

Figure 13.3 provides an example of an Initial Consensus Ranking Summary that creates the starting Sector Ladder. The end result is a hierarchical set of initial search priorities very similar to a Mattson Consensus, except that verbal cues are turned into numbers instead of using numbers directly.

The example in Figure 13.3 shows the results for two participants rating four sectors and four routes. Based on their input, Route 2 (R2), a trail, would be the highest priority for sending in search resources. Route 4 (R4) would have the lowest priority for initial response searching. Sector A and Route 1 have "equal," rank in third place (3=) and would receive equal priority behind the first and second ranked locations.

Note also that ROW is included as the last sector, reflecting the view that the subject is more likely to be along one of the routes or in one of the other sectors than anywhere else. As routes and sectors are adequately searched, ROW will move up the ladder. In the case where there are many sectors and planners feel that the likelihood of the subject being out of the search area is greater than being in some of the lower priority sectors, ROW can be assigned higher than last. The Sector Ladder is a tool to assist planners in creating a reasonable set of search priorities. Like all tools, it should be controlled by the user to reflect their best estimates of what is happening in the field.

Figure 13.3

Sector Ladder
Initial Consensus Ranking Sample:
Summary Sheet with 2-Participants

Sector/ Route	Dave	Pete	Total Score	Rank
A	5	6	11	3=
B	6	7	13	2
C	5	3	8	6
D	3	4	7	7
R1	6	5	11	3=
R2	7	7	14	1
R3	5	4	9	5
R4	2	3	5	8
ROW	--	--	--	9

Summary

Segmentation of the search area into manageable units allows search planners to

- Assign priorities to segments (POA).
- Keep track of search coverage (cumulative POD).
- Minimize gaps in coverage.
- Provide unambiguous assignments to search teams.

Segments should:

- Have boundaries that are clearly identifiable in the field.
- Be small enough to be covered by a single resource in 4 to 6 hours.
- Include trails, lake edges, and other areas that will be searched separately.

Probability of Area (POA):

- Refers to the probability that the subject is located in each of the segments.
- Should be assigned to each segment, including the "Rest of the World" (ROW) for most land searches.
- Should be determined by consensus.

Mattson Consensus:

- Provides an unbiased method for creating an initial set of search priorities using input from a group of expert evaluators through a mathematical rating scheme that sums to 100% POA with ROW.

- The Modified Mattson (O'Connor) Consensus substitutes letters, corresponding to verbal cues, to provide a relative rating scheme that creates similar results to a Mattson Consensus, while avoiding the potential for mathematical errors.

Sector Ladder: Initial Consensus:

- Provides a non-mathematical method for creating an unbiased set of initial search priorities, using input from up to five expert evaluators, who rate sectors and routes using verbal cues which reflect the likelihood of finding the subject in each location.

Advanced Planning Concepts

- The concept of Scenario Analysis is presented in Figure 13.4.

Figure 13.4

ADVANCED PLANNING CONCEPTS: SCENARIO ANALYSIS

As discussed in this chapter, probability of area (POA) refers to the chances that each, respective segment contains the lost subject. POA is an important planning tool for prioritizing the search area and assuring that the search is conducted in a systematic and efficient manner. However, assigning POA can be quite difficult when search planners are unsure about the circumstances surrounding the missing person's disappearance. Often, for example, there may be conflicting eyewitness accounts that put the subject in two different locations simultaneously, heading in opposite directions! In this example, areas with a high POA under one condition may have a low POA under another. In this case planners may develop two, alternative search plans and proceed to conduct what amounts to two separate searches.

To do this, we need a system for assigning POA estimates that takes into account competing scenarios (defined as "hypothetical sequences of events resulting from the missing subject's behavior or mishap"). In a previous article (Hill, 1992), Hill proposed a technique called scenario analysis, which is based loosely on search procedures developed by the U.S. Coast Guard. To apply scenario analysis, the Planning Chief describes the alternate scenarios to those search planners participating in the consensus assignment of POA to the segments. Planners then assign POA to the individual segments (including the ROW) as usual, but they repeat the process for each scenario, and their POA estimates are always based on the assumption that the scenario in question is the correct one. Once finished, they then estimate the relative probabilities for each of the scenarios.

For example, let's assume that we have a lost hunter whose LKP is his automobile. The car is parked on a road that runs north and south. The two scenarios in question are: (1) he went east, and (2) he went west. The area is divided into six segments plus the ROW. Each of the search planners then proceeds to assign POA to the segments while considering one scenario at a time. Once all segments have been assigned POA for each scenario, the planners then go through the alternate scenarios and rate the relative probability of each, out of 100%. The probabilities of each scenario are multiplied by the segment POA for each segment. These weighted POA are then added across scenarios to obtain the final, planning POA for the search.

(continued)

Figure 13.4 (cont.)

The table below presents hypothetical POA for one planner. This person has assigned a probability of 0.7 to the East scenario, and 0.3 to the West scenario (notice that his scenario probabilities add up to 1.0 or 100%). His un-weighted POA assignments appear in the second and third columns from the left. In the second column, for example, these POA estimates are made under the assumption that the East scenario is valid, while POA appearing in the third column pertain to the West scenario. As can be seen from this table, weighted POA are obtained by multiplying the POA for each segment by the appropriate scenario probability, and doing this for each scenario. Finally, the resulting or <u>planning</u> POA are computed by adding the weighted POA per segment across scenarios. **The Planning POA are the figures that will be used for computing the consensus POA, which will be shifted as the search proceeds** (as will be discussed in Chapter 16).

Segment	Initial POA East	Initial POA West	Weighted POA East (p = .70)	Weighted POA West (p = .30)	Planning POA
1	0.30	0.10	0.70 X 0.30 = 0.210	0.30 X 0.10 = 0.030	0.210 + 0.030 = **0.240**
2	0.25	0.05	0.70 X 0.25 = 0.175	0.30 X 0.05 = 0.015	0.175 + 0.015 = **0.190**
3	0.20	0.05	0.70 X 0.20 = 0.140	0.30 X 0.05 = 0.015	0.140 + 0.015 = **0.155**
4	0.10	0.30	0.70 X 0.10 = 0.070	0.30 X 0.30 = 0.090	0.070 + 0.090 = **0.160**
5	0.05	0.25	0.70 X 0.05 = 0.035	0.30 X 0.25 = 0.075	0.035 + 0.075 = **0.110**
6	0.05	0.20	0.70 X 0.05 = 0.035	0.30 X 0.20 = 0.060	0.035 + 0.060 = **0.095**
ROW	0.05	0.05	0.70 X 0.05 = 0.035	0.30 X 0.05 = 0.015	0.035 + 0.015 = **0.050**

Note: p = probability that scenario is valid; ROW = "Rest of the World".

See the original article (Hill, 1992) for an extended discussion of scenario analysis, including a small computer program listing for simplifying the process.

Questions for Discussion:

1. What are some additional benefits of area segmentation not mentioned in this chapter?

2. How is it possible to estimate the number of searchers necessary to search a particular segment within a reasonable period of time?

3. In your own words, what is the purpose of assigning POA values to each of the segments in the search area?

4. Why is it important to consider the "Rest of the World" (ROW) segment when assigning POA?

5. What kinds of lost person "scenarios" are good candidates for scenario analysis?

Part III: Managing Plans & Operations

CHAPTER 14

ALLOCATING RESOURCES
(SEARCH TACTICS)

In this chapter we focus the discussion primarily on **how to best allocate and utilize resources**, a critical component of **search tactics**. Once incident objectives are written and priorities have been set, it becomes the Operations Section Chief's job to decide how best to use available search resources, in the correct order, to get the job done.

CHAPTER OBJECTIVES:

When you finish studying this chapter, you should be able to:

1. Discuss how the emergency nature of the lost person incident affects the allocation of search resources.

2. Describe methods of attraction, confinement, and active searching.

3. Discuss the difference between clue finders and subject finders.

4. Describe the differences between hasty, loose grid and tight grid resources.

5. Identify the keys to successful searching.

6. Understand how sign cutting can be a major factor in reducing a search area.

SEARCH IS AN EMERGENCY!

During the initial response phase of any search mission there are a great number of unknowns. Because an individual's life may depend on time, it is extremely important to consider these unknowns constantly:

- The subject may need immediate emergency care.
- The subjects may need protection from the environment and even themselves.
- Time and weather can destroy valuable clues (and witnesses may leave the scene).
- Urgent response to a lost person incident reduces the uncertainty of large search areas.

Since not every jurisdiction is blessed with an excess of SAR resources, an urgent response is crucial for efficiency's sake as well as for the greatest benefit to the missing subject. Proper allocation of resources, generally the responsibility of the Operations Section Chief (OSC), is crucial.

Considerations in Allocating Resources

The following factors will influence how the OSC allocates and deploys his or her resources.

- Search Urgency
- POD of resources available
- POA of segments to be searched (search priority).
- Terrain analysis:
  — difficult to search
  — density of vegetation (from air and ground)
  — hazards.
  — travel aids available to the subject.
- Subject' condition (assumptions developed in Chapter 8):
  — mobile and responsive.
  — mobile and unresponsive.
  — immobile and responsive.
  — immobile and unresponsive.
- Kinds of resources available (capabilities and equipment).
- When resources can arrive.

Respond Urgently & Gather Resources

Given a search emergency, an Incident Commander should:

- Respond urgently.
- Conduct a thorough investigation.
- Search both night and day.
- Aid searchers any way possible.

The following rules should always be considered as the Incident Commander initially evaluates needs and gathers resources:

- Determine the right kind and type of resources required, then order the correct resources for the job.
- Diversify the resource options.
- Back-up and support the resources.

Organizing Resources

Any human, animal or physical assets that are committed to on-scene support of search operations should be considered resources and used appropriately. Realizing that committing resources to the field is essential to finding a lost subject, it is equally important to assign the proper personnel and equipment simultaneously to the function of providing management. If the entire effort is to run smoothly, then this control function must be firmly established early on.

There are few things more frustrating for a SAR resource than to arrive at base camp ready to depart into the field, and then have to wait for several hours while someone establishes tasks and makes field assignments. The Incident Commander should always define more task assignments than available resources. When the appropriate resource arrives, the Incident Commander will be ready.

Operations Section Chief (OSC) – The Manger of Resources

In order to properly manage the specialized resources that are either on-scene or on the way, it is advisable to assign an Operations Section Chief as early in the incident as possible. Previously, we have described the job of the Operations Section Chief in Chapters 4 and 9. Here, we will discuss in further detail the functions of the "Ops Chief" as applied to the allocation of search resources.

Generally, **the OSC supervises and adjusts tactical operations** as necessary, based on changes in the incident situation and the status of the resources.

Related functions include:

- Evaluate the overall effectiveness of tactical operations and adjust as necessary for next operation period.
- Evaluate the progress of operations based on situation reports and comments of operations personnel.
- Estimate immediate and long-range operational resources and logistical requirements.
- Request additional resources as needed to provide lead time for meeting incident objectives.
- Advise incident communications unit and resources unit of all changes in status of resources assigned to the operation.
- Update the IC on current problems, resource needs, and accomplishments.
- Inform the IC as soon as possible on problems and accomplishments.

The Operations Section Chief should immediately assume or assign the responsibilities of staging area manager. This function is responsible for ensuring that all arriving resources are accounted for, are ready for field assignment and are able to respond within minutes of management's request. If aircraft have been requested to assist in the search effort, then consideration should be given to establishing an **Air Operations** branch. If only one aircraft is requested or used, then the Operations Section Chief may simply assume that position. If several aircraft are needed, then a specialized branch may be established to manage the following functions:

- Establishing helibases and helispots.
- Operating helibases and helispots.
- Maintaining records on both fixed-wing and helicopter aircraft.
- Maintaining required liaison with fixed-wing aircraft that are using off-scene facilities.
- Maintaining all timekeeping for aircraft assigned to the search.
- Establishing all logistical and supply needs for air operations.
- Managing the tactical operations of the aircraft.

Resource Priority & Categories

An aggressive response in the initial stages using actions and resources listed in Figure 14.1, can help keep the search area manageable and often results in finding the subject quickly.

Figure 14.1

INITIAL RESPONSE
Resources and Actions

Used immediately and aggressively to find the subject quickly

Most effective resources:
• Tracking teams
• Clue-aware hasty teams
• Air-scenting dog teams (with clue-aware handlers)
• Trailing dog teams (with clue-aware handlers)
• Helicopters with trained spotters
Combined with actions including:
• Confinement
• Attraction
• Binary search (sign cutting)
• Hasty search

We've discussed the concept of establishing where to look and which segments on the map to give high search priority. At some point the IC or the Operations Section Chief has to make the decision about which resources will be committed to the field, and

in which order. This is a critical step in the management of search operations.

An essential part of this decision process is a full understanding of resource capabilities and limitations. Definitions and resource typing per NIMS should be used to assist in determining capabilities.

Search Initiation Guide (SIG)

Another approach to the initial response is called "SIG" for Search Initiation Guide which was written and compiled for ERI International, Inc., and is excerpted here with their permission. SIG is based on a six-step process.

Search Initiation Guide (SIG)
(Extracted from *Search Management for the Initial Response Incident Commander* © 2001 ERI International, Inc.. Written and complied by: Hugh Dougher, Rick Goodman, Rick LaValla, Chris Long, Dave Perkins, Pete Roberts. Contributors: Rick Hood, Richard Smith.)

Current research indicates that most SAR incidents (90% +/-) are concluded within 24-48 hours by exploiting clues and leads identified through investigation and initial search efforts. Quite often then, the advanced application of formal search theory (including the math necessary to support it), which forms the bulk of most traditional search management courses, is not used. However, regardless of how large or lengthy a search may become most operations are started in a similar way.

The methods presented are designed to provide SAR incident commanders with the tools they need to rapidly initiate operations aimed at finding the lost subject as quickly as possible while providing the structure to expand the search operation if that becomes necessary. Management as well as tactics are required to get the operation going efficiently and effectively.

The Incident Response Process

This six-step Incident Response Process is a problem solving model developed by the International Association of Chiefs of Police (IACP) which is very similar to Troop Leading Procedures as taught by the various branches of the armed forces. It might also be compared to similar processes or models presented in most first aid instruction (i.e. the "A-B-Cs.")

> *"Problems by their very definition, imply a state of instability. Any problem-solving situation can be improved by the use of an organizational technique that frames the unstable problem within a stable system. In other words, trying to impose order on chaos."*
> Jeff Isaac
> The Outward Bound Wilderness First-Aid Handbook (Revised Edition)

The Incident Response Process is a logical sequence of actions and thought processes followed by the incident commander in developing and executing a plan. The purpose is to ensure the best use of time and resources in accomplishing the incident objectives. All the steps are covered, even if each takes only a few seconds. Some steps may be taken concurrently. The process is not rigid: modify it to fit the mission, situation and available time. Not all the tasks listed for each step will apply to every "cycle" of the six step process or to every mission. Take what's useful, add to it as you gain experience. Rather than a checklist, view the six steps as a continuous process. As you complete one "cycle" you immediately start the process again. As you gain experience you will find it becomes virtually instinctive.

The Incident Response Process is taught in the IACP's course Critical Incident Management and was included in the Federal Emergency Management Agency's courses Incident Command System For Law Enforcement Agencies, Incident Command System For Public Works and Decision Making in a Crisis. We'll discuss the "generic" system first and then show how it could apply to a SAR mission. (Note: some terminology has been updated to conform to NIMS.)

INITIAL RESPONSE PROCESS

1. Size-up the situation.

What is the nature of the incident?

What hazards are present?

What hazards exist for response personnel and the public?

Do warnings need to be issued?

Are there injured people who need to be treated or assisted?

Is evacuation required?

How large an area is involved?

Will the area be isolated?

What location would make a good staging area?

What entrance and exit routes would be good for the flow of response personnel and equipment?

2. Identify contingencies.

Consider what *could* happen.

Remember Murphy's Law – anything that can go wrong may go wrong at the worst moment. Have a backup plan!

3. Determine incident objectives and strategy.

4. Identify needed resources.

What resources are needed?

Where will we get them?

How long will it take them to get here?

Are there any special resource requirements?

5. Build a plan and structure.

Responsibilities and tasks.

Chain of command.

Coordination.

6. Take action.

SAR INITIAL RESPONSE

This process is adaptable to virtually any incident. It is especially useful in the initial response phase of a SAR mission. For example, a Hasty Team leader arriving at a trailhead from which a reported lost person departed, quickly runs through the process to determine where to employ his resources: which trails to run, buildings to search, high hazard areas to check, etc.

The Incident Commander, while the Hasty Team is still in the field, uses the process to plan the next phase of the search. Here is an example of the type tasks that may be considered when we apply the Six Step Incident Response Process to the initial response phase of a SAR mission. (Remember: Not all these tasks listed under each step will apply to every "cycle" of the six step process or to every SAR mission. They are meant only as memory aids. Take what's useful, add to it as you gain experience.)
First Notice: This is the critical first step in each mission. First notice can come to you thru the 9-1-1 center, a call to the local sheriff

or police station, in person while you are on patrol, thru a third party, etc. regardless of how you receive notice, remember, time is a critical element. SEARCH IS AN EMERGENCY!

Once you are advised of the mission, begin the Six-step Incident Response Process.

The SIG Six Step process with SAR-specific tasks:

1. Size-up.

Do we have a SAR mission? Search or Rescue? Or is this an abduction, runaway, etc.?

If unable to talk to the reporting party, use dispatch. But ensure the RP is anchored! Phone number, address, etc.

What is the urgency of this situation?

Plan use of available time.

Are there subjects requiring immediate medical aid/evacuation?

Where is the Last Known Position/Point Last Seen (your Initial Planning Point).

What hazards to responders are present? The subject? In particular, what hazards are present that which could greatly increase the subjects risk?

Where is a good location for a staging area? Incident Command Post? Routes in and out? Control your responding resources and protect the PLS/LKP.

What resources, if any, are on scene or enroute?

Do a thorough map study. Consider weather, terrain, history of the area, lost person behavior stats.

Define the potential search area. Can you quickly confine/contain the subject?

Based on your size up, you may alert or mobilize resources at this time. This is especially true if you have a preplanned response that includes a trained hasty team.

Issue warnings to responders.

Have resources report to a staging area or an off-incident mobilization center/rendezvous. Protect the PLS/LKP!

2. Identify Contingencies.

What are possible scenarios to account for the facts observed in Step 1?

What could happen to make this situation worse?

Consider weather, remaining daylight, terrain.

Remember Murphy's Law!

3. Determine Incident Objectives and Strategy.

What are we here to do? Why (purpose)? By when?

How will we do it?

What are the priorities of action?

Speed is essential: the search area is getting larger and the subject is getting weaker.

Basic Strategies:

Investigation

Confinement

Hasty Search

Ensure investigation is ongoing.

4. Identify Needed Resources.

Are resources on scene/enroute sufficient?

If not, where/how do you get additional resources?

How long will it take for them to get there?

Are there special resource requirements? Trackers, dogs, etc.

Don't forget command and general staff. If you think you might need them, order them now.

Have resources report to a staging area or an off-incident mobilization center/rendezvous. Protect the PLS/LKP!

5. Build a Plan and Structure.

Select/refine tactical objectives/tasks based on Incident Objectives, selected Strategy and available resources.

Tactical objectives/tasks. Some initial tasks in a SAR operation require minimal information about the subject and can be started quickly and conducted concurrently with more specific search planning activities (lost person behavior studies, scenario analysis, etc.):
Establish command.

Establish/maintain communications.

Contact RP, possible witnesses: Investigation!

Identify/secure LKP/PLS.

Identify staging area.

Set up entrance/exit/safe routes.

Mobilize resources.

Issue warnings.

Search obvious high probability and high hazard points.

Assign resources to tactical objectives.

Review span of control - designate strike teams, task forces, groups, divisions, and/or branches if/as necessary.

Coordinate logistics, medical, transportation etc. Develop Logistics Section structure as required by mission and span of control factors.

Document! Use ICS Form 201 if available.

Select end of Initial Response Phase / start of 1st operational period!

Chain of command. Requirements for command and general staff personnel.

Select staging area(s) and route(s).

Assign staging area manager.

Initial response Incident Action Plan briefing should include:

Situation
Subject name, searching data, map orientation, weather, hazards, etc.

Mission/Execution
Command: Incident Commander / Immediate Supervisor; Leader's intent:
Incident objectives / strategy
Specific tactical assignments,
Coordinating instructions

Communications
Communication plan
Tactical, Command, Air-to-

ground frequencies,
Cell phone numbers
Medevac plan

Service / Support
Other resources working adjacent, and those available to order Aviation operations, Logistics, Transportation, Supplies and equipment

Risk Management
Identify known hazards and risks
Identify control measures to mitigate hazards / reduce risk
Identify trigger points for re-evaluating operations
Questions or Concerns?

6. Take Action.

Issue IAP: Ensure that your intent and tasks to be performed are well understood. Ask questions. Get feedback.

Supervise and coordinate.

Evaluate progress.

Continue size-up: begin planning for next operational period.

Again, remember that these six steps are a continuous process. As time goes on you will learn more information and more resources will become available.

Continue the Mission. As you progress through the mission:

Maintain "situational awareness."

Continue the investigation.

Develop clues/leads.

Repeat 6 step process.

Continue assigning resources to tactical objectives/tasks in priority.

Maintain span of control - build organizational structure accordingly

Remember logistics.

Transfer command?

Rescue operation: 6 step process.

Transition To Formal Search Planning.

At some point in the operation, if you haven't found the subject, you will begin to exhaust all clues and leads. It is at this juncture you will need to develop your own "clues and leads" through the formal search planning process. Here are a few points to consider:

Don't permit a lag or gap in the operation. Anticipate the need to expand the planning function and order the appropriate resources.

One of the first steps in the formal planning process will be the development of a Probability of Area consensus among search planners. Ensure you can clearly and concisely explain your search efforts to date.

Don't let the formal planning process distract you from your other responsibilities. As Incident Commander you are equally responsible for current operations, future operations (planning), and logistical support. Delegate!

"Search and rescue is both an art and a science. There are theoretical approaches and practical ones. As one must compromise between optimum and realistic planning, one should also compromise between the art and the science. Search directors should never become slaves to tradition."

William G. Syrotuck
An Introduction to Land Search Probabilities
and Calculations

Resource Categories

As mentioned in Chapter 4, resources are generally classified into three basic categories:

Single Resources: The lowest common denominator, a resource or unit that can be used effectively independently from other resources (for example, one search dog with handler; one human tracking team; one investigator).

Strike Team: A number of the same kind of resources working together under a common supervisor or leader with common communications.

Task Force: Any combination of different kinds of resources under one leader and with common communications put together for a specific assignment.

Resource Identification

Each resource that is available to a jurisdiction should have key information readily available to the IC. It should be an addendum to the Preplan or available in a resource file which is quickly accessible, especially if the IC. function may fall on any one of several personnel. The following is an example of key information for one particular resource.

Hasty Team

This is an initial response team of well-trained, self-sufficient, and highly-mobile searchers whose primary responsibility is to check out those areas most likely to produce a subject first (for example, trails, trailheads, roads, forks, intersections, campsites, lakes, clearings, and other likely spots). Their efficiency and usefulness is based upon speed of response and accuracy of first-hand information acquired at the scene.

Recommended Hasty Team skills:
- Track and sign awareness
- Clue and subject oriented.
- Ability to interview effectively.
- Familiarity with the local terrain and inherent hazards
- Completely self sufficient
- Advanced first-aid skills
- Pinpoint navigation skills.
- Self-reliance; not requiring supervision.

Equipment:
Minimum: 24 to 48 hour pack (as required).
Radio communications.
First-aid supplies.
Orienteering compass.
Accurate map of the area.
Essential climbing gear (if near steep terrain).
Optimal: 72 hour pack.
Ground to air communications.
Medical supplies, including rescue gear.
Gridded high-scale topo map of the area.
Global Positioning System (GPS) receiver.

The best way for an agency to learn the capabilities of surrounding resources is to involve them in the preplanning phase and train with them.

Resource Allocation Tactics

Tactics

Search tactics refer to the techniques, procedures, and methods used to actually find the subject or clues. Again, all tactics employed should refer specifically to at least one of the incident objectives in the search plan.

Some common examples of search tactics:
- Use air scent dog teams first in the high probability areas.
- Run all trails and ridges for tracks and sign.
- Establish track traps at major trail junctions.
- Re-search two areas with different resources (diversify).
- Interview subject's acquaintances for favorite area information.
- Interview all hikers in the area.
- Assign personnel to follow up on all physical clues.
- Sound patrol vehicle sirens once every hour from the same location.
- Concentrate the helicopter on open drainages twice a day.
- Have fixed wing aircraft fly 200 feet contour patterns in extremely steep terrain.

Experience and the review of previous case studies continually point out the need for using **the right resources in the right order.**

Search Tactics –
Indirect & Direct

There are two basic search tactics. Indirect tactics use relatively passive methods for eliciting a response from the subject or allowing him/her to intercept stationary resources. Direct tactics entail active "looking" for the subject. Both types of tactics should be used simultaneously.

Indirect Tactics (Passive) –
Let the Subject Come to You

The two main indirect tactics are **Confinement and Attraction**: You let the subject come to you . . .
— Wait, watch, and listen
— Confinement (block trails)
— Attraction (noise, lights)

In many jurisdictions, historical data has defined areas of common confusion or terrain that funnels a subject into a specific location. In general, within a certain period of time these subjects might be expected to walk out or show up. In these cases a passive tactic like attraction may prove helpful. Indirect tactics allow the subject to come to you, walk out on their own, or allow you to provide attraction points to guide and encourage mobile subjects to move to a certain location. Additionally,

these efforts can provide encouragement to immobile victims, who are assured that searchers are on their way.

Direct Tactics (Active) –
Searching for the Subject

Direct tactics require that someone commits resources to actively search for the lost person.

The decision to use Direct or Indirect tactics largely depends on:
• relative urgency of the incident.
• quantity, quality, and availability of search resources.
• existing hazards (weather, man-made, or natural hazards).
• assumed status of the subject (mobile, immobile, responsive, unresponsive).

Attraction

Attraction is an indirect search tactic that seeks to call the subject's attention to the searchers. It can range from emergency vehicle lights and loud sounds to the smell of hot dogs roasting on a campfire. Some examples of Attraction:

Visual Attraction
— lights   — beacons
— aircraft   — flares
— strobes   — balloons
— fires   — smoke

Sound Attraction

— horns   — P.A. systems
— voice   — sirens
— gunshots   — whistles

When using sound devices, remind team leaders that they **should not forget to listen for a response by the subject** for some time after making noise. Also, do not overlook the fact that in valleys, canyons, and mountains, noises reflect and echo, which can cause added confusion for the subject. The direction of the source of a sound can be especially difficult to determine at night.

As a final note on the use of attraction, remember that attraction as a search tactic might not always be your best option. There may be some hazard to the subject who is trying to find the source of your sound — especially at night, or in steep terrain. You may be drawing the subject out of a cozy shelter into bad weather in a vain attempt to find you. As such, attraction methods go against the admonition taught in woods safety programs that lost people should "stay in one place" and wait for searchers to find them. In any case, if you do decide to use attraction, then be sure that the sound source is stationary. More than one lost subject has been bewildered by a police siren attached to a car that is traveling up and down a highway!

Combining Attraction with Active Search Methods: The Sound Sweep

Searchers have long been aware of the advantages of making sounds, such as calling the subject's name or blowing whistles, while conducting search patterns. Frequently, the first signal received from a subject is a response to such sounds, long before the visual detection of the subject himself. Colwell (1993) has conducted studies on the effective use of sound while conducting grid searches with wide spacing (between 47 and 100 meters/51 and 109 yards) for subjects who are alert, conscious, able to respond, and expecting a whistle blast. In his studies, each searcher was equipped with a VHF radio and a loud whistle. A coordinator using the base radio cued the searchers to blow their whistles simultaneously every two, three, or five minutes, as they swept through the search area. When the cue was received over the radio, each searcher would stop, blow their whistle, and then wait briefly for an audible response from the "victim." Colwell's studies reveal an extremely high success in all time intervals used: from 87% (five minute interval) to 100% (two minutes between blasts). These are high POD's indeed, especially considering the wide spacing between searchers! Consider whether these POD numbers are credible after reading Chapter 15 on the derivation of POD. The logic behind the sound sweep is as follows. By controlling the time between whistle blasts, and requiring searchers to blow simultaneously, sound waves from the whistles reach every part of the search area at an audible level at least once. Shortening the time intervals between blasts increases redundancy, so that subjects standing in any one location will hear whistles more than once. Such redundancy is comparable to that obtained by using narrow spacing between searchers in a grid line, where there is some overlap in the visual detectability of clues (that is, more than one searcher can see the same clue).

The sound sweep method can be an effective tactic when the subject can be reasonably expected to respond to sound. An advantage of the sound sweep is that it lets the subject know that someone is looking for them. However, this may not work for some subjects like young children, despondents, hunters who are ashamed to admit they are lost, and others who do not want to make contact with a stranger. It may also not work for various walkaways such as Alzheimer's patients and mentally challenged subjects who do not care if anyone is looking for them, for subjects who are hard of hearing, for subjects who are not alert, and for anyone who is unconscious or otherwise unable to answer the sound. Searchers using whistles should be forewarned that their decibel level can be far higher than that considered safe.

Hearing protection is recommended when repeatedly blowing whistles in a sound sweep. However, the devices must be removed to listen for the subject in between blasts.

Why Limit the Search Area?

The smaller the area to be searched, the smaller the amount of time needed to effectively cover it. In addition, the numbers of searchers required will be less and the chances of finding the lost person are improved. With limited resources, the efficient OSC may have no other viable alternative than to aggressively confine the designated search area until more crews arrive. It is imperative that an effort be made to establish a search area with specific boundaries beyond which the missing subject has not passed. Once the search area has been defined, numerous methods can be employed to ensure detection should the subject pass through the perimeter. Use confinement tactics while you amass sufficient resources to employ direct tactics, but keep the confining resources in place throughout the search if possible. If the subject is presumed to be mobile, then this procedure requires prompt initial reaction combined with an accurate analysis of the surrounding terrain. Rapid confinement presents no conflict with other search methods and dramatically reduces the chance of an expanded search area.

Confinement – A Passive (Indirect) Tactic to Limit the Search Area

Confinement is an effort to establish a search perimeter which encompasses the subject and beyond which he or she is unlikely to pass without being detected.

Just One More Step . . .

When the lost subject steps one foot past one mile from the IPP, they've increased the search area by over 33,000 square feet!

Guidelines for Confinement:

1. It should not conflict with active search methods.

2. It starts at the perimeter of the theoretical search area, and works inward toward the PLS or LKP.

3. It should focus at least out to the distance represented by the 75th percentile of the subject's category.

4. It requires prompt initial reaction to set up, but will help to decrease the need for a massive search.

Primary Methods of Confinement: Road Blocks, Trail Blocks, Camp-Ins

Any roads, drainages or clear pathways provide routes by which a subject can depart an area. Many subjects have walked out on a road, caught a ride with the first vehicle contacted and completely left the area, an example of a subject being in the ROW. Establish road blocks and patrols on all roads and trails leading into and out of the confinement perimeter. Assigning some resources to set up camp in selected areas provides an opportunity for attraction while acting as a barrier to subject travel. These so-called camp-ins can be assigned to volunteers who may not have formal SAR training but are competent outdoorsmen like recreational campers, hunters, and advanced Scouts. In the case of wilderness areas, setting up trail blocks, patrols, and camp-ins (for example, in a specified drainage) will serve to identify and preserve perimeter boundaries. When assigning patrols use sufficient observers so that some personnel can watch the area to the rear. Some people who do not want to be found will cross roads after the patrol has passed.

Do not assume that a trail or road will necessarily serve as a natural perimeter. There have been numerous reported instances where a lost person has come to a road or trail, crossed it, and continued to wander. Assign patrols, establish track traps, post notices, expand the search beyond these "barriers," and implement other actions to minimize this possibility.

Also consider waterway and shoreline boat patrols when appropriate. Water edges or "blue lines" also provide excellent natural track traps (described in the next section).

Other Methods of Confinement

Look-outs

Where existing National Forest and Park Service look-out stations exist, notify these sites of the missing subject and ask for observation assistance. Posting of spotters with binoculars in strategic locations on high ground is also a viable method of monitoring a perimeter. This tactic is particularly valuable in search areas above timberline or otherwise void of timber.

Track Traps

A track "trap" is any area where tracks are easily made and easily perceived, such as a river bank or a sandy area. The U.S. Border Patrol developed the method of laying down artificial track traps. This involves brushing off bare areas and dragging road edges or lightly traveled back roads. The intent is to frequently check for footprints in the brushed areas for any indication that someone has passed through. Mark the edges of track traps with a few rock cairns. This will alert searchers to avoid the traps without alerting others.

String Lines

An excellent method of confinement has also been developed by the Explorer Search and Rescue (ESAR) Organization. Spools of string are mounted in a backpack or container worn on the hip ("hip chain"). As the searcher walks through an area, the string unrolls, leaving a visible trail. Other searchers can follow behind and place the string waist high on brush, perhaps putting paper arrows with self stick note paper on the string pointing toward a road or base camp. It is expected that the subject will follow the arrows. At the least, the string makes a visible perimeter or segment edge.

The effectiveness of this technique is increased if the paper arrows include specific directions, such as "Mr. Smith: We are searching for you. Please follow this string in the direction indicated. Stop when you reach the road. We are patrolling the road, and will find you there. If you cannot travel, then wait here — we check this string line daily." Include the date and time.

Committing Resources to the Field

Initial tactics include determining the subject's most likely direction of travel by sign-cutting the PLS. High probability locations (including trails and other travel aids) are then identified for searching by hasty teams. Simultaneously, confinement tactics are initiated.

It is important that the Operations Section Chief knows how each resource operates, including their limitations. For example, a tracking team relies on subtle physical clues left behind by the subject, such as tracks, broken twigs, leaves, or other disturbances.

The air scenting search dog relies on a plume of scent emanating from the subject in the field. It would be a waste of valuable resources to rely on a tracking team after an area had been systematically worked by a several ground search crews. Aircraft can be crucial in some terrain. Each type of initial response team has its advantages and should be applied to the areas that best suits their expertise. Proper application of SAR resources to field operations is the foundation of effective search management.

Figure 14.1 presented a list of initial response resources and recommended search tactics. Using those initial actions as a guide, resources should be used in the following order if possible:

Clue Finders
— These resources are called first and they respond quickly.
— They are skilled.
— They are small in number (logistical needs are fewer).
— Primary function: to find clues, or to determine a direction of travel.
Examples:
> — hasty team
> — trailing dog team
> — tracking team
> — sign cutting team
> — investigation team

Clue/Subject Finders
— Main function: to search areas identified by clue finders.
— Provide on-going information and possible routes or barriers to subject travel; subject attractions: further clues left by subject (this should help to further reduce search area size).
Examples:
> — air-scenting dog team
> — hasty team
> — clue-aware grid team
> — helicopter with trained spotters

Subject Finders
Generally, these resources provide a relatively low probability of detecting clues (other than the subject), either due to the nature of the resource or a lack of training.
Examples:
> — grid searchers
> — helicopters and fixed-wing aircraft
> — forward-looking infrared (FLIR)
> — untrained searchers (for example, spontaneous volunteers)

The IC or OSC should consider several important points in allocating resources:
> - Determine what kinds of resources are required for the high priority search areas.

- Consider all available initial resources (should be contained in a good preplan) and their capabilities.
- What kind of training and how much have they had (as determined by NIMS resource typing)?
- What can the resources provide in relation to what is required? (Technical expertise vs. clue awareness.)
- What information can a particular resource provide that will contribute to the overall search effort? (If a resource simply reports that "they did not find the subject" then they may not have provided information that could lessen the search difficulty and may have, in fact, destroyed clues).

Direct Searching (Active) Tactics – Detection Procedures

In using direct searching tactics, detection procedures are those methods designed to seek out the subject or clues generated by the subject in the probable search area, while at the same time reducing the potential area as much as possible. Direct detection procedures involve overt commitment of resources into the field and very specific actions by those searchers. There are three distinct procedures: hasty team searching, loose sweep searching and tight sweep searching.

1. Hasty Searching (Speedy)
Involves a rapid response to areas of high probability by immediately available, highly trained resources.

Hasty Searching Considerations:
1. The assumption is (depending on elapsed time between when the subject became missing and when the incident was reported) that the subject is responsive.
2. It provides an immediate show of effort.
3. It can help define the search area by gathering intelligence or locating clues, or in follow-up after a clue is located.
4. Clue-consciousness is critical.
5. It often results in determining where not to search further.
6. Preplanning is crucial for the availability and effective use of Hasty Team resources.

Hasty Techniques:
1. Investigation.
2. Thorough checks of LKP (for clues, tracks, direction of travel, etc.)
3. Follow known (or suspected) route.
4. Trail running.
5. Perimeter check (often used with confinement).

6. Sign-cutting

7. Road patrols.

8. Check attractions.

9. Check hazardous areas.

10. Check drainages.

11. Ridge running.

12. Check for bogus search.

13. Locating any clues.

14. Electronic signal detection (ELT/PLB/EPIRB).

15. Trailing dog from LKP

Sign Cutting

Sign cutting is a procedure used by human trackers to detect the route of the subject by finding small disturbances (sign of passage) on or around the ground. It can be used during the initial response when hasty teams are deployed in an effort to determine direction of travel, but it is generally more thorough, painstaking and time-consuming than typical hasty tasks like trail running or checking a parking lot.

Most Effective Hasty Resources:

1. Investigators.

2. Trained (clue-conscious) composite hasty teams.

3. Human trackers.

4. Dogs (both trailing and air scenting).

5. Aircraft.

6. Other highly mobile, trained resources.

2. Loose Sweep Searching (Efficient)

This type of search involves a fast, systematic search of high probability segments using techniques that produce high probabilities of detection per searcher-hour of effort.

Loose Sweep Searching Considerations:

1. Often employed after Hasty efforts in some segments, especially if speedy tactics found clues.

2. In other search segments, particularly heavily vegetated ones, it may be the initial search tactic used.

3. Should be used when subject responsiveness is assumed to still be high.

Techniques:

1. Use in a defined segment of the search area.

2. Use to follow up in a segment where a clue has been found.

3. Uses an open grid, with relatively wide spacing between searchers (or critical separation).

4. Search routes often are followed using compass bearings.

Most Effective Loose Sweep
Resources:

    1. Investigators.

    2. Clue-conscious teams.

    3. Search dog (K9) Teams.

    4. Trackers, sign cutters.

    5. Aircraft.

    6. Trained grid teams.

    7. Other trained searchers.

3. Tight Sweep Searching (Thorough)

Involves a slower, highly systematic
search, using high coverage
techniques.

Considerations:

    1. Should be used when
    thoroughness (high
    Coverage/high POD) is
    desired, or after less-thorough
    techniques have not been
    successful.

    2. Usually searches are
    extremely destructive to clues,
    especially when searchers used
    are not trained to be clue-
    conscious.

Techniques:

    1. Closed grid or sweep search.

Most Effective Tight Sweep
Resources:

    1. Trained grid search teams.

    2. Law enforcement cadets
       and supervised Explorer
       Scouts.

Six General Principles for Applying SAR Resources

1. The OSC should determine resource requirements based on a hazard analysis done in the preplanning phase, and ensure that those resources have been properly trained.

2. Know where outside resources are located, what they can and cannot do, and how to obtain their services as back-up.

3. Include all required resources and how they will be used in a preplan.

4. Match the resources and their capabilities to the needs of the jurisdiction and the kinds of searches most likely to occur.

5. Initial tactical actions of resources should require minimum direction and control by the search IC.

6. The more diverse and flexible in skills that resources become, the more useful they become.

When Applying Resources, Always Consider Whether:

• Is it better to use the resources I have available now to keep the search area from getting bigger? (indirect, passive tactics)

        OR,

• Whether I should use the existing resources to try to find the subject? (direct, active tactics)

Keep The Organization Running Smoothly

What follows are some important points to remember when trying to keep the search organization running smoothly using all resources:

- Team efforts are more efficient and more effective than the same number of individual efforts.

- Team efforts utilize the "buddy system" with a safety factor not available with individuals.

- Use the chain of command when dealing with organizations, and include their leadership in regular briefings as well as search strategy formulation.

- Make sure each resource has a well-defined and reasonable task to perform.

- Never ask a person or unit to attempt a function they are neither trained nor equipped to do, especially if there is any question of safety.

- Early delegation of functional assignments to trained personnel is a key to success.

Four Factors that are Essential for a Successful Search Operation

1. Quick Response: Keep the search area small and find the subject fast in many cases.

2. Resources: The right ones responding at the right times in the right places.

3. Communications: Of all types to all search members plus feedback to the IC.

4. Management: Searches fail because of poor management more than any other reason.

Figure 14.2 provides a summary list of eight critical keys to conducting a successful search.

Figure 14.2

KEYS TO SUCCESSFUL SEARCHING

1. Respond quickly

2. Confine movements of subject and witnesses

3. Find clues

4. Protect clues

5. Diversify the response

6. Have back ups ready to fill personnel gaps and avoid delays

7. Use hasty teams to flag routes

8. Start and continue an intensive investigation to gather and analyze information (clues of all kinds)

Summary

In this chapter we discussed the appropriate use of search resources during the lost person incident. We began by describing various influences affecting the allocation of resources, including search urgency, desired PODs (covered in Chapter 15), POAs of segments to be searched, terrain analysis, assumptions about the subject's condition, and the types and availability of resources to be employed. The important tactical role of the Operations Section Chief was discussed, as were the three basic categories of resources

under the Operation Chief's control (single resources, strike teams, and task forces). With respect to single resources, we described the important role of the hasty team in modern search methods, including requisite skills and equipment. In addition, we presented some guidelines for gathering clue information, including factors related to the category of the subject, determining the point last seen, the circumstances under which the subject went missing, the physical condition and health of the subject, the subject's personality, his or her clothing and equipment, and analysis of the terrain in the area.

With respect to deciding upon specific tactical operations, two search tactic groups were described: (1) Indirect tactics using Attraction and Confinement, and (2) Direct tactics using active searching techniques. Attraction was described as the process of having the subject come to the searcher, a tactic that should be used with caution. The sound sweep, a tactic that may be employed when the subject can be assumed to be responsive to searcher's whistle blasts, was described as a means of combining the indirect technique of attraction with direct searching methods. Methods of confining the subject were discussed, including road blocks, trail blocks, camp-ins, look-outs, track traps, and string lines.

We discussed the order in which resources should be committed to the field, including clue finders, clue/subject finders, and subject finders, respectively. Regarding direct searching procedures aimed at detecting clues, we described three classes of resource actions: Hasty (speedy), Loose Sweeps (efficient), and Tight Sweeps (thorough). The appropriate resources for these actions and considerations in using them were also discussed. Finally, we ended the chapter with numerous recommendations regarding the efficient allocation of resources.

Questions for Discussion:

1.What is the difference between search Strategy and search Tactics?

2. With respect to the question, "Is it better to use resources to confine and limit the search area, or to actively look for the subject?" how should the category of the lost person affect your answer?

3. Describe some ways of using <u>spontaneous volunteers</u> during the lost person incident. What are some disadvantages in using them for searching?

4. Why is it important to <u>diversify</u> resources?

5. What are the differences between clue finders and subject finders?

CHAPTER 15

MEASURING SEARCH COVERAGE: ESTIMATING THE PROBABILITY OF DETECTION (POD)

Probability of Detection is the **single most important concept** in modern search theory because it is a **numeric representation of what is happening in the field**. Its values have critical implications that affect incident objectives, indications of search progress, and measures of the quality of search resources and the tactics employed.

CHAPTER OBJECTIVES:

When you finish studying this chapter, you should be able to:

1. Define the concepts of Probability Of Detection (POD).

2. Discuss the importance of quantifying POD.

3. Discuss the three concepts critical to understanding POD (Sweep Width, Coverage, and the Exponential Detection Function)

4. Use the Exponential Detection Function to determine POD from Coverage.

5. Compute the Cumulative POD of a segment that has been searched more than once.

6. Explain the significance of POD for effective search management.

7. Estimate the POD for various search resources.

8. Describe factors that can decrease coverage, reducing POD.

Probability of Detection (POD)

The Probability Of Detection (POD) is the conditional probability that a SUBJECT or CLUE will be detected by the search action, given that the person or the object is in the area being searched. POD is expressed as a decimal, between zero and one, or as a percentage value (for example 0.50 or 50%), but in calculations POD is always in decimal form. POD is a measure of resource effectiveness in the field.

Attempts to estimate POD directly, through hunches or gut feelings, have often been wildly inaccurate, usually on the high side. Personnel who work on searches are highly motivated and want to be perceived as doing a good job in their efforts to find the subject. This natural tendency to want to please and succeed can translate into overestimation of POD.

Searchers may be reluctant to report a low POD out of fear of looking bad in the eyes of a search manager. This is a misconception that needs to be addressed by every new generation of searchers. Reporting a low but realistic POD is much more helpful to search managers and the fate of the subject than reporting an unrealistically high POD.

Overestimation of POD can bias the search away from areas that may contain the subject and need to be re-searched. Errors in initial estimates of the Probability Of Area (POA) can self-correct through "shifting" as will be discussed in Chapter 16, but errors in POD do not self-correct.

A bad POD will typically remain in the calculations for the entire search, making the entire effort less effective than it could have been, and may even lead searchers away from the subject! In formal searches the Probability of Success (POS) is repeatedly calculated as the product of POA times POD. Good estimates of POD are essential for effective resource management. Clearly, POD needs to be estimated in a consistent and reliable way that minimizes subjective hunches.

The Wartes Planning Formula and its Limitations

In the 1970's, John Wartes attempted to make the estimation of POD less subjective by conducting experiments in moderate to dense underbrush in the Pacific Northwest with an eye to determining a relationship between grid searcher spacing and POD. The resulting planning formula has been used in numerous land searches over the years. This formula claimed that POD could be calculated as 100 minus one half of the spacing between grid searchers walking parallel to one another. For example, if searchers were spaced twenty feet apart, then half of that distance (ten feet) would be subtracted from one hundred to yield a POD of 90%. This is likely to be a reasonable estimate under most conditions where searchers have a clear line of site to the ground ten feet on either side. It may even underestimate POD under conditions of good lighting and sparse vegetation. However, the Wartes formula is limited by the fact that it was based on only one or two environmental conditions in which the detection results were averaged for two types of subjects of the same-size: responsive and unresponsive adults. Because of these limitations, the resulting numbers from Wartes' planning formula are best limited to an environment similar to the one used in the tests, and in daylight where a mentally alert adult subject is assumed to be responsive to searcher calls. While the development of this formula was a step toward a more objective approach, the need still remained for a POD estimation methodology which was linked to an appropriate detection function and attuned to more than one or two local environments and one or two subject types.

Scientific POD: Bernard Koopman and Operations Research

The scientific development of POD estimates for objects of different sizes dates back to the research of the mathematician Bernard Koopman during World War II. Koopman created a method for determining the optimal track spacing of reconnaissance aircraft needed to ensure a high POD when searching for the wakes of enemy ships. Koopman's pioneering experiments lead to the field of Operations Research which to this day continues to solve complex problems for the military and business. At the heart of Koopman's method are the concepts of Effective Sweep Width, Coverage, and a set of detection profile curves that relate Coverage to POD.

Effective Sweep Width (ESW)

Effective Sweep Width (ESW) is a non-intuitive concept that must be determined by experiment involving hundreds of detection opportunities. ESW is not a "one-size-fits-all" concept because it must be computed for each object under consideration given its size, colors and other characteristics, and for each combination of environmental conditions (terrain, vegetation, visibility) that may be encountered by a human grid searcher. Figure 15.1 depicts an idealized effective sweep width result, with a searcher track

heading North inside a perfect rectangle with an arrow to the right (R) and one to the left (L) representing the "looks" or "glimpses" to either side of the track. The total width of the rectangle represents the ESW, while the distance from the searcher track to either side represents one-half the ESW. Experiments to determine ESW are typically conducted along winding trails and not inside a perfect rectangle that is used here only to simplify the visual example.

Figure 15.1

Idealized Depiction of Effective Sweep Width

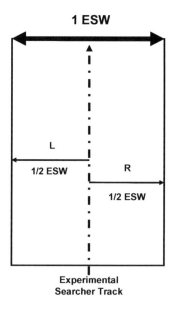

A typical experiment to determine ESW might involve twenty or more experimental searchers and data loggers proceeding through a pre-designed course with thirty or forty objects of two or three different types placed in randomized locations along either side of the track.

Note that we have not assigned any numbers to the value of ESW in Figure 15.1, because that width will vary by object type and prevailing environment at the time of each experiment. The derived ESW would be very different for a mouse (small number, difficult to see) or an elephant (large number, can be seen from a long way off). They would be different again if the long range visibility was restricted by fog. A grey elephant's ESW in fog might be close to that of a mouse's ESW on a clear day.

Coverage: A Ratio of Areas

While search areas are almost never perfect rectangles, using one reminds us that we are dealing with two-dimensional spaces and simplifies the calculation of area to a single length times a single width.

Coverage is the ratio of two areas: search effort as track length times a width, divided by the total area searched. When the width equals ESW, then the Coverage=1 for a POD of 63%. In an actual incident, if the rectangle in Figure 15.1 was searched along the entire track (at a speed consistent with the ESW experiment) at

a width of one ESW, then the ratio of searched area (length times width) to total area (length times width) would equal one, the value of Coverage. **The importance of Effective Sweep Width is that it provides an effective measure of search object detectability that is useful for determining appropriate searcher spacing and numbers of resources required to attain a desired Coverage and POD.** Often, a Coverage of 1.0 is appropriate. In this case, the track/searcher spacing equals 1 ESW if the tracks are perfectly straight, parallel and evenly spaced. Coverage is also equal to 1.0 if the area effectively swept (searched at 1 ESW) equals the area of the segment, provided that the searching effort is approximately uniformly spread over the segment.

However, before exploring this relationship it is also important to gain an understanding of Coverage numbers by looking at a specific resource, grid searchers. Imagine, based on the current conditions, that a grid team's ESW is 40 feet. This means that, if the team members are 40 feet apart and they sweep their assigned search area, they will have Coverage of 1. Now consider two different scenarios. In the first scenario, there are insufficient searchers to sweep the area with 40-foot spacing. There are only enough searchers to sweep the area with 80-foot spacing. Here the search area remains the same, but the search effort is one half the value when the Coverage was one (because half the number of people are used), so in this case the Coverage is 0.5. In the second scenario, there are more searchers than are needed to sweep the area with 40-foot spacing. In fact, there are enough searchers to sweep the area with 20-foot spacing. Again the search area remains the same, but the search effort is twice the value when the Coverage was 1.0 because twice the number of people are used, so in this case the Coverage is 2.0.

The Exponential Detection Function

As mentioned previously, Koopman developed a family of detection profile curves for relating POD to Coverage. The most useful of these curves for land searches is the Exponential Detection Function (EDF) because it naturally incorporates some of the random influences that can occur in both searcher effectiveness (fatigue, attention lapses, variations of actual searcher tracks from those assigned, etc.) and the environment (terrain, vegetation, etc.). Furthermore, it enables us to calculate the POD of a resource based on its Coverage.

Figure 15.2 depicts the EDF, which, for the mathematically curious, is given by the formula $POD = 1 - e^{-C}$, where "C" is the

coverage and "e" is the base of the natural logarithm. To use this curve for finding POD, first compute Coverage and then find the point where that value intersects the curve. Note the bold arrows in the figure. One points upward from the horizontal axis at a Coverage of 1, and the other points across from the vertical axis to meet at the intersection where the POD is 63%. Thus, a resource with Coverage of 1 has a POD of 63%.

By using the EDF, search planners have a statistically based tool that relates search effort to POD while accounting for average random variations spawned by the searchers themselves and the prevailing detection conditions.

Linking the EDF to site-related field tests of how detectable a person or object is under the prevailing conditions provides a robust method for estimating Coverage and resultant POD. This is superior to using a formula based on a snapshot of data from a single eco-region's environment that in all likelihood will not be similar.

Figure 15.2

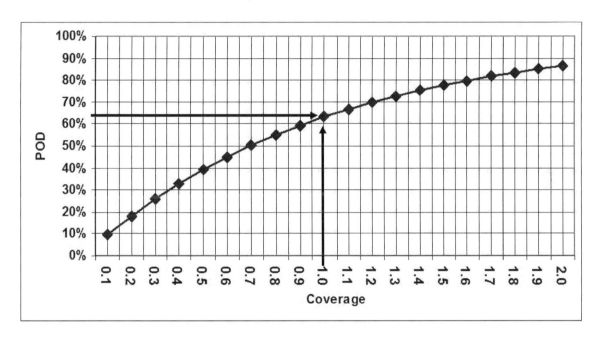

POD vs. Coverage
The Exponential Detection Function

Limitations of ESW

Use of Effective Sweep Width (ESW) in ground-based land searches is highly limited by the fact that ESW can only be determined by experiments that are complicated to set up and analyze. Although research is on-going, only a handful of sweep width tables exist for land grid searching under specific conditions compared to the myriad combinations of varied terrain, visibility and subject types that may be encountered. Koopman's

methodology requires an estimate of ESW as an input to computing Coverage, which then allows POD to be read from the EDF curve. If an ESW estimate is not readily available for a particular environment and subject type, a surrogate must be found if we want to use the Koopman method.

Critical Separation

Fortunately, Perkins and Roberts have devised a very fast technique called Critical Separation for determining searcher spacing for an efficient search that can produce line-of-sight Coverage values in the range of 0.5 to 0.7. With this method there is no fixed distance that yields a particular POD, because spacing is determined by a searcher's ability to detect a sample object near the limit of its visibility under any conditions. Doubling the average distance at which an object is just perceptible yields one Critical Separation distance (1 CS). Figure 15.3 provides a not-to-scale generalized graphic of how Critical Separation (CS) compares to Effective Sweep Width (ESW).

Figure 15.3

Comparison of Critical Separation to Effective Sweep Width

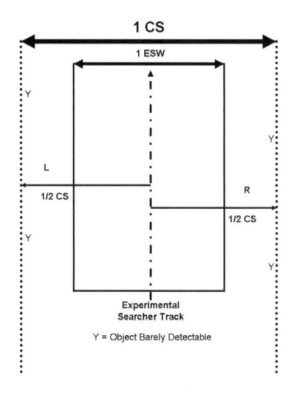

Critical Separation will always be some distance longer than ESW. Therefore, a spacing of 1 CS will always yield a lower Coverage and POD than a spacing of 1 ESW. **In the absence of an experimentally determined value for ESW, it may be estimated to be 0.5 to 0.7 times the Critical Separation distance.**

Determining Critical Separation for prevailing conditions for a representative object can be done in a matter of minutes, usually by two persons trained in the technique. Both circle opposite one another around a sample object so it remains just visible in terrain where the search takes place. Spacing of 1 CS is the distance between them. To use 0.7 CS as a substitute for ESW, a team must not only be expert at determining 1CS, but also at consistently maintaining 0.7 CS separation throughout the assignment.

> **Critical Separation is TWICE the average distance at which a representative person or object can just barely be perceived.**

An analysis by Charles Twardy suggests that 1.5 times the Average Maximum Detection Range (AMDR) may also be a good surrogate for ESW. AMDR is based on a sampling of the maximum distances at which an object is just detectable along eight radial lines separated by angles of 45 degrees. These eight values are then averaged. When determining CS or AMDR for a particular environment, accuracy can be enhanced through use of a laser rangefinder.

Purposeful Wandering

To increase the chances of finding a lost subject, Perkins and Roberts have added a technique to gird searching at Critical Separation distances called "Purposeful Wandering". This allows searchers to deviate from their search track to inspect areas of interest (under ferns, in logs, behind rocks, etc.) before centering back onto the original track. Perkins and Roberts have concluded that the use of Purposeful Wandering, with spacing derived from Critical Separation, can be expected to add 0.4 or more equivalent units to Coverage, making the combined technique roughly equivalent to Coverage at one ESW or higher. The incremental increase to Coverage provided by Purposeful Wandering can be estimated from the additional distances traveled, and increased effort expended by searchers, in their wanderings off of the assigned track.

Helpful Characteristics of the EDF curve

Besides providing a mathematical basis for deriving POD, the Exponential Detection Function (Figure 15.2) has four additional characteristics that are helpful in managing POD estimates in land searches:

1. The EDF graph in Figure 15.2 stops at a Coverage of 2.0 and corresponding POD of 86% because higher coverage on any single search assignment usually represents an over-concentration of effort. POD values for cumulative Coverage greater than 2.0 may be computed using the PODcum formula: $[POD = 1 - e^{-C}]$ where "c" equals Coverage and "e" equals the base of the natural log.

2. As the most conservative detection function, accounting for randomizing influences, a Coverage of 1.0 on the EDF curve corresponds to a POD of 63%. This should **help to discourage overblown estimates of POD** from the field. Values above 63% need to be carefully justified or discounted by search planners.

3. The EDF curve provides **a handy tool for computing Cumulative POD**, which reflects the effect of multiple search resource sweeps in a single area. Consider a segment that was searched with a Coverage of 0.8 (55% POD) by one resource and then searched by another resource at a Coverage of 0.4 (33% POD). To find Cumulative POD for that segment, first add the two Coverage values together (0.8 + 0.4 = 1.2) then find the POD for that Coverage on the

EDF curve. In this case, a Coverage of 1.2 results in a Cumulative POD of 70%. Cumulative POD's greater than 86% can be garnered from Figure 15.4 or the PODcum formula, as needed.

4. The EDF curve also provides for a quick visual understanding of the impact of additional search effort on POD. Because the graph is not a straight line, an increase in search effort does not translate into a proportional increase in POD. Starting at a Coverage of 1.0, increasing the effort by 100% (from a Coverage of 1.0 to 2.0) causes the POD to increase from 63% to 86%, a difference of 23% in POD, which represents a only a 37% percentage jump from the base of 63%. At this level, POD only increases by a little over a third with a 100% increase in effort. This demonstrates **the law of diminishing returns** in which more effort results in smaller incremental additions to POD. This impact reinforces a Coverage of 1.0 as a good balance between thoroughness and efficiency, making Coverage of 1.0 (63% POD) appropriate as a target for planning in most cases.

Besides using the EDF curve to find Cumulative POD, the value can be computed using the following mathematical formula: $POD_{cum} = 1 - (a \times b \times c \dots \times z)$ where

$a = (1 - POD)$ of first search, $b = (1 - POD)$ of second search, $c = (1 - POD)$ of third search and $z = (1 - POD)$ of final search in the sequence.

Example: A segment has been searched three times by:

1. Helicopter: 30% POD
2. K9 Team: 30% POD
3. Grid Search: 70% POD

What is the cumulative probability of detection (POD_{cum})?

$$POD_{cum} = 1 - [(1 - 0.30) \times$$
$$(1 - 0.30) \times (1 - 0.70)]$$
$$= 1 - (0.70 \times 0.70 \times 0.30) = 0.85$$
(or 85%)

This is the same value that is obtained from the EDF curve by summing the equivalent Coverage for the three PODs (0.35 + 0.35 + 1.2), which equals 1.9 as total cumulative Coverage, corresponding to a POD of 85%. Cumulative POD may also be estimated from the table of values in Figure 15.4 or by the formula $[POD_{cum} = 1 - e^{-C}]$ where "c" is the sum of the individual Coverage values.

Coverage as an Incident Objective

Incident objectives should be expressed as desired Coverage. This does not need to be a numeric value, which is the responsibility of the Planning Section to compute. Rather, teams could be asked to search in terms of "high, moderate or low" Coverage values. Priority areas need to be identified and the expectation of Coverage, in descriptive terms like "high" or "low," with which they should be searched, should also be specified. This provides <u>measurable</u> objectives for the individual teams and the Operations Chief to work with when considering tactics. Also, when objectives are defined in terms of desired Coverage, decisions regarding possible <u>expansion</u> or <u>suspension</u> of the search are facilitated and more easily justified.

Search resources should be <u>briefed</u> in terms of desired Coverage, rather than merely being given a task description like, "search with 50-foot spacing." Team leaders should also be informed of the specific Coverage objective for the assignment. This allows the leader some flexibility when the team arrives in the field and begins their assignment. For example, the terrain or vegetation may require closer spacing or more people than expected to obtain a Coverage of 1.0. If the vegetation is less dense than expected, wider spacing can be used to obtain the same Coverage, requiring fewer searchers who could be deployed somewhere else. Briefing in terms of some descriptive level of Coverage is especially important when searchers will be using a critical separation tactic.

Searchers should be <u>debriefed</u> in terms of what they experienced in the field: what was the CS or AMDR used? Have them describe the terrain and vegetation, the estimated searching speed, the total time spent searching, whether fatigue was a factor and what portions of the assigned area were not searched. From this information the Planning Section can estimate the Coverage attained for the assignment.

It is critical that search planners be able to estimate the potential Coverage that a search resource is capable of obtaining, as well as being able to accurately determine the POD once a search assignment has been completed. While some information is known about the probability of detection for some search resources (discussed later), there are no precise formulas or tables for determining the Coverage, and subsequent POD, for all types of resources under all conditions. Search managers should be able to assess the value of a resource with respect to its ability to detect clues, as well as having a good understanding of how such conditions as terrain, vegetation, weather, searcher fatigue, and time of day may affect Coverage and the subsequent POD.

Figure 15.4 provides a convenient method for computing cumulative POD. The intersection of POD from the vertical axis with the POD from horizontal axis provides cumulative POD for any two listed values. For example, searches by two resources in a segment at a POD of 50% and 40% would result in a cumulative POD of 70% for that segment.

Figure 15.4

Table for Estimating Cumulative POD

POD	5%	10%	15%	20%	25%	30%	35%	40%	45%	50%	55%	60%	65%	70%	75%	80%	85%	90%	95%
5%	10	15	19	24	29	34	38	43	48	53	57	62	67	72	76	81	86	91	95
10%	15	19	24	28	33	37	42	46	51	55	60	64	69	73	78	82	87	91	96
15%	19	24	28	32	36	41	45	49	53	58	62	66	70	75	79	83	87	92	96
20%	24	28	32	36	40	44	48	52	56	60	64	68	72	76	80	84	88	92	96
25%	29	33	36	40	44	48	51	55	59	63	66	70	74	78	81	85	89	93	96
30%	34	37	41	44	48	51	55	58	62	65	69	72	76	79	83	86	90	93	97
35%	38	42	45	48	51	55	58	61	64	68	71	74	77	81	84	87	90	94	97
40%	43	46	49	52	55	58	61	64	67	70	73	76	79	82	85	88	91	94	97
45%	48	51	53	56	59	62	64	67	70	73	75	78	81	84	86	89	92	95	97
50%	53	55	58	60	63	65	68	70	73	75	78	80	83	85	88	90	93	95	98
55%	57	60	62	64	66	69	71	73	75	78	80	82	84	87	89	91	93	96	98
60%	62	64	66	68	70	72	74	76	78	80	82	84	86	88	90	92	94	96	98
65%	67	69	70	72	74	76	77	79	81	83	84	86	88	90	91	93	95	97	98
70%	72	73	75	76	78	79	81	82	84	85	87	88	90	91	93	94	96	97	99
75%	76	78	79	80	81	83	84	85	86	88	89	90	91	93	94	95	96	98	99
80%	81	82	83	84	85	86	87	88	89	90	91	92	93	94	95	96	97	98	99
85%	86	87	87	88	89	90	90	91	92	93	93	94	95	96	96	97	98	99	99
90%	91	91	92	92	93	93	94	94	95	95	96	96	97	97	98	98	99	99	100
95%	95	96	96	96	96	97	97	97	97	98	98	98	98	99	99	99	99	100	100

Instructions: Find the existing POD prior to the current search along the left vertical axis and the POD for the current search along the top horizontal axis. The intersection of the two is the Cumulative POD. Example: For a prior POD of 65% and a current POD of 45%, the Cumulative POD is 81%.

Thoroughness vs. Efficiency

Research by Wartes and Koopman revealed an interesting relationship between the thoroughness of a grid search (defined in terms of POD) and its efficiency (defined in terms of the amount of searcher effort that must be expended in order to obtain a certain POD). Succinctly stated, as thoroughness increases, efficiency tends to decrease. That is, increasing the POD by narrowing the spacing between searchers requires either more searchers, or more time to search, or a smaller segment to cover. Moreover, the inverse relationship between thoroughness and efficiency is governed by a principle of diminishing returns, meaning that small increments of POD must be "purchased" at the cost of increasingly higher amounts of searcher hours and effort. This law of diminishing returns is readily visible in the EDF curve as seen in Figure 15.2. Increasing Coverage from 1.0 to 2.0 (a doubling of effort) only results in a 37% increase in POD from 63% to 86%. There may be times when high search intensities are advisable, resources permitting. In the case of a lost toddler with nightfall approaching, obtaining and assigning enough resources to attain a Coverage of 2.0 or higher might be prudent. In other situations, like that of a fully equipped lost hiker, an efficient approach at a Coverage of 1.0, which allows fewer resources to cover more territory in the same time frame, may be appropriate. These are the kinds of resource deployment decisions that a search manager must make based on an overall understanding of the subject's type and the circumstances that caused the subject to be reported missing.

Search Planning Formulas

How do search planners estimate the number of searchers needed, or the time it will take to search with a given number of searchers, or the area that can be searched in a given time with the available resources? Fortunately, we can derive formulas based on a given search speed or number of hours per mile. Figure 15.5 shows the various formulas for determining the relationships between number or searchers, searchable area, hours of searching, and searcher spacing. The finding by Wartes that it takes about 3.5 hours for a grid searcher to travel one mile when searching (which means the searcher speed is 0.286 mph) is useful for planning purposes. From this speed of 0.286 mph we get the "3.5-hours-per-mile" rule-of-thumb which can be used in these formulas for estimating any one of the following when the remaining three are known: (1) the number of searchers necessary for the task, (2) the size of the segment to search, (3) the spacing between the searchers, and (4) the amount of time the task should take. The value of 3.5 hours per mile can be replaced by another, more accurate value, if the search planners have access to better information about how many hours that it takes a resource to search each mile.

Figure 15.5

Grid Search Planning Formulas

$$\text{Searchers} = \frac{\text{Area (sq mi)} \times 5280 \times 3.5}{\text{Spacing (ft)} \times \text{Hours}}$$

$$\text{Area (sq mi)} = \frac{\text{Spacing (ft)} \times \text{Hours} \times \text{Searchers}}{5280 \times 3.5}$$

$$\text{Hours} = \frac{\text{Area (sq mi)} \times 5280 \times 3.5}{\text{Spacing (ft)} \times \text{Searchers}}$$

$$\text{Spacing} = \frac{\text{Area (sq mi)} \times 5280 \times 3.5}{\text{Searchers} \times \text{Hours}}$$

The value for spacing, the distance between searchers, can be computed, but its relationship to Coverage must be determined based on a value for ESW or a surrogate such as a field sample of CS scaled back between 0.5 to 0.7, or a multiple of AMDR. For example, if the ESW or its surrogate was 40 feet (Coverage of 1) and the Spacing formula yielded 80 feet, then the Coverage for the area searched at that distance between searchers would be 0.5 (40/80). If the Spacing formula yielded a value of 20 feet, then the Coverage at that distance between searchers would be

2.0 (40/20). Use the formulas in Figure 15.5 for each of the four planning calculations when it is reasonable to assume a searcher speed of one mile every 3.5 hours (0.286 mph).

Many untrained or inexperienced search planners often overestimate the ability of grid searchers to cover an area, assigning too few people to too large a segment with too narrow a spacing to complete a task in too short a time. These planning formulas help to provide an objective measure of requirements.

Sample Grid Search Planning Problems

1. Twenty five novice grid searchers are available for 7 hours. From on site trials, the Critical Separation distance has been determined to be 120 feet. What size area can this grid team search at Coverage of 1.0 in the allotted time? The search area

is groomed farmland with straight, parallel fields making it easy for searchers to maintain equally spaced searcher tracks

Solution 1: Since half of the CS distance is a surrogate for ESW with novice searchers, the ESW would be estimated at 60 feet. Therefore, the spacing should also be 60 feet to get a Coverage of 1.0 when all of the assigned area is swept with straight, parallel, equally spaced searcher tracks. Applying the Area formula: $(60 \times 7 \times 25)/(5280 \times 3.5)$ we find $(10,500/18,480) = 0.57$ sq mi, so they can search a little under 0.6 square miles in 7 hours.

2. The IC is under pressure to find a Congressman's lost relative. She wants an 80% POD from a segment that is one square mile. She has given you 100 grid searchers for the task, and wants them all to search in the same line because the national media has a helicopter in the air and will be taking pictures. As in the first question, the ESW is estimated to be 60 feet from a CS test. The IC has given you two minutes to figure out how long it will take to complete that task.

Solution 2: First use the EDF curve to do a back conversion of POD to Coverage. A POD of 80% corresponds to Coverage of 1.6. Because 60 feet is the spacing expected to produce a Coverage of 1.0 if the entire assigned area is searched at that

distance between searchers, we need to compute the spacing at a Coverage of 1.6 (POD of 80%). This is done by dividing ESW by desired Coverage, that is, 60 divided by 1.6, giving 37.5 ($60/1.6 = 37.5$), indicating that about 38 feet between searchers is necessary to produce an 80% POD. Next, use the Hours formula with that spacing: $(1 \text{ sq mi} \times 5280 \times 3.5)/(38 \times 100)$, which simplifies to $18,480/3,800 = 4.9$ Hours. Tell the IC that you can do it in 5 hours at 80% POD.

3. From eco-region tables for your area, the value of ESW is listed as 50 feet for the prevailing conditions. Seventy five searchers are available to go into the field for 5 hours. What would be the POD for this team searching 2 square miles? What would be the Cumulative POD if they did the same task twice with the same POD each time?

Solution 3: From what is known, the spacing required for 75 searchers to search 2 square miles in 5 hours can be computed using the Spacing formula. Once this spacing is known, expected Coverage can be computed by dividing the ESW of 50 by the desired spacing. From this Coverage the POD can be read from the EDF curve.

Starting with the Spacing formula: $(2 \text{ sq mi} \times 5280 \times 3.5)/(75 \times 5)$ we find

36,960/375 = 98.6 feet of spacing between searchers. Coverage at this spacing is computed as (50/98.6) = 0.51. Referring to the EDF curve in Figure 15.2, Coverage of 0.51 yields a POD of 40%. If the same task was repeated, then add the Coverage for each task and find the POD for that sum on the EDF curve. In this case, (0.51 + 0.51) = 1.02, for a PODcum of about 64%. Alternatively, use the Cumulative POD table in Figure 15.4 to find the intersection of 40% prior POD and 40% current POD to give a Cumulative POD of 64%.

4. The Planning Section Chief would like a 3-square-mile segment to be searched at a Coverage of 1.0 (63% POD) in 6 hours. The Critical Separation value has been determined to be 72 feet by experts who will be team leaders. How many grid searchers are needed to complete this task in the allotted time?

Solution 4: Since we know the Critical Separation value is 72 feet, determined by CS experts who are expected to maintain assigned separation as team leaders, we can use 0.7 times 72 feet to convert from CS to ESW. Since 0.7 x 72 = 50 feet (rounded) that value will be used as a surrogate for ESW providing Coverage of 1.0 where 50 foot spacing is maintained. Using the Searchers formula: $(3 \times 5280 \times 3.5)/(50 \times 6)$ we find 55,440/300 = 184.8. Operations will need to deploy 185 grid searchers to complete the task at Coverage=1.0 in 6 hours.

Air Scenting K9 POD

The POD of air scenting search dogs has been a topic of much discussion for many years. A major problem for the search planner has been the lack of a reliable method for estimating POD coverage by this important resource, because numerous atmospheric and environmental conditions will affect the dog's ability to detect airborne scent.

Research by Hatch Graham (1994) suggests a useful method for estimating air scenting K9 POD using daytime sun angles (to estimate convective activity), wind and cloud cover (to estimate likely scent propagation in the absence of strong convection) during the duration of the sweep pattern employed by the K9 team. Some advanced K9 handlers are known to take a laminated copy of the full Hatch Graham tables into the field for estimating POD. We will not reproduce the entire set of tables in this manual. A shortcut set of tables for aiding search managers is shown in Figure 15.6 for three scent detection ranges under various conditions. In the absence of any further research in this area, worst case Coverage for a particular POD is back calculated from the EDF curve for reference. These values are then scaled up to conform to the EDF curve, with a "best case" coverage of 2.0, for a POD of 86%.

Figure 15.6

Simplified K9 Coverage Estimation for Search Managers, After Hatch Graham

Estimates of Coverage for K9 Scent Detection at 100, 50, and 25 meters Downwind of the Scent Source under Various Environmental Conditions

Factor	**POOR**	**FAIR**	**GOOD**
Sun Angle	High	Medium	Low
Wind	Less Than 4 mph	4 to 10 mph	11 to 20 mph
Cloud Cover	Clear	50% Low Clouds	Overcast or Night
Downwind Distance	Estimated Coverage	Estimated Coverage	Estimated Coverage
100m	**0.1**	**0.3**	**0.5**
50m	**0.2**	**0.6**	**1.0**
25m	**0.4**	**1.2**	**2.0**

Adapted from Graham (1994) and conformed to the Exponential Detection Function

The sun angle can be calculated using a formula based on the geometry of shadows. For any vertical height (this can be a person, a yardstick, etc.) that casts a shadow on horizontal ground, consider the length of the shadow as the base of a triangle. The ratio of the height over the base can be used with Table 15.7 to determine one of three sun angle values: High, Medium, or Low in Table 15.6. For example, a 36-inch yardstick that casts a 30-inch shadow has a height over base ratio (36/30) of 1.2, which, according to Table 15.7 corresponds to a "medium" sun angle because the ratio is between 0.71 and 1.71.

Figure 15.7

Sun Angle from the Ratio of Vertical Height Divided by Shadow Base

Height over Base Ratio	Greater Than **1.71**	From **0.71** to **1.71**	Less Than **0.71**
Sun Angle	**HIGH**	**MEDIUM**	**LOW**

Adapted from Graham (1994)

Note though, for a shadow reading in the morning, the sun angle will be moving towards higher values. Conversely, in the afternoon, the sun angle will be getting progressively lower. Whether or not the sun angle moves from Medium in the morning to High by mid-afternoon depends upon geographic latitude and the time of year. Generally, the hours from 10am to 2pm in the summertime are subject to high sun angles, which produce high convection currents. These thermal currents move scent particles vertically upward rather than horizontally outward. High sun angles, which produce high convection, are associated with poor conditions for air-scenting.

K9 POD for SAR Managers

Let us now put the Hatch Graham methodology and the EDF curve together to show how SAR managers can use them to make informed judgments about K9 POD. Imagine that you have been asked to debrief a K9 air-scenting team that has come in from the field at 3pm on a clear, hot, windless summer day, somewhere in the northern hemisphere. The team has been out for four of the hottest hours of the day and the handler claims a 95% POD for their task. Is this credible? The likely answer is: probably not! Referring to Figure 15.6, all of the factors are Poor for this air-scenting assignment. Even at a downwind range of 25 meters/82 feet, the Coverage is estimated to be no better than 0.4, corresponding to a POD of 33%. There may be mitigating factors why the team's POD could be higher than 33% (for example, if the spacing between scent sweeps is less than 25 meters), but a 95% POD would be wildly unrealistic under those conditions.

The values in Figure 15.6 are not meant for computing exact Coverage based on the Hatch Graham methodology and are intentionally more conservative than Graham's maximum POD values. Higher values can be accepted, but they should be justified by K9 handlers. The data is there to provide search managers with a set of guidelines to gauge the credibility and reasonableness of each air-scent K9 team's estimates of their own effectiveness under various environmental conditions.

Helicopters and POD

Research by John Bownds and his colleagues has provided much information on the ability of helicopters to detect lost subjects. Particularly useful for planning purposes are their data on searching for simulated "subjects" in forested, mountain areas of Arizona (Bownds, *et al*, 1991). The search pattern involved contour searching mountainous or hilly terrain, and route searching of trails and canyon bottoms. Their major results can be described as follows:

- Waving, Upright Lost Persons:
  24 persons were found out of 40: 60% POD

- Persons in Spread Eagle ("Cookie Cutter") Position in Plain View:
  17 persons found out of 21: 81% POD

- Motionless, Unresponsive Persons Under Cover (But Not Hidden):
  0 persons found out of 7: 0% POD.

These results confirm the value of helicopters as a search resource when it can be assumed that the subject is responsive and motivated to be found. They also support the use of helicopters for large, open areas, where even

unconscious subjects may be spotted if their posture resembles the "spread eagle" position.

The fact that in the Sonoran Desert the POD on a bright sunny day when looking for subjects who are not responding and under cover (which is true most of the time) is only about 30%, usually surprises many ground based resources, and helps them to reconsider their own POD estimates more realistically. The study by Bownds et al can be accessed at: http://math.arizona.edu/~dsl/casie/helicop. htm.

Factors that Lower POD

Search planners should be acutely aware of the many factors that may easily decrement or reduce the expected POD of a search team. When such factors are perceived to exist, the theoretical or reported POD should be adjusted downward accordingly. Some of these factors include:

- Weather, terrain, vegetation
  Can affect visibility, ease of travel, and searcher morale.

- Sensitivity to Time of Day
  Some resources, such as air scent dogs and visual trackers, work best in the morning, late afternoon, and at night.

- Glaring Sunlight

  Aircraft spot more subjects on hazy, overcast days than on bright, sunny days.

- Searcher fatigue

  Searchers are optimally effective for the first hour or two. Effectiveness starts to decrease rapidly after four hours, and "bottoms out" after about eight hours.

- Searcher expectations

  Searchers who do not expect to see a clue will not be disappointed.

- Searcher training

  Poorly trained searchers are "subject finders" at best. To be effective, searchers need to learn good scanning techniques, how to minimize distractions and how to reorient and concentrate on searching after being distracted. Preoccupation with cell phones, GPS units or other equipment severely deteriorates effectiveness.

- Poor leadership

  When team leaders and search managers do not know the appropriate tactical procedures, or in some way show deficient management skills, searchers will perform less effectively regardless of training and motivation.

Summary

In this chapter we discussed the important concept of Probability of Detection (POD). We began the chapter by addressing the limitations of a single formula to determine searcher spacing. The research of Bernard Koopman was introduced with the concepts of Effective Sweep Width (ESW), Coverage, and the Exponential Detection Function (EDF).

Critical Separation was defined and we noted that 0.5 to 0.7 of a Critical Separation distance is acceptable as a reasonable surrogate for ESW, based on a team's level of experience. With this knowledge we were able to demonstrate the calculation of Coverage using an on-scene sampling of a person's or object's detectability. Once Coverage is known, we showed that POD can be determined using the EDF curve.

We discussed methods of calculating cumulative POD when a segment has been searched more than once, then described the importance of such POD measures to many components of search management. We stated that incident objectives should be expressed as Coverage values, and that search resources should be briefed and debriefed in terms of expected Coverage.

Methods of estimating Coverage and deriving POD for specific resources were discussed, including grid search teams, for which planning formulas were provided, critical separation tactics, hasty teams, air scenting dog teams, and helicopters. Finally, the chapter ended with a discussion of factors that can lower Coverage and subsequent POD. These can include weather, terrain, vegetation, time of day, searcher fatigue, searcher expectations, searcher training, and poor leadership.

Questions for Discussion:

1. What factors will affect whether a particular clue is detected?

2. Under what circumstances might you decide to search a segment a second time?

3. What kinds of factors would lead searchers to expect <u>not</u> to find clues? What can crew leaders or search managers do to prevent declining expectations? Would prior experience in searching be an important factor.

4. On a clear, sunny day, an air scent dog team has just completed their search of a segment, which they swept moving upwind at 100 meter intervals. The five-foot-five handler notices that her shadow is approximately 3 feet in length, and that the wind in the search area is at least 10mph. Assuming that the team is well trained and highly qualified, what is a good estimate of the team's approximate Coverage and POD? Would Coverage of 0.2 and a POD of 18% be a reasonable estimate?

CHAPTER 16

CHANGING SEARCH PRIORITIES: SHIFTING THE PROBABILITY OF AREA (POA)

As search resources are applied to the field and the subject is not found, search priorities have to change accordingly. In this chapter we introduce **three methods of systematically "shifting" the probabilities of area** for each of the segments in the search area.

CHAPTER OBJECTIVES:

When you finish studying this chapter, you should be able to:

1. Explain why POA should change as segments are searched.
2. Provide a conceptual (non-mathematical) explanation of how POA are shifted.
3. Describe three methods of shifting the POA.

Shifting the Probability of Area (POA)

An important component of tracking search progress involves a systematic and consistent reassessment of probability of area (POA) whenever segments are searched and the subject is not found.

Remember that the purpose of assigning POA to segments (as well as to the "Rest of the World" or ROW) is to quantify — or translate into percentages — the search planner's implicit "probabilities" (hunches or beliefs) about the possible location of the lost person.

Quantifying the POA forces the search planner to consider and compare every possible segment within the designated search area, as well as assessing the possibility that the subject is outside the area. However, once the initial POAs are assigned and segments are searched without finding the subject, the planner is confronted with the problem of reassessing or changing the respective POAs. The problem is magnified by the requirement that, not only must the searched segment's POA be *decreased* by some number, but the POAs for the remaining segments, including the ROW "segment", must be simultaneously <u>increased</u>, however slightly. This chapter is intended to provide a conceptual (non-mathematical) understanding of the mathematics of shifting the POA. Readers interested in the mathematics are referred to the section on Bayes' Theorem.

Post-incident critiques of unsuccessful searches commonly reveal that persons managing the search used no consistent system

for reassessing search priorities as the incident proceeded. Typically, the same favored areas were searched repeatedly, while attention to less favored areas was overly delayed, and the designated search area was not extended soon enough to find the lost person alive. Shifting the POA is intended to help search planners avoid these potentially fatal errors.

What Happens When POA is Shifted?

1. **The POA of the searched segment is** <u>decreased</u>. Prior to being searched a targeted segment will have a specified number of points (the POA). After it is searched, a number of these points must be subtracted and redistributed to the remaining segments, leaving the targeted segment with a new POA, lower than the old one. **The number of points to subtract from this segment's POA will depend on the effectiveness of the search resources, that is, their POD.** A highly thorough search (for example, a POD of 80%) should result in a significant decrease in that segment's old POA, while a less thorough search will result in a smaller decrease.

For example, a search planner believes that a particular segment is "hot," with a very high chance that it contains the lost person, because its POA is 50%. He tasks a search

team to grid the area with spacing of 10 feet between searchers, where the ESW is known to be 30 feet. The Coverage is 3 (30/10), so the POD is 95%. When the team returns without the subject, the planner should now have much less confidence that this segment contains the subject than he would if the search had been less thorough. Translating this example into numerical terms, a segment with a prior POA of 50%, searched with a POD of 95%, will result in a new (or shifted) POA of less than 5%, which comes from using Bayes' Theorem. However, if the segment had instead been searched with a POD of 20%, then the new POA would be about 45%, suggesting that the segment still has a high possibility of containing the lost person.

2. **The POA of the remaining segments is** <u>increased</u>. As stated previously, the probability "points" that are taken away from the searched segment must be redistributed to the remaining segments (including the ROW "segment"). How should these points be distributed? It might seem logical to distribute them equally among the remaining segments. However, a little thought should reveal the fallacy of spreading them out evenly among segments. Consider, for purposes of illustration, a search with only three segments (typically, a search incident will have many more segments than three). Segment 1 has a prior POA of 40%, segment 2 also has a POA of 40%, while segment 3 has a POA of only 1%, (the POA for the ROW is therefore

19%). Segment 1 is then searched with a POD of 35%, causing the new POA for segment 1 to be 30%, a decrease of 10 percentage points. If we were to evenly distribute these 10 points to the remaining segments and the ROW, then segment 2 would show an increase of only about 8%, while segment 3, originally considered only a remote possibility, has now increased by about 300%! Clearly, the probability points taken away from segment 1 should be redistributed in a fashion that takes into account the prior POA for the remaining segments.

The correct formula that redistributes POA to the remaining segments and ROW, assigns the POA in proportion to the respective sizes of their prior POA values. Thus, segments with high POA prior to a particular search will receive proportionately more probability points when POA are shifted than will segments with lower POA.

Summary of Shifting POA

> **Determine the new or shifted POA of the segment that was just searched.** This will involve taking some number of POA points <u>away</u> from the segment, depending upon the thoroughness of the search.
> **Determine the new or shifted POA of the remaining segments, including the ROW** This will involve redistributing the POA that has been

taken away from the searched segment, thereby **increasing** the POA for all remaining segments. The specific amount of POA to be added to each segment will depend on the prior size of each segment's POA.

A Note on the Formula for Shifting POA

The formula that is used to shift the POA is called **Bayes' Theorem** (see Figure 16.1). While nearly anyone can "crunch the numbers" using Bayes' Theorem and a calculator or computer, an appreciation of how the theorem works requires an understanding of algebra as well as conditional probability theory. Although the formula is not particularly complicated, trying to compute the shifted POA by hand can be an extremely onerous and error-prone task, because the formula must be applied to every segment in the search area following each search. Fortunately, there are numerous computer programs and spreadsheets available that simplify the shifting of POA, as well as many other search management tasks. One application that does the mathematics for you is "Computer Aided Search Information Exchange" or CASIE for short. A very user-friendly Windows version of CASIE is available free via download at http://wcasie.com. Besides shifting POAs, CASIE includes features that allow users to quickly create an initial consensus and do virtually all of the search planning math.

Figure 16.1

APPLYING BAYES' THEOREM TO SHIFT POA

STEP 1: Find the new Probability Of Area (POA) of the segment (X) that has just been searched with a particular Probability of Detection (POD X):

$$POA_{new} \; X = \frac{(1 - POD \; X) \cdot POA_{old} \; X}{1 - [(POD \; X) \cdot POA_{old} \; X]}$$

STEP 2: Find the new POA for each remaining segment (Y) — including the ROW — as a result of segment X having been searched.

$$POA_{new} \; Y = \frac{POA_{old} \; Y}{1 - [(POD \; X) \cdot POA_{old} \; X]}$$

Notes on terminology:

POA_{new} : the new or "shifted" POA after segment X is searched.

POA_{old} : the old POA for the segment, prior to segment X being searched.

$POD \; X$: the probability of detection by which segment X was searched.

Note: for purposes of computation, numbers in this formula are expressed as decimals. For example a POD of 75% would be written as 0.75. The total POA would therefore be expressed as 1.00 rather than 100%.

Shifting POA Without a Computer: THE SHORT FORMULA

Greg Shea (1988) has developed a useful "short formula" of shifting the POAs that does the mathematical computations inherent in Bayes' Theorem in a simple, efficient, way.

Using just a calculator, the search planner can quickly shift the POA for several or more sectors at a time, without having to make the calculations after each tasking. The process requires two steps, with a practical example provided in Figure 16.2:

Step 1: Compute POA′

(pronounced POA "prime") for each segment, using the formula:

$$POA' = (1 - POD_{cum}) \bullet POA_{old}$$

where POD_{cum} is the cumulative POD for the segment and POA_{old} is the POA prior to being shifted.

Step 2: Normalize the POA by performing the following sub-steps:

(a) **Sum the POA′** across all segments, including the ROW. The total will be a decimal number less than one, and is called the **normalization factor**, designated **S**.

(b) **Divide each segment's POA′ by S**, which yields the new, shifted POA. These values are identical with the ones that would have been obtained using Bayes' Theorem at each step

Figure 16.2

<u>Example of Applying the Short Formula for Shifting POA</u>

In this example, there are four segments, plus the ROW. Segments 1 and 2 have been searched once, segment 3 has been searched twice, and segment 4 has not yet been searched. The search manager (a) calculates the cumulative POD for each segment (the POD for the ROW is always zero), (b) then calculates POA′ for each segment and the ROW. (c) After summing the POA′ to obtain the normalization factor **S**, (d) divide each POA′ by **S** to obtain the new, shifted POA. This shifted POA becomes the "old" POA the next time the calculations are performed.

Segment	POA_{old}	POD_1	POD_2	POD_{cum}	POA′	POA_{new}
1	0.40	0.60	–	0.60	0.16	0.32
2	0.20	0.85	–	0.85	0.03	0.06
3	0.10	0.60	0.75	0.90	0.01	0.02
4	0.20	–	–	0.00	0.20	0.40
ROW	0.10	–	–	0.00	<u>0.10</u>	0.20
					S = 0.50	

Note that POA′ must be calculated for every segment each time that POA are shifted, regardless of whether the segments had been searched during that particular period. Consequently, using the "short formula" can become tedious when there are a large number of segments. However, the method has the advantage of permitting <u>periodic</u> updating of POA rather than requiring it after every tasking (note, for example, that four POD's were recorded before the POA were shifted). It is an excellent procedure when computers (and computer users) are not readily available.

Shifting POA Without Numbers:
The Sector Ladder

Dave Perkins and Pete Roberts of Northumberland SAR (United Kingdom) have proposed a method of shifting priorities as segments or "sectors" (the U.K. term) are searched and the subject is not found. The method is elegant in its simplicity, yet maintains many of the advantages of the more rigorous approaches described previously.

The first step in applying the sector ladder approach is to order the respective sectors and routes from highest to lowest priority into a single list or "ladder," which was explained in Chapter 13. After sectors at the top of the ladder are searched, those sectors are dropped to the bottom "rungs" of the ladder. Eventually, low-priority sectors at the bottom of the ladder work their way to the top in a systematic fashion.

Based on the initial rankings in Figure 13.2, Figure 16.3 shows how the Sector Ladder might be updated by phase when the top three sectors or routes are searched. The Initial Phase shows the starting consensus search priorities. In Figure 13.2, Sector A and Route R1 were tied for third place. Since there are only three resources available for each phase in this hypothetical example, we have arbitrarily assigned Route R1 to be fourth in rank.

In this example, sectors/routes R2, B and A are identified by consensus as high-priority sectors. During the initial phase, there are only enough search resources to search these three sectors. When these resources fail to find any clues, the search planner checks them off and makes up a new list (Phase 2). Sectors/routes R2, B and A are dropped to the bottom of the ladder, while sectors R1, R3 and C are promoted to the high-priority rungs. Again, in this example, resources are tasked to the three top sectors, but no clues are found

---

Figure 16.3

A Sector Ladder Example:
Shifting Search Priorities
(Three Resources Available per Phase)

Rank	Initial Phase	Phase 2	Phase 3	Add E & F
1	R2	R1	D	D
2	B	R3	R4	R4
3	A	C	ROW	E
4	R1	D	R2	F
5	R3	R4	B	R2
6	C	ROW	A	B
7	D	R2	R1	A
8	R4	B	R3	R1
9	ROW	A	C	R3
10	--	--	--	C
11	--	--	--	ROW

Note, once Phase 2 is over without any clues being found, that the lineup for Phase 3 has ROW as the third ranked sector. When using this method for shifting POA, the presence of ROW at or above the middle of the ladder is a good indication that the search may need to be expanded. Before proceeding with searches in Phase 3, two new Sectors E and F are carved out of the ROW and added at the rank of ROW, in this case ranking slots 3 and 4. This represents an expansion of the search area with ROW dropping back to the bottom. With three resources available, sectors/routes D, R4 and E would be searched in Phase 3. A full explanation of this method with guidelines for shifting sector priorities and handling clues can be found in the paper, "A New Look at the Sector Ladder," by Dave Perkins and Pete Roberts (revised 2005).

The usefulness of the sector ladder approach becomes most apparent when clues are found, or for whatever reason search planners come to believe that any sector (whether previously searched or not) has a different priority than is represented by its position in the ladder. Suppose, for example, that information is obtained from friends — after the initial phase — that the subject may have camped in sector B. Although this sector has already been searched, the search planner may wish to upgrade the priority of sector B, and to send resources back to search sector B more thoroughly for clues. This decision would result in a revised Phase 2 list with Sector B going back to the top of the list, rather than

automatically going to second from the bottom. After they are searched, sectors are dropped to at or near the bottom of the ladder based on the estimated POD. The exact location depends upon the thoroughness of the searching that has taken place in the sector. A very high POD, as reported on the debriefing, would indicate a very low likelihood that the sector contained the subject, pushing the sector to, or close to the bottom. By the same token, a low POD search would indicate that there was still a good chance that the subject might be in there. Under these conditions, the sector would not be dropped to the bottom but to somewhere in the middle of the ladder, reflecting the need for additional resources to search there again until the cumulative POD reaches an acceptable level.

Advantages of the Sector Ladder Approach

- It is easily learned and applied.

- It does not require mathematics or computers.

- It takes into account both clues and the impact of negative information on the changes to search priorities.

Disadvantages of the Sector Ladder Approach

• Unlike the shifting POA approach, there is no precise system for adjusting a segment's priority according to the specific POD of a search. Without doing the mathematics, any attempts to shift the priority of a searched sector will be at least partly subjective.

• Unlike the shifting POA approach, it does not automatically yield measures of each segment's coverage (cumulative probability of detection). However, this could still be computed separately if accurate records are maintained.

• The approach may become cumbersome in large incidents with many segments and resources in the field.

The Sector Ladder approach to shifting search priorities represents an important tool for search planners. It may be especially useful during the early phases of the search, before the planning section becomes fully functional, or when computing equipment is not available.

Summary

In this chapter we provided the rationale for shifting probabilities of area after search resources return from high-priority segments without finding the subject. We described three methods of systematically shifting POA, including (1) the classical Bayesian approach, which requires computer software as well as computer savvy search planners, (2) a "short formula" for calculating the Bayesian probabilities, which can be easily performed with a calculator, and (3) the sector ladder approach, which can be applied without any calculations.

Questions for Discussion:

1. Without any reference to numbers, explain what happens when segment POA is shifted shifted.

2. What kinds of problems or errors does the search planner attempt to avoid by using the shifting-POA methods in this chapter?

3. What other factors, besides relatively high POA, should be considered when deciding which segments to search?

CHAPTER 17

BRIEFING AND DEBRIEFING

Briefing and debriefing are two critical components of information management. All resources used on the search should be briefed prior to each operational assignment and debriefed at the assignment's conclusion. In this chapter we will describe the **significance of adequate briefings and debriefings**, and describe the types of information that should be exchanged.

CHAPTER OBJECTIVES:

When you finish studying this chapter, you should be able to:

1. Discuss the important elements and procedures of the SAR briefing.
2. Discuss the important elements and procedures of the SAR debriefing.

The Importance of a Briefing

An effective incident briefing will summarize the situation, past and present, and provide all information necessary to orient personnel to all environmental and strategic aspects of the situation. **A complete briefing will provide:**

a) Situation status.
b) Objectives.
c) Strategy.
d) Tactical assignments

The type of briefing conducted depends on the size and complexity of the operation. Briefings may be oral, written, or a combination of both. Written briefing statements and task assignments reduce confusion and improve communication.

Written briefings also help ensure that search personnel do not overlook important items, as well as providing the ability to review assignments once the team or search crew gets into the field. ICS Form 204, the task assignment list, should be used to document the briefing essentials.

A proper briefing can determine the outcome of an operation. A poor briefing can result in — among other things — poor search implementation, gaps in coverage, misuse of or destruction of clues, and ultimately, the failure to find the subject in good condition.

For Searchers, Who Briefs Whom?

Formal briefings are coordinated by the Planning Section and usually presented by the Operations Section Chief (OSC) or delegate, with assistance from the Planning Section Chief (PSC). All involved personnel must be briefed. Factors determining who will attend the formal briefing are (1) the size of the operation, (2) the number of personnel involved, and (3) the location of the resources requiring a briefing. In large operations, all personnel down to the division/group supervisor level should attend the formal briefing. In smaller operations, the Planning Section may brief all personnel down to individual crew leaders (team leaders). In either event, division/group supervisors or crew leaders would subsequently brief those who had not attended the formal briefing to ensure that everyone receives critical operational information.

What Information Must be Presented?

Briefings should cover all pertinent aspects of the operation. The Incident Action Plan, especially the incident objectives, is actually a ready-made briefing statement and should be used as a guide. The following information is of interest to all personnel and should be included:

- The situation status and predictions of the future course of the incident.
- Incident objectives and strategies should be discussed so that personnel know why they are being assigned specific tasks and how those tasks relate to the success of the overall incident.
- Tactical assignments should be outlined and specific instructions provided which are explicit and include the exact results expected (for example, the desired POD or Coverage for a search activity).

- Information about the subject that will help searchers recognize the subject, find clues, or determine the subject's behavior should be provided, generally as a handout containing:
-- Complete physical description.
-- Clothing and equipment (clothing carried or worn and underneath).
-- Physical condition.
-- Mental condition.
-- Behavioral traits.
-- Circumstances causing a search.
-- Medical concerns (such as health problems or medicine the subject may require).

Clue considerations:
- Sole pattern of subject's footwear. If other family members wear the same style footwear, secure a pair of the subject's to more accurately portray the foot print pattern.
- Items carried by subject that could be dropped or left behind.
- Procedures for reporting clues and a Clue Management Plan.
- Instructions on logging clue locations and times found.
- How to protect clue locations for follow-up.
- Subject's trip plans.
- Hazards that may be encountered.

- Safety instructions, including emergency procedures to be followed if a member of the team is injured in the field.
- Weather information, both current and expected.
- Map version, scale & datum for programming GPS units.
- Specific equipment needs for personnel to carry out their tactical assignment.
- Communications details such as frequencies, radio designators, contact persons, radio procedures and Command Post cell phone while noting that updates will be transmitted as conditions change.
- How to deal with the media and family, if they are encountered during the incident.
- Review emergency procedures for handling a subject found alive and the need for securing the area if the subject is found deceased.
- Transportation details setting out how personnel are to get to their assignments and back to the base or camp.
- Reporting locations and times.
- The length of time that personnel can expect to be in the field.
- Demobilization procedures.

- Instructions about where and when the debriefing will occur.
- Prepare them at the briefing for the debriefing so they will be better prepared to debrief.

Briefing Protocols

Location - Conduct briefings at a designated area, with plenty of room, which is sheltered, quiet, and free from interruptions. The briefing site should be large enough to accommodate all personnel expected to attend.

Timing - For crew leaders, briefings should be conducted just prior to the crew's leaving for their search area. For others, briefing could be conducted after crews move out to the search area, or when the overhead team changes shifts.

Time limits - Briefings normally should take no longer than one-half hour in order to:

1. Maintain or improve morale of personnel.
2. Maintain management credibility in the eyes of subordinates.
3. Ensure timely response into the field and maximize time for task accomplishments.

Briefing Techniques

In every case possible, distribute written briefing statements, diagrams, maps, photos, or sketches to convey information. Examples include:

> Photo of subject.
> Briefing statement photocopied.
> Sketch of sole pattern.
> Maps, reproduced showing assigned area and searching details.

This requires adequate maps, materials and photocopying capability at the search base, and sometimes this can prove difficult logistically. But having reliable information for search personnel to constantly refer to will greatly reduce mistakes and omissions. Remember: written briefings will reduce confusion and questions as well as improve communication.

Other useful techniques for briefers include:

> Use an outline for your oral presentation to help keep the briefing on track.
> Summarize the most important information at the end of each major briefing segment to ensure understanding.
> Be clear and direct. Use specific, concrete language. Speak in short sentences and omit needless verbiage and acronyms.

DEBRIEFING

A debriefing is a complete and thorough interview of what resources have done in the field. The purpose is to gather all of the information necessary for developing a complete and accurate understanding of each resource's field activities, information necessary for planning future search strategy and tactics. Without thorough information, subsequent planning may be unrealistic, misdirected, inadequate, or incomplete.

Who Conducts and Who Receives the Debriefing?

Debriefings are normally coordinated by someone in the Planning Section. To ensure consistency, one person, or a small cadre of persons should debrief all teams. All field personnel need to be informed that the successful direction of the mission depends upon the results of field activity, the accurate assessment of that activity in the debriefing and results from the on-going investigation.

Depending on factors such as team size and type of operation, either the entire team, or just the crew leader (team leader) can be debriefed. If the debriefing will be limited to the crew leader, then that person should first debrief the team members to ensure that all pertinent information will be passed on to the Planning Section.

Each team, resource, or search crew should be debriefed individually, rather than en masse (such as several crew leaders together). The resulting information will usually be more specific and complete. Trained debriefers for specialized resources may uncover more detail when allowed to de-brief their own crews.

What Information Needs to be Obtained?

As a minimum, the following specific information should be obtained from the search teams:

- A marked up map or a sketch of the actual area covered by the team.
- An estimate of the POD or coverage for the effort.
- The location and description of any clues found, regardless of how insignificant they may seem.
- Search difficulties or gaps in coverage encountered.
- Hazards in the area.
- Problems encountered with communications.
- Suggestions, ideas, or recommendations for future searching efforts.
- List any injuries sustained or any equipment damaged.

Debriefing Protocols

Location - Conduct debriefings at a designated area, with plenty of room, where it is sheltered, quiet and free from interruptions.

The area should include a smooth work surface to use for sketching and updating maps. Have plenty of water available for the teams being debriefed. The area should also be secured from intrusion by family, media, or onlookers to prevent the inappropriate release of raw, unanalyzed, or sensitive information. The briefing site should be adequately sized to accommodate all personnel expected to attend.

Timing - Debriefings should be conducted as soon after the teams come out of the field as possible, while the information is still fresh in their minds and before they have much chance to talk with other search teams, which may tarnish their information.

Time limits - Debriefings are generally not time limited. It is important to take whatever time is needed to develop the needed information from each team. However, debriefers should always be conscious of the fact that searchers who have just returned from the field are likely tired and may be frustrated if the search has, so far, been unsuccessful.

Establishing a written record - Written information documents activities and becoming part of the incident record. **Debriefings should be written in order to reduce confusion, misinformation, and misinterpretation.** It is best if a standard set of open ended questions are developed, and used for each team/individual. These can be distributed at the beginning of the operational period with the incident action plan or briefing packet.

The ICS form 214 (Activity Log) is intended to be a written record of significant events encountered by a search crew or team, and should be included in the debriefing documentation. **A widely used debriefing form for SAR purposes, which complements ICS Forms 214 and 204, is contained in Appendix C.**

Document team accomplishments on transparencies overlaid on a master map, supported by written notes. Transparencies are very useful because they allow "stacking" of assignments for various analyses.

Note: —————— Debriefing by radio should be avoided, if at all possible. It takes precious radio time and results in imprecise information. If radio debriefing cannot be avoided, then use it to obtain only minimum essential planning data and follow it up with a formal debriefing as soon as possible. A better alternate is to transport a member of the Planning Section to the location where the debriefing needs to take place.

Debriefing Techniques

Debriefing is an interview: a face to face meeting designed to elicit information. It is a tool for evaluating success and lays the foundation for future plans. In some cases, the IC or Planning Chief may wish to assign a trained interviewer as the debriefer. Note too that search resources who are not debriefed may resent the omission and feel that their

effort was of no value. It's important to debrief everyone who comes in from the field, primarily for information that can assist the search, but also for maintaining morale.

It is important to place the team or crew at ease and to convey a positive sense of urgency about the information they are about to provide. In addition, the debriefer should be respectful of the team's physical and mental condition and supportive of their need to feel a sense of accomplishment. Be professional, but also be somewhat assertive. A life is at stake. It is important to obtain all relevant information, even if some of it is offered reluctantly. **Stay neutral and objective and remember that a debriefing is a type of "interview."**

Crew leaders are sometimes reluctant to give a quantitative estimate of POD. Figure 17.1 shows various factors that can affect an air crew's effectiveness. Totals less than 100% can be used to reduce Coverage estimates to account for negative influences detracting from search effectiveness. For the results in Figure 17.1, a calculated Coverage equal to 1.0 might be reported as 0.76 to account for non-optimal factors that lower the crew's effectiveness. Team leaders should be asked about factors that can reduce coverage like sloppy spacing, lack of access to an area (which will require a segment split), worsening conditions, faster than planned speed and other negative influences like searcher fatigue.

Figure 17.1

__Search Effectiveness Factors for Air Crews__

The following describes a procedure that is sometimes used for estimating air crew search effectiveness. The debriefing officer, in conjunction with the aircrew, will apply a value to each factor listed, as in the example. The sum of the values equals estimated effectiveness. The optimum values is 10, decreasing to 0 for no value. Weights can be added to each factor to further distinguish relative importance of them.

1. Ability to maintain optimum altitude and airspeed. 8
2. Favorable visibility and weather conditions. 6
3. Nature of terrain and sea conditions. 5
4. Optimum track spacing and track spacing flown. 9
5. Qualification and availability of scanners. 9
6. Accuracy of navigation (consider aids used and available). 8
7. Enough time in area to allow thorough search. 9
8. Attitude and physical condition of search crew after flight. 6
9. Adequate crew rest before flight. 10
10. Quality of lunches, coffee, water, etc. <u>6</u>
   TOTAL - 76/100 =76%

For land search teams, Richard Toman has compiled a list of relevant factors, by various resource types, that can be used in a similar fashion as the air crew factors to discount and otherwise reduce (or in some cases increase) the calculated Coverage value, and related POD, due to sub-optimal (or in some cases better than anticipated) influences. Called "POD Factoring," the method includes rating factors similar to those of an air crew like weather, terrain/vegetation, crew fatigue, and some things not encountered in the air, like contamination by other humans, animals, waste products, exhaust fumes or chemicals at or near the surface. Factors for air-scent K9, mounted equine and grid search teams are shown in figure 17.2. More information on this technique for use in debriefing can be found at http://podfactoring.org/.

Figure 17.2

Search Effectiveness Factors for Land Based SAR Teams

K-9 Air-scent Factors

Rate the first 6 factors on a
scale of 1 to 10:

- Wind
- Humidity
- Vegetation
- Established Spacing,
  Width of Search Pattern
- Team Wellness
- Contamination

Rate these 8 factors on a scale of 1-5:
- Hazards
- Handler/K-9 Experience
- Light
- Weather/Temperature
- Terrain Features
- Area Size/Time allotment
- Team Fatigue
- Other Variables

Equine Mounted Factors

Rate the first 5 factors on a
scale of 1 to 10:

- Rider Training and Experience
- Mount Experience
- Mount Management
- Terrain
- Vegetation

Rate these 10 factors on a scale of 1-5:
- Contamination
- Hazards
- Rider "SAR" Training
- Light
- Weather
- Fatigue
- Humidity
- Area Features
- Wind
- Other Variables

Grid Search Factors

Rate the following 10 factors
on a scale of 1-10.

- Terrain
- Hazards
- Vegetation
- Weather
- Team Composition
- Light
- Area Size
- Tactics
- Spacing
- Instinct and Other Variables

Summary

Briefing and debriefing are two of the most important functions necessary for effective searching. Those who conduct briefings must be thorough enough to provide search teams with an adequate description of the subject and specific task goals for searching an assigned area. Information from debriefings, when those resources return from the field, provides the data needed to shift segment POA and develop search assignments for the next operational period. **The briefing and debriefing function is the critical link between field operations and the command post.**

Questions for Discussion:

1. What are some additional advantages of providing crew leaders with written briefings?

2. Why should debriefing of search resources be done individually, rather than as a group?

CHAPTER 18

DOCUMENTATION

It is difficult, if not impossible, to generate accurate records of a search after it is over. Therefore, **it is essential that the search effort be accurately documented** throughout and that records be kept in a usable, easily retrievable form. In this chapter we will describe the **rationale for incident documentation** and the methods for accomplishing it.

CHAPTER OBJECTIVES:

When you finish studying this chapter, you should be able to:

1. Discuss the reasons for documenting the entire search effort.
2. Describe the methods of documentation.
3. Describe the advantages and methods of visualizing the status of search resources.

Why Document the Entire Search Effort?

1. Documentation assists with the on-going planning effort and:
- It allows for personnel shift changes without a loss of continuity.
- It makes it possible to disseminate accurate information to searchers.
- It allows for the review of actions at critical times, such as whether to suspend the incident or to expand the search area.

2. Documentation enables you to reconstruct the search effort at a later time and:
- For review purposes; in determining what was right, or wrong, and why.
- To aid improvements with those aspects that need work, to update the preplan, and increase effectiveness on future search incidents.
- Evaluate the effectiveness of resource utilization and update or refocus training as necessary.

Documentation is also important in the event of litigation proceedings with respect to the manner in which an incident was handled. Court cases rarely occur immediately after a mission. More common is the requirement to testify in cases that occurred many months if not years earlier. If documentation does not exist, then details and possible critical information is lost.

Documentation can provide some protection against after-the-fact criticism of incident decisions. Knowing the information that was available at the time of the decision facilitates the justification of the actions taken.

> # If it isn't documented, then it's difficult to prove it happened.

Documentation will aid you in gathering data on subject behavior and provide you with one of the most important methods of establishing probable search areas for future incidents.

What Should You Document?

Documentation is an ongoing process. It begins with the initial reports and ends with the revision of the Preplan.

The ICS protocols help by providing a large amount of required documentation. All units of the ICS organization are responsible for documentation. Starting with the initial mission request, there are several units within the plans section that generate documentation on a regular basis:

The Situation Unit is responsible for the collection and organization of incident status and situation information and the evaluation,

analysis and display of that information.

The Resources Unit is responsible for:
1. Establishing all incident check-in activities
2. Preparing and processing resource status change information
3. Preparing and maintaining displays, charts, and lists that reflect the current status and location of resources, transportation, and support vehicles.
4. Maintaining a master check-in list of resources assigned to an incident.

The Documentation Unit is responsible for :
1. Maintaining accurate and complete incident files.
2. Providing duplication services to incident personnel.
3. Packing and storing incident files for legal, analytical, and historical purposes.

> ## Note: the Documentation Unit is the collector of information, not the creator.

The key to documenting ongoing events is the use of the ICS 214 Activity Log (see the ICS forms shown later). Minor items documented on an ICS 214 may not seem critical at the time, but if not recorded, that information will not be available if needed later. Everyone involved in the incident should be recording their actions on the ICS 214. A new ICS 214 is generated for each operational period. It is important to document key decisions and the time they were made, in addition to the available data and prevailing conditions under which those decisions were made.

The ICS Forms

As mentioned in Chapter 4, the ICS provides a set of forms for documenting virtually any event or contingency during an emergency incident. Although the forms were originally developed for use during wildland fires, they have been adapted to SAR incidents with only minor cosmetic changes. This uniformity in documentation will be especially useful for organizations (such as parks services and police) that handle other types of emergencies besides searches. Similar to using the same language, uniformity in documentation also facilitates communication between agencies or groups that do not routinely work together. For these reasons, we recommend the use of the ICS forms as they stand, with some modifications to the assignment briefing form, and a debriefing form specific to SAR.[4]

What follows is a list of the major ICS forms that should normally be employed during the

search incident. All NIMS ICS forms are readily available online at the following link: **http://nimsonline.com/download_center /index.htm#forms** for downloading and printing. Some of the key forms are:

> **ICS 201 — Incident Briefing.** This is a collection of important documents intended largely for the briefing of a new overhead teams (for example, for the second operational period). All important information is summarized succinctly on just a few pages. These include:
> — Map sketch.
> — Resources summary.
> — Summary of Current Actions.

> **ICS 202 — Incident Objectives.** This form contains the summary of overall search strategy for that operational period, and includes weather and safety information.

> **ICS 203 — Organization Assignment List.** Typically, the second page of the IAP listing incident management and supervisory staff for that operational period.

> **ICS 204 — Assignment List.** This form is used to provide written briefings of task assignments by resource, its team leader and assigned personnel.

---

[4] See Appendix C for a SAR Debrief form.

ICS 205 — Radio Communications Plan. This form contains all information pertaining to the assignments of frequencies or radio channels to specific resources.

ICS 206 — Medical Plan. This form describes those contingencies in the event of injury to a <u>searcher</u> or other personnel assigned to the incident. Briefly, it identifies the locations of first aid stations, ambulances, and hospitals, and describes procedures for treatment or evacuation.

ICS 207 — Organization Chart.

ICS 209 — Incident Status Summary. This form summarizes the status of search resources assigned to the incident. See Figure 18.1, "Visualizing Data" for additional methods of presenting summaries, such as using T-cards, which provide a way to quickly identify an track resources using a set of color coded index type cards.

ICS 211 — Check-In Lists.

ICS 214 — Activity Log. Used to record all major decisions and events during the incident, including the discovery of clues.

ICS 215 — Operational Planning Work Sheet. This document is a worksheet used to plan resource needs and assignments for the next operational period. Final assignments are transferred to ICS Form 204 for each team.

ICS 218 — Support Vehicle Inventory

ICS 219 — Resource Status Cards

ICS 220 — Air Operations Summary

ICS 221 — Demobilization Check-Out

Figure 18.1

VISUALIZING DATA
IN THE SITUATION UNIT

By Hugh Dougher

Just as a picture is worth a thousand words, information presented visually is easier to retrieve, compare, and conceptualize if transferred to charts, map symbols, and colors, rather than to text. Here are some suggestions:

1. Assignments and Accomplishments. List summaries of team assignments both on notepaper for records, and in large letters on flip chart paper or blackboard for quick scanning. Post this list in the Planning Section. Keep up-to-the-minute record of accomplishments and the status of field terms in the same manner.

2. Maps. USGS 7.5 minute topographical maps are best. Whichever type of maps are used, they can quickly become a nightmare of scribbles, coloring, and general clutter. Data may be lost or poorly recorded, on different maps and forgotten. People will regularly discard used maps for new ones. To avoid these problems, limit all writing to transparencies placed over the maps. The only notations allowed on the maps are marks indicating where the corners of the transparencies should be placed, the PLS or LKP, and possibly a few other important landmarks. This system has many advantages:

a. Each effort can be recorded on a separate transparency. Important notes can be added to the corner of the transparency, and the transparency can then serve as a detailed record of that effort.

b. Information can be gathered simultaneously using more than one map station. The completed transparencies are then routed to the Situation Unit and can be used by the Situation Unit, Plans, Records, and others as needed.

c. Efforts can be analyzed in different combinations to visualize the types and number of times each segment has been searched, reveal holes in coverage, etc.

d. The Planning Section can record each assignment on a separate transparency. These transparencies are placed over a map and photocopied. The photocopies are given to team leaders during assignment briefing. This simplifies operations duties, and minimizes confusion and misunderstanding.

(continued)

(Figure 18.1 cont.)

   e. The transparencies provide a detailed step-by-step record of both the planning and the accomplishments of the search.

   f. The Situation Unit should set up at least four map tables: A master map for the Situation Unit's exclusive use, two for use by debriefing, and one for the Planning Section. Additional map stations can be added as needed. Each map should be taped to a table top.

  3. Color Codes. Color code resources for quick recognition. ICS Color codes have been adopted for standardization of colors both in mapping and on T-cards with a 219- prefix:
  -2 (green) search crews, -3 (rose) search patrol, -4 (blue) helicopter, -5 (white) personnel,
  -7 (yellow) trackers, -6 (orange) aircraft, -8 (tan) K9 teams.

  4. Map symbols. Boundaries, areas covered, and successive cumulative coverage can be indicated by using hachure lines. To keep current, Situation unit needs to constantly monitor radio traffic.

Resource Status

The Resource Unit Leader is responsible for maintaining current information on the status of resources. The T-card organizer is very effective for this and cards within the organizer can be grouped into three general categories:

  1. En route
  2. On-scene
  3. Released

Within the "On-scene" category, resources should be listed according to their status, as follows:

  1. Assigned
  2. Available
  3. Out of service

Summary

In this chapter we described the importance of maintaining adequate documentation during the search incident. We explained how documentation assists with the on-going planning effort and enables search managers to reconstruct important events at a later time, including the rationales for critical decisions. With respect to what gets documented, we described how different components of the Planning Section have their respective areas of responsibility, including the Situation Unit (documents that keep track of the status of the incident), the Resources Unit (documents that track search resource use), and the Documentation Unit (which collects and maintains documents generated by the other planning units). Finally, we described some major <u>ICS forms</u> for use during the first operational period.

Questions for Discussion:

1. What are some complaints concerning having to do "paperwork" during an emergency incident? How would you respond to such complaints?

2. What are the advantages and disadvantages of altering the ICS forms — or introducing altogether new forms — for search management?

CHAPTER 19

SUSPENDING THE INCIDENT

Not all search incidents, no matter how well managed, are resolved successfully in a reasonable period of time. Search managers must be prepared for the fact that **the incident cannot continue indefinitely**. One of the most difficult decisions an IC will have to make is whether to suspend the search and demobilize resources without finding the subject. In this chapter we will discuss the manner in which this decision should be made.

CHAPTER OBJECTIVES:

When you finish studying this chapter, you should be able to:

1. Describe reasons why subjects sometimes are not found.
2. Identify the key factors involved in deciding whether to suspend a search incident.
3. Outline the elements of a limited, continuing search.

Why Haven't You Found the Subject?

There are seven reasons why missing subjects occasionally are not located despite massive search efforts:

a) The lost subject is outside the search area perimeter, or the search area has not been expanded far enough. **This is the single most common reason why subjects are not found early in the incident.**

b) The subject has been missed due to a gap in search coverage. This includes cases where subjects are missed because they were hidden under brush, in crevasses or mine shafts, under water, or inside buildings or vehicles.

c) The area where the subject is located has not been searched sufficiently (low POD), or has been searched by inadequate or inappropriate resources.

d) The subject has traveled into a segment or area that has previously been searched thoroughly.

e) The subject is actively hiding from searchers (most common for mentally retarded individuals, suicidal subjects, or adolescents in conflict with their families).

f) The subject is not in the area, but is in the ROW: it is a "bogus" search. For example, the subject may have walked out to safety alone and gone to a friend's house, or changed their trip plans without informing friends or family.

g) The subject is missing due to some criminal activity, such as being abducted or murdered. Despite the fact that this scenario is extremely rare (compared to the other reasons enumerated previously), the possibility of abduction becomes increasingly "likely" (in the minds of searchers) when children are not found early in the incident.

To Suspend OR NOT to Suspend?

The following considerations are presented as a guide to the IC who is faced with the responsibility of suspending the mission when the subject has not been located.

Two Basic Questions to be Answered

First, you need to ask, "Are we searching (at this point) for a person who has any reasonable chance of being alive?"

Second, "Is the evidence now pointing to the conclusion that the subject is no longer in the search area?"

Four Main Considerations for Suspending

There are four main considerations to be evaluated before suspending the search:

1. **What are the chances of the subject being alive?** Do not underestimate the subject's ability to survive (see Figure 19.1, "Survivors").

2. **What is your assessment of search area coverage?**
   — Have you extended the search area far enough?
   — Are you satisfied with the thoroughness of your search (PODs)?
   — Are there any gaps in coverage?

3. **What is your assessment of searcher safety?**
   Fatigue, discouragement, and stress contribute to accidents. Have conditions changed in the search area that create an unsafe environment for searchers?

4. **What is the overall family, media, agency and political climate?**
   — What pressures or counterpoints are being exercised?
   — What does your Agency Administrator say?
   — Does suspension require Agency Administrator concurrence?

Other Factors to Evaluate in Considering Suspension of a Search Incident

- Have all segments been searched and re-searched?

- Has there been a thorough and effective execution of the search plan?

- Has the question of survivability of the missing person been thoroughly researched and studied?

- Are you compromising the safety of your searchers?

- Are there any unresolved or unanswered clues?

- Have your search resources been depleted? Is there increasing pressure to release searchers and equipment?

- What is the availability of replacement resources?

- Are there political or family pressures to continue the search?

- Do you have other SAR incidents occurring simultaneously which demand a higher priority?

- Has the current and forecasted weather been examined in light of continuing the search?

- Are there any serious equipment malfunctions?

- Is a continued search effort affordable or practical from a cost standpoint?

- Are there any other considerations that affect your decision to suspend the search?

The Decision to Suspend a Search Usually Involves A Combination of All of These Factors

---

When deciding on whether to suspend the search incident, consider the following "survivor" stories from the SAR annals in Figure 19.1.

Figure 19.1

SURVIVORS

Case #1

A 4-year-old boy became lost after following a deer into the woods of Nova Scotia. A massive search conducted in three days of freezing weather yielded no clues. On the morning of the fourth day, the boy came out of the woods and stopped a passing automobile.

Case #2

An autistic 10-year-old boy became lost in a Florida swamp teeming with poisonous snakes. He was found in good health on the fourth day.

Case #3

A 10-year-old boy became lost while camping in Plumas County, California. After a week of cool weather, he was found 1.8 miles from his campground. He had survived by covering himself with leaves.

Case #4

Two girls (9 and 13 years old) became lost in the Amazon jungle after their adult leader died of malaria. They finally came out to safety after a month of wandering in the jungle.

Fig. 19.1 (cont.)

Case #5

    A 48-year-old male hiker became lost near Bishop, California. The search was suspended after five days. He came out to safety after two weeks of being missing.

Case #6

    A 65-year-old man in New Brunswick, Canada, was found in good condition 10 kilometers from the PLS. He had been missing for five days.

Case #7

    The search for an 80-year-old mushroom picker in Virginia was suspended after four days. Searchers suspected that the victim had drowned. The man eventually found safety after 39 days.

Case #8

    A 2-year-old toddler in diapers wandered off into a remote region of the Arizona desert in the middle of the summer with daytime temperatures over 100F. The parents showed no interest in the search. An investigation revealed that they had taken out a large insurance policy on the life of the child. Every night mountain lions were heard in the search area. However, after over four days of 'round-the-clock searching, the child was found, dehydrated but otherwise unharmed.

And if you still need convincing . . .

Case #9

    Two small children, a boy (6 years) and his sister (4 years), became lost in the mountains of Argentina. They walked 95 kilometers before taking shelter in an abandoned hut, where they were found. Their ordeal lasted three weeks.

Never underestimate the subject — You may be searching for a Survivor!

Each incident is unique and the decision to suspend must be based upon the combined facts and considerations specific to your situation.

Group Consensus Recommended

Try using a group consensus method as a means to helping you make the decision whether to suspend the incident. Have each person review each of the significant factors, assign his or her percentage of probability or value ranking (scale 1 = low; 10 = high), or simply list the pros and cons. If possible, bring in an outside search expert who was not involved in the incident to offer a neutral assessment, prior to suspending.

Factors For & Against Suspension

The following factors can be evaluated to help justify continuing or suspending the search. For example, if conditions had changed so as to make the search area unsafe for searchers, then suspension of some, or all, of search operations might be wholly justified.

1. Safety of searchers
2. Weather
3. Unresolved clues
4. Gaps in coverage
5. Other factors (list)

Scaling Down the Search

As an IC who is considering suspending the incident, the first decision you have to make is rarely whether to simply terminate the search and go home. There is usually a transitional, "scaling down" phase in which resources are used more safely, such as not tasking searchers at night or during harsh weather. Fewer search resources are ordered in, while new, specialized resources may be employed, such as dive teams. The family of the subject should be included in honest discussions pertaining to scaling back or suspending the search.

The Limited, Continuing Search

When the time does arrive to withdraw resources from the field and demobilize the incident, it is not simply a matter of going home and forgetting about the missing subject. This can be demoralizing for searchers who have spent many hours on the incident, and psychologically devastating for the subject's family. In particular, friends and family of the subject must be made to feel that, in the absence of closure on the subject's whereabouts or condition (although, by this time, they are usually starting to accept the possibility that the subject is deceased), efforts will still be made toward the eventual <u>arrival</u> at closure. For this reason, we recommend the limited but continuing search, including:

Overflights — over the search area on an intermittent or occasional basis.

Detection of clues — A modest search effort for any "new clues" under better conditions, such as when snow or ice melts.

Signs — Post signs at the campgrounds and trail heads to inform the public that a person is missing in this area.

Informing the public and media — Particularly people who may be going into the search area (such as during hunting season.)

Using the search area for training exercises — Further search training programs could be conducted in the area.

If you decide to use the **limited, continuing search** technique, rather than simply terminated search efforts, then you are:

- Suspending the incident, but not the search.
- Continuing the search, although on a limited basis.
- Keeping the case "open."

This concept of a **limited, continuing search** is important because if additional clues are found or information becomes available, then you are **ready to take additional action**. You are communicating the message that **you have not given up on the subject.** Keep in mind that there have been a number of limited continuing searches in which participants in SAR training, hikers or hunters have found human remains.

Summary

In this chapter we discussed the difficult decision of suspending the search for the missing subject. We began by describing

seven reasons why subjects are sometimes not found, then discussed the two basic questions that should be addressed when suspension is being considered. Regarding the latter, the possibility of the subject's survivability, considering the elapsed time since they became missing, as well as the chances of a false or "bogus" search should be weighed against the threat to searcher safety and the depletion of search resources.

Toward addressing these questions, we listed numerous factors that that should be considered. We proposed a consensus technique for an orderly and readily documented decision as to whether to suspend.

Finally, we discussed the process of scaling down the incident, rather than merely terminating search activities, and the advantage of a limited, continuing search once the incident has been suspended.

Questions for Discussion:

1. What information should be conveyed to family members of the missing subject when a decision has been made to suspend the incident?

2. How would you respond when family or other external influences unreasonably insist that a search be actively continued?

CHAPTER 20

DEMOBILIZATION

Demobilization — or **the orderly release of resources** — is not just a mirror image of mobilization. When we mobilize for a search, a number of individuals in widely separated places direct, coordinate, and provide transportation to get search and rescue resources to a single point. Demobilization is the responsibility of a few people to **get these same resources back to the same widely separated places they came from**. While command and communication channels remain the same as with mobilization, the procedures may be quite dissimilar.

CHAPTER OBJECTIVES:

When you finish studying this chapter, you should be able to:

    1 Explain why it is necessary to plan for demobilization early in the incident.

    2. Describe the principles and techniques of demobilization.

    3. Discuss the benefits of holding a closeout operational review.

    4. Develop a Demobilization Plan.

Two Types of Demobilization – Sudden or Gradual

1. Termination (sudden): The subject has been located.

2. Scaled down or suspended (gradual): The search is gradually being reduced in size.

Each type requires different demobilization approaches. For example, there may be different priorities for the release of resources than for their callout. Coordination and organization may be more or less difficult depending on sudden termination versus a scaled down operation.

Principles of Demobilization

Timing: Information regarding places of origin, methods of travel, and travel times for search resources should be collected at the time they initially check-in at the incident. Collecting and organizing travel manifests may be a simple way of accomplishing this task. Records on the unit must be complete, showing place of origin, method of transportation to search area, home unit, and other significant information. Formal demobilization planning should begin early in the incident, rather than waiting until the last minute.

Control: Control over resources is an absolute necessity. This control should be exercised from incident to home base. In addition to the obvious need for control to ensure safety and cost effectiveness, there are the concerns of units away from home about being available for a new assignment in their own area. There are many unforeseen delays that could occur and priority adjustments can only be met through strict control. Special resources, particularly Type I, are in high demand and, if paid, need to be released on a high priority basis. Out of area resources should also be given high priority for release back to their home agencies.

Communications: Adequate, rapid communications among all key personnel and facilities involved in the demobilization effort are essential. Demobilization communications are markedly different from those involved during search activities, requiring a separate communications plan.

Staffing: Staff the demobilization organization to fit the needs of the incident. For example, you may need to assign additional people to assist with signing out search personnel, to help with transportation and traffic management, to inventory equipment and supplies, to monitor safety considerations, to collect and organize documentation, and to perform many other functions that should be identified in the demobilization plan. Loaned or borrowed equipment must be returned promptly,

especially if it was provided by an out of area resource.

Safety: Tired people make mistakes and are often impatient. Adequate rest prior to demobilization takes on added importance when long travel times are anticipated. Do not sacrifice safety and cost effectiveness for speed. Keep the resources on the incident until transportation arrangements are confirmed. Standardized work and rest guidelines have been developed for wildland fire incidents and should be followed in lost person incidents as well. The following **Work/Rest Guidelines** are from "The Incident Business Handbook," Chapter 11, Part 12.7-1:

Work/Rest Guidelines

To maintain safe, productive incident activities, incident management personnel must appropriately manage work and rest periods, assignment duration, and shift length for crews, overhead personnel, and support personnel. **Plan for and ensure that crews, overhead personnel, and support personnel are provided a 2 to 1 work to rest ratio (for every 2 hours of work or travel, provide 1 hour sleep and/or rest).**

Provide the opportunity for **a minimum of 1-hour of rest for every 2-hours of work or travel regardless of work performed** (incident/non-incident), incident type or jurisdiction, time of incident or operational period, or regular work schedule. **Work shifts, including the first operational period, will not exceed 24 hours.**

Ensure that all drivers are well rested before they leave the incident. The state of Virginia lost one of its incident commanders to exhaustion in 1994 after she fell asleep at the wheel returning home from a search and fatally crashed. The National Multi-Agency Coordination group produced the Incident Business Handbook quoted above, which insists upon **one hour of rest for every two hours of work or travel.**

Techniques for a Final Operational Review Session

Consider including, as part of your demobilization process, a final "closeout" operational review for personnel involved in the incident. Among other things, the review provides closure for personnel who participated in the incident and who may not understand the reasoning underlying some of the decisions that affected their search assignments. Such a review would be especially appropriate when the outcome is not viewed as successful, such as when the subject is found deceased, or when problems impeded search efforts. Generally, the review provides an excellent opportunity to discuss the incident while events are still fresh in everyone's mind, and to benefit from whatever lessons can be learned.

The review is normally provided as a group session by the IC, in consultation with the Planning Section (particularly the Documentation Unit). This is discussed in more detail at Chapter 25.

Objective of the operational review: To collect, record, and exchange information on what happened during the search, to identify problem areas, and to assess the effectiveness of strategies and tactics.

- Review the exact terrain covered, referring to maps, worksheets, and activity logs.
- Review coverage and cumulative probabilities of detection (POD_{cum}).
- Describe clues that were discovered during the search.
- Discuss any safety hazards discovered by searchers.
- Discuss the performance of crew leaders (team leaders) and management personnel (but remember: praise should be public, but criticism — however "constructive" — should be private).
- Discuss other operational concerns or events relative to the team.
- Identify areas where improvement is needed.
- Summarize information obtained from individual debriefings. In particular, identify those factors that were novel or unique about this incident.

Summary

Too frequently there is little or no planning for demobilization until the incident is actually over and there is an uncoordinated rush as personnel head for home. Things often are left to simply fizzle out. This lack of planning and coordination can result in incomplete information, missing equipment, dissatisfied searchers, traffic accidents (searchers falling asleep at the wheel), poor image of the agency in charge by the responders, and many other problems, including legal liability.

In this chapter we discussed the need for an orderly and well planned demobilization process. We described the need to control the timing of resource release, the use of a separate communications plan, and requirements for adequate staffing (such as sign-out personnel and additional logistics support). We also described how proper demobilization is especially important for safety considerations. Finally, we outlined the benefits and methods of conducting a final closeout review session for search personnel.

Questions for Discussion:

1. What problems can you foresee with ensuring that searchers are not too fatigued to drive home from the incident? How would you deal with these problems?

2. What additional staffing, besides those mentioned in this chapter, would be useful for demobilization?

Part IV: Other Management Considerations

CHAPTER 21

MANAGING INCIDENT FACILITIES

Virtually all search operations require support, most of which are supplied by the Logistics Section. In this chapter we will describe the **various support functions** that need to be performed and the base facilities that should be established and staffed.

CHAPTER OBJECTIVES:

When you finish studying this chapter, you should be able to:

1. Identify the various types of incident facilities and explain their uses.

2. Describe the major functions of incident facilities.

3. Discuss the factors to be considered in selecting locations of incident facilities.

4. Describe safety considerations when establishing incident facilities.

The Logistics Section

Most lost person incidents start small. However, the first IC must plan for the possibility of a large and rapid increase in the growth of the incident. Logistics should not be allowed to lag behind the escalation in operations, as failure to adequately support the incident will greatly hamper search efforts.

The IC should appoint a Logistics Section Chief early enough to keep up with demand for support. Remember that it will take time for the Logistics Section to set up and function efficiently. As with all general staff functions, the section chief must perform any role not delegated to someone else.

Factors that should be considered when establishing incident facilities include:

- The requirements of the incident.
- Time frame the facility will be used and its ability to grow.
- Costs to establish the facilities.
- Environmental considerations.
- Who owns the land?
- Are there existing facilities that can be used (such as fire halls)?
- Public access and security (or lack of it).
- Communications.
- Safety and sanitation.
- Adequate size for functions ranging from planning to staging.

Types of Search Operation Facilities

As mentioned in Chapter 4, there are six basic types of incident facilities:

1. Incident Command Post
2. Staging Areas
3. Incident Base
4. Camps
5. Helibases
6. Helispots

Each facility has a unique purpose on an incident. These six types should fulfill virtually any incident facility requirement.

The Incident Command Post

The Incident Command Post, generally simply called the "Command Post" (CP), is the location at which the primary command functions are performed. The IC will normally be located at the CP.

All incidents must have a designated location for the CP. **There will only be one CP for each incident.** This also applies on multi-agency or multi-jurisdictional incidents operating under a single or a unified command.

Initial location for the CP should consider the nature of the incident, whether it is growing or moving, and whether the command post location will be suitable in size and safe for the expected duration of the incident.

The CP may be located in a vehicle, trailer, tent, or within a building, for example. On longer incidents, it is desirable to provide an CP facility that will provide adequate lighting and protection from the weather. Larger and more complex incidents will often require larger CP facilities. Examples of incidents that usually require an expanded CP facility include:

- Multi-agency incidents run under a unified command.
- Long-term incidents.
- Incidents requiring an on-scene communications center.
- Incidents requiring a separate planning function.
- Incidents requiring the use of
- Command Staff and Agency Representative positions.

Some incidents may be large enough to have an on-site communications center to dispatch assigned resources. The Communications Center is often associated with or adjacent to the CP. Also, some incidents will require space at the CP to allow for various Command Staff and Planning Section functions. Due to impaired radio reception in hilly and mountainous terrain, the communications center may need to be located at a considerable distance from the command post and incident base. Appropriate relay equipment may be needed.

Characteristics of the CP

Both the Command and Planning functions are normally conducted at the CP. It should contain situation and resource status displays necessary for the incident, and other information used by the Planning Section, as well as room for agency representatives who are also normally located at the CP.

Guidelines to be used in Establishing the CP

- Position it away from the general noise and confusion associated with the incident.
- Position it away from potential hazard zones.
- It should be expandable as the incident grows.
- It should be possible to provide security for the CP and to control access.
- Identify its location with a distinctive banner or sign.
- If possible, announce CP activation and location via radio or other communication so all appropriate personnel are notified.

Staging Areas

A staging area is a temporary location at an incident where personnel and equipment are kept while awaiting tactical assignments.

- Staging areas should be located within five minutes travel time to the area of expected need.
- An incident may have more than one staging area.
- In locations where major incidents are known to occur frequently, it is advisable to designate possible staging area locations, and to plan their layouts in advance.
- Resources in a staging area are always "in or on an available status," which means they are ready for assignment within three minutes. This is an important consideration for resource use planning and should be closely adhered to.
- Staging areas may include temporary fueling and sanitation facilities.
- All staging areas will have a Staging Area Manager.
- Check-in stations are frequently located in a staging area.
- Staging Areas will be given a name that describes their general location, for example, Webster Park Staging Area.
- The Staging Area Manager reports to the Operations Section Chief, or to the IC if an Operations Section has not been established.
- A Staging Area may be in the same general area or adjacent to other incident facilities; however, it should have its own separate location and name.

- Some incidents may use staging areas for only certain kinds of resources. For example, all police vehicles or ambulances may be located in one staging area. A staging area could be established in a harbor location for boats used in a water-related incident.

Staging Area Guidelines

- Be close to the location of tactical assignments (within five minutes).
- Be located outside the area of any hazards to minimize risk.
- Be relocated if necessary.
- Have different access routes for incoming and outgoing resources.
- Be large enough to accommodate available resources and have room for growth.
- Be clearly marked.
- Be located to minimize environmental damage.
- Have necessary security controls.

Benefits of Using Staging Areas

- Provide locations for immediately available resources to await active assignments.
- Provide locations to allow resources to be formed into operational units such as task forces and strike teams.
- Provide for greater accountability by having available personnel and resources together in one location.

- Provide safe locations for personnel and equipment to await assignments.
- Prevent resources from freelancing or "doing their own thing."
- Minimize excessive communications of resources calling for assignments.
- Control and assist the check-in of personnel who arrive at the incident via private means.
- Allow the Operations Section Chief or IC to properly plan for resource use, and to provide for contingencies.
- Segregate search personnel from the media and the subject's family.

The Incident Base

All primary services and support activity for the incident are usually located and performed at the base. In particular, the Logistics Section will be located at the base (not necessarily within the CP).

Normally, the Incident Base is the location where all uncommitted (out of service) equipment and personnel support operations are located. For example, tactical resources assigned to the Incident Base (not to staging areas), will normally be out of service.

There should be only one base established for each incident, and normally the base will not be relocated except under unusual circumstances. In locations where major incidents are known to occur frequently, it is advisable to pre-designate possible base locations, and to plan their layouts in advance.

The management of the base comes under the Logistics Section. If an Incident Base is established, then a Base Manager will be designated. The Base Manager in a fully activated ICS organization will be in the Facilities Unit of the Logistics Section.

Camps

Camps are temporary locations within the general incident area that are equipped and staffed to provide sleeping, food, water, and sanitary services to incident personnel. These are separate facilities not located at the Incident Base. Camps may be established when they are seen as logistically more efficient, or when there is significant in-transit time to remote areas from the Incident Base. Camps may be in place for several days, and they may be moved depending upon incident needs. Very large incidents may have one or more camps located in strategic areas. All ICS functional unit activities performed at the base may also be performed at camps.

Each camp will have a Camp Manager assigned. Camp Managers are responsible for providing non-technical support and coordination of all organizational units operating within the camp. As part of the incident's Logistics Section, Camp Managers will report to the Facilities Unit Leader. If that position has not been activated, then the

Camp Manager would report to the Logistics Section Chief.

Initially, personnel requirements for Logistics Section units located at camps will be determined by the incident General Staff, based on the type and size of the incident and expected duration of camp operations. After a camp is established, additional personnel and support needs would normally be determined and ordered by the Camp Manager. If logistics units are established at camps, then they would be managed by assistants.

Helibases

A helibase is the main location within the general incident area for parking, fueling, maintaining, and loading of helicopters. It is often located at or near the Incident Base. However, an incident helibase can also be located at a nearby airport, or at another off-incident location.

A helibase will be used to load helicopters with personnel, equipment, and supplies necessary for incident operations.

The helibase will be managed by a Helibase Manager. The Helibase Manager will report to the Air Support Group Supervisor in the Air Operations organization if that position has been activated. If not, then the Helibase Manager reports to either the Air Operations Branch Director (if activated) or to the

Operations Section Chief. (Note that helicopter support, like staging areas, are the responsibility of the Operations Section rather than Logistics).

Helispots

Helispots are temporary locations in the incident area where helicopters can safely land and take off. Helispots can be used to load or off-load personnel, equipment, or supplies.

Helispots will be managed by Helispot Managers who will function on the ground at the helispot. The Helispot Manager will report to the Helibase Manager. If an incident has no established air operations organization but does have one or more helispots designated, then the Helispot Managers will report to the Operations Section Chief.

Facility Safety Guidelines

Ensure that all personnel are briefed about "in-base" rules, pertaining to items such as fires, sanitation, quiet hours, smoking, prohibition of alcoholic beverages, supplies, area hazards, and evacuation plans.Ensure that all hazards in the area have been identified and mitigated:

- — Flood, flash flood
  potential.
- — Fire potential, both
  structural and wild land.
- — Hazardous plants, insects
  and animals.
- — Hazardous trees & limbs.
- — Fuel storage, chemicals.
- — Severe weather hazards.
- Produce a base map, showing evacuation routes, and listing base rules.
- Establish speed limits.
- Ensure that service vehicles have "back-up alarms" and are guided by persons on foot.
- Test all water sources regularly.
- Designate smoking, no smoking areas.
- Designate open fire areas, ensure adequate fire fighting equipment is immediately available.
- Establish camp security.
- Keep list of camp safety rules current; circulate and post.
- Ensure that all flammables are clearly marked and stored in supply area; post and enforce no smoking; ensure that storage areas are shaded.
- Properly store liquid petroleum gas (LPG) tanks; ensure that only trained personnel handle and light stoves, heaters, and lights, powered by LPG.
- Ensure that sanitation rules for cooking and washing are followed.
- Provide for proper camp hygiene; chemical toilets, latrines, showers, wash areas; monitor, service 2 or 3 times daily.
- Clearly mark or flag ditches, holes, stumps, and similar hazardous areas.

- Provide for night lighting of camp area, especially pathways.
- Locate generators so that noise and exhaust will not affect personnel.
- Provide proper grounding for electrical tools and generators.
- Locate all electrical cords and inspect them for shock potential; mark them well.
- Ensure that tents and temporary shelters are secure and anchored against wind.
- Flag or mark all anchor ropes, guy lines, pegs, and braces.
- Pick up garbage daily. Clearly mark the designated garbage disposal area.
- Be on the alert for lightning storms and other weather hazards
- Ensure that food is stored properly.
- Maintain a visible and well-stocked first aid station staffed by trained personnel.
- For safety and noise abatement reasons, ensure that helicopter operations do not depart or arrive over the incident base or other manned facilities.
- During periods of high alert for forest fires, direct all vehicles to park "facing out" to facilitate a quick evacuation of the base or camp if it becomes necessary. This should be a general rule in forested areas where flammable ground fuels are suspected.

As the size and scale of the incident increase, so will the complexity and difficulty in managing facilities. Preplan your resources. Incident facilities are similar to those of fire operations; identify those possible resources that can manage and operate your facilities. Apply the best resource available to the job.

The Long Range Patrol Camp: Learning from "Lurps"

The long range reconnaissance patrol (LRRP or "Lurp") is a venerable military tactic going back at least to the 17th Century, receiving much wider application during the Vietnam War, by both adversaries. The LRRP consists of a small group of highly trained personnel (typically Army Rangers) that operate independently of the main force, some distance away from the command center, and requiring little or no logistical support. The concept of the long range patrol has been applied to SAR by Millen, Gilmore, and Seitz (1995). According to these authors, there are many situations where the LRRP may be useful, such as: searching long trails with many offshoots or spurs; searching a series of likely spots that are far away from the search base; installing and monitoring passive search devices, such as string lines and track trap; and setting up remote camps for searcher rehabilitation without leaving the field.

The advantage of using Long Range Patrols is that they can be logistically more efficient than merely tasking such crews from the search base. They can greatly reduce time in transit, thereby increasing the proportion of time that searchers are actually in the field looking for clues. Once set up, a LRP Camp can provide feeding, shelter (usually tents and lean-tos), and improvised latrines ("catholes"), so searchers will not have to make the long trek back to the base for these amenities. All of the ICS functions may be performed, particularly Command and Logistics. The Communications function will be especially important for such remote camps, as it may be necessary to install portable mast antennas and maintain diversified communications systems, such as HF and VHF radios, as well as cellular telephones.

Millen, Gillmore, and Seitz suggested that movement by such LRRP's would be largely restricted to areas open only to foot travel, but in some circumstances it might be possible to employ more efficient modes of transportation to support remote camps, such as helicopters, all-terrain vehicles,

snowmobiles, portable boats and horses. The Long Range Reconnaissance Patrol Camp may well be a viable solution to what might otherwise be a logistical nightmare.

Summary

Most incident base facilities and support services (with the exception of helibases, helipads, and staging areas) are the responsibility of the Logistics Section. We discussed how important it is for the IC to anticipate rapidly growing needs for such support, usually requiring the early appointment of a Logistics Section Chief.

We described the six basic types of incident facilities, including the Incident Command Post, the Incident Base, staging areas, camps, helibases, and helispots. Finally, we described numerous safety guidelines with respect to managing the base.

Questions for Discussion:
1. Describe some ways that poor or inadequate support can impact negatively on search operations.

2. What logistics functions are especially important during the first few hours of the incident? How do logistical needs change later in the incident?

CHAPTER 22

MANAGING SEARCHER STRESS

Emergency response is, by definition, a stressful activity. Even a successful search can be stressing to those involved, and the psychological impact of an unsuccessful incident can be devastating. In this chapter we will discuss the concept of **critical incident stress** as it applies to SAR responders involved in a lost person incident.

CHAPTER OBJECTIVES:

When you finish studying this chapter, you should be able to:

1. Define the concept of critical incident stress (CIS).
2. Describe common symptoms of CIS.
3. Identify sources of CIS in the lost person incident.
4. Describe methods of preventing CIS in SAR responders.
5. Explain why and when a SAR demobilization should include a stress defusing.

Critical Incident Stress (CIS)

Critical incident stress (CIS) refers to a stress reaction experienced by emergency responders, which may have debilitating psychological and physiological effects upon them. The stress can be a reaction to a single, highly traumatic SAR incident, or to a series of incidents with less impact experienced over a period of time — even years. This chapter will focus on the prevention of CIS in emergency personnel responding to a single lost person incident.

At the very least, CIS can lead to diminished job performance, decreased motivation, apathy, and a reluctance to participate in future emergency incidents. In more extreme cases it can cause serious psychological disorders, marital problems, chronic depression, and even suicide.

> **All emergency responders, even the most experienced and emotionally stable, are vulnerable to the effects of critical incident stress.**

Common Symptoms of CIS

A partial list of CIS symptoms includes:

- Insomnia, nightmares, other sleep disorders.
- Irritability, anger, displays of temper, other inappropriate emotional reactions.

• Recurring and unwanted memories of the incident ("flashbacks").
• Poor concentration and memory loss.
• Changes in appetite (increased or decreased).
• Increased smoking or alcohol consumption.
• Social detachment.

Some of these symptoms, particularly social detachment, memory lapses, and irritability, may be shown while the incident is still in progress. For example, the "stressed-out" responder may be sitting apart from his or her colleagues, staring vacantly and silently at the ground. Some people may forget the names of co-workers, or show inappropriate emotional responses, such as giggling, or becoming angry or abusive over trivial matters.

It is important to remember that these are normal reactions to an abnormal situation. Whenever possible, the responder showing CIS symptoms should be relieved of duty in a non-punitive fashion, and provided with a critical incident stress debriefing.

Sources of CIS

Sense of isolation. Most lost person incidents occur in rural or wilderness areas, often at night. Searchers working in small teams may travel for extended periods with minimal contact with each other. Combined with other stressors, such as fatigue, a feeling of isolation can contribute to a CIS reaction in some searchers.

Loss of spatial orientation. Merely becoming confused about one's spatial position can be a source of stress. In wilderness SAR, maintaining a constant "fix" on one's position (dead reckoning) is not always possible, as searchers must focus their attention on looking for clues. Consequently, search teams frequently experience periods of spatial disorientation, intending to recover their orientation when necessary. Also, the prospect of becoming "lost" looms as a threat to self-esteem and a source of derision from unsympathetic colleagues. Competence with GPS and recurrent map and compass training can reduce this source of stress.

Extremes in temperature. Both hot and cold weather conditions can contribute to stress. Searchers working in desert conditions may have to cope with daytime heat and nighttime cold, thus contending with the threat of both hyperthermia and hypothermia. Also, cold weather brings a number of additional stresses, such as forcing searchers to carry additional clothing and equipment, thus increasing their susceptibility to fatigue. In addition, factors associated with cold weather may increase stress, such as having to traverse icy terrain or frozen lakes.

Death of the subject. This can be an extremely traumatizing experience for searchers, especially those who have had infrequent experience in dealing with deceased subjects. Under some conditions, however, the death of the subject can be especially stressing, regardless of searcher experience, such as when the subject:

- is a child.
- is found alive, but dies during rescue.
- is found in an area that had previously been searched.

Death or injury of a co-worker or colleague. Surveys of emergency responders reveal that injury to a fellow responder, especially someone they know, can be a major source of CIS, often even more stressful than the death of the subject. This type of event will create significant incident-wide stress for everyone involved.

Prolonged incidents. Lost person incidents that extend over several or more days can provide several sources of stress, including:

- *mental fatigue.* Searchers and management personnel who have participated in a prolonged incident frequently report a "sense of unreality" resulting from alternating their time on the search with their off-duty time.

- *media attention.* Prolonged searches almost invariably become a media event. The longer the search proceeds, the more negative media attention is likely to become. Responders on a prolonged lost person incident frequently have to contend with negative media reports while the incident is still in progress.

- *when the lost subject is not found.* Having to leave the search scene without having found the subject is not an uncommon source of CIS, particularly if the searcher does not agree with the decision to suspend the search.

The Stress of Command

Search management personnel often report that **management is *more* rather than *less* stressful than their experience as a searcher in the field.** While the search team that finds the lost person is usually given credit for a successful find, there is a tendency to blame search managers for a search with negative outcomes (for example, the subject is found dead or not found at all), regardless of how efficiently the search was organized.

Specific factors increasing the stress of search managers include:

- High pressure early in the search to gather information and employ resources quickly, often contending with the presence of highly distraught members of the subject's family.

- Tracking search progress through flawed or otherwise imperfect communication systems (for example, failing radios).

- Making critical decisions without having adequate information available (for example, tasking search assignments in the absence of adequate maps and other planning data).

It has been observed that a number of emergency incident management personnel have become CIS peer counselors to assist their own organization in symptom recognition and providing appropriate referrals to mental health professionals. By networking across organizations, access to peer counselors on short notice is enhanced.

Preventing CIS

Reduce opportunities for negative imagery and "flashbacks." Note that any of the senses can be a source of negative imagery, but particularly what the searcher sees, smells, hears, and touches. Do not let personnel come near a deceased subject unless it is absolutely necessary. Responders involved in the recovery of a body must wear proper personal protective equipment and may need to take additional measures to mask the smell of a subject who has been dead for some time, whose remains may emit a distinct and disturbing odor. Searchers should be instructed not to attempt "black humor" or make other unnecessary comments, as many SAR responders have reported remarks like these imply a callous disrespect for the dead which can increase CIS for those who don't share the dark humor.

Employ the Incident Command System effectively. A major goal of ICS is to reduce the level of stress experienced by management personnel and searchers alike. This can be done through good preplanning and by maintaining a modular organization with a manageable span of control in each operational period.

Consultation and discussion with peers on potential or actual sources of incident stress is also advisable to help prepare for and defuse its impact.

Debrief and defuse. Whenever possible, contact a professionally trained CIS de-briefer to respond ASAP to the scene. Establish a preplan action to have a person with this qualification on standby. Many agencies have professional counselors and chaplains available. The debriefing of responders should be aimed at getting them to understand how their respective roles "fit into" the overall strategy, such that they will not feel the need to "make sense of it" after they leave the search scene. **The debriefing should be done with the Planning Section Chief or the IC in charge, and not be relegated to someone who was not directly involved with decision making during the incident.**

After the incident objectives are described, with discussion of individual tasks performed, personnel should be encouraged to ask whatever questions they may have. No reasonable question should be ignored or ridiculed. For large groups, **be prepared to spend as long as it takes to address everyone's questions.** During this time, note taking and any kind of recording should be discouraged to allow a more open exchange of information and any emotional "unloading."

The demobilization should include consideration of whether to hold a stress defusing, depending on the nature of the incident. A defusing is a short meeting (30 to 60 minutes) held within several hours after demobilization, and presided over by qualified peer counselors (SAR personnel trained in stress counseling). The defusing focuses only on those people who were most directly affected by the incident, and may be assumed to be experiencing stress. The goal of a defusing is to get search personnel "back to

normal" by having them discuss their emotional reactions to the incident in a group context. A secondary goal is to determine whether a formal CIS debriefing may be necessary.

Searchers and management personnel who show symptoms of CIS should be identified and immediately referred for a CIS debriefing, conducted by qualified mental health professionals and peer counselors. Many of these mental health support professionals mya be available for free through Employee Assistance Programs. **The preplan should address the requirements for defusing stress by conducting an all-hands debriefing and include the telephone numbers of qualified CIS debriefing counselors.**

> **Defusing the effects of stress is aimed at preventing a full-blown CIS reaction, involving the possible loss or diminished performance of your most important resource: PEOPLE.**

Summary

Critical incident stress (CIS) refers to a stress reaction experienced by emergency responders, which can have long term debilitating effects upon them. We described various symptoms of CIS, including sleep disorders, inappropriate emotional responses, flashbacks, poor concentration and memory lapses, changes in appetite, increased smoking or drinking, and social detachment. We also discussed various sources of stress that may be caused specifically by involvement in a lost person incident, including a sense of isolation, loss of spatial orientation, extremes in temperature, death of the subject or co-worker, and factors associated with prolonged incidents. Perhaps most stressful of all is the role of search management, caused by high pressures to gather information and employ resources quickly but effectively, contending with poor or delayed communications, and making critical decisions in the absence of adequate information — all while dealing with

external influences, such as the subject's family. Finally, we described methods of preventing or alleviating CIS, including reducing opportunities for negative imagery, employing an effective management system (ICS), and providing debriefings and actions to defuse stress.

Questions for Discussion:

1. What additional sources of stress, not mentioned in this chapter, are sometimes experienced by SAR responders?

2. For agencies and search teams without ready access to qualified mental health professionals and peer counselors who can conduct CIS debriefings, what can they do to remedy this problem?

CHAPTER 23

MANAGING EXTERNAL INFLUENCES

As mentioned in the previous chapter, **influences external to the incident can be highly stressful to managers and searchers alike**, impeding efforts to resolve the search successfully. In this chapter we'll describe the major types of influences and make suggestions as to how they may be managed.

CHAPTER OBJECTIVES:

When you finish studying this chapter, you should be able to:

1. Describe the outside influences that might indirectly affect the outcome of a search.

2. Discuss possible methods for managing external influences.

Types of External Influences

Typically, there are four categories of influences that search managers must be prepared to manage:

1. Media.

2. Relatives or friends of the lost subject.

3. Political influences.

4. Persons claiming parapsychological powers (for example, psychics and astrologers)

Managing the Media

Media pressure will not usually develop to significant levels during the first operational period, although mistakes made with the media early in the incident can have long term negative effects. Therefore, it's critical that the initial IC understand and apply principles of media management so that serious problems can be avoided.

Understanding the News Media

Commonly referred to as "the press," the news media is the link between information and the public. It is largely responsible for determining what is "newsworthy" and how it is reported.

Dealing with the news media is a fact of life for public officials and those in the emergency response professions. Whether it's a phone call late at night, flashbulbs popping at a news conference, or a microphone thrust in your face, eventually every IC is going to be confronted by a reporter asking questions. Some officials have learned to use the news media as an effective tool for communicating with their constituencies. Others ignore the questions and hope the reporters will simply go away. But reporters do not go away, because the activities of emergency responders is considered the public's business, and the public has a "right to know" what we are doing on the lost person's behalf. This often involves disclosing how responsible officials are handling (or mishandling) an incident and providing expanded or in-depth perspective.

The media will always get their story. How they do so, and how accurate and complete it is, depends to a large degree on how the incident staff interacts with reporters. A hostile relationship is likely to produce a hostile story.

Characteristics of the Major Media

Each of the three major media has a different audience, different deadlines, and different needs.

Newspaper: Generally only one or two major dailies cover an area, but there may be a local newspaper which may have more interest in the search. They have a critical need for pictures, quotes and details, and their deadlines are tight. Deadlines for local papers, which are typically published weekly, are not as tight as those of dailies, unless the search occurs near press time.

Radio: Most areas have a number of stations that provide immediate coverage. They will be especially interested in actual voices from the

major players to give their story maximum impact.

Television: Generally there are only two or three stations in an area with any significant news capability. Here the need is for short film clips of the story for coverage on the noon or evening news. There is a growing trend, however, toward live coverage whenever a story is in progress. More than most type of emergency incidents, the search for a lost person is likely to be long enough for such live "in progress" reports.

The larger the media coverage area, the more aggressive the media will likely be. For example, reporters associated with networks are likely to push harder than the local television reporter (although some local reporters revel in "scooping" the networks).

What Media Coverage Can You Expect?

Media reporting of lost or missing persons often will go through three fairly distinct phases:

Early concern for the lost person. They will focus on the concern for the subject and show genuine sympathy for you, your people, and the job you have to do.

Next: accusation. This will arise if the subject is not found quickly. Generally the media will assume something has gone wrong. Expect to be asked, "Why haven't you found this child yet?" or "What kinds of problems are keeping you from finding this person?"

Then: the story behind the news. After the initial two phases, the search for controversy expands and revealing the story behind the news will start. What really happened and why? Who really was involved? Why and what are you covering up?

If we reflect for a moment, then we realize that these three phases are logical processes that our own minds follow as we witness news unfold. We should not be surprised nor upset that the media seeks information to support these needs.

Recall, for example, the early November 1994 case of two missing (later found murdered) young boys in Union, South Carolina. This case took on a typical (though clearly more highly emotional) progression:

> Report of the "abduction" of the children captured the audience and generated sympathy for the mother, father, and townspeople.

> National coverage galvanized the population, generated thousands of reports of sightings of the "abductor" or of the children, and expressed

widespread early support for the way officials were handling the incident.

With an absence of evidence, resulting in NOT finding the children, or the "abductor," or the vehicle after several days, the media focused on officials' failure to solve the case and on the possibility that family or friends were involved.

Following the confession by the boys' mother, the media delved into investigative reporting about nearly every person even remotely involved.

Communicating the Message

When speaking to the media, much is communicated besides the actual verbal statement. For example, it has been estimated that word choice contributes only 10% of what the recipient of a message "hears," while voice tone makes up 35% of the message, and body language contributes 55%! Clearly, just "saying the right things" is not sufficient to communicating the intended message. A competent media representative or Public Information Officer will apply the following nonverbal components to their communications:

> Natural gestures.
> Sincere facial expressions.
> Expressive voice.
> Constant eye contact.

General Principles for Managing the Media Response to the Search Incident

1. At the moment you begin to feel any pressure of any kind from the media, order a qualified Public Information Officer to take that pressure off of you. Generally, the local host agency will want to have one of their people perform the PIO function. This makes perfect sense as they may already have a working relationship with the media representatives. It is up to the IC to ensure that the local PIO gets all of the relevant information on the roles of the agencies involved in the incident.

2. Always designate only one person as the primary media liaison — the Public Information Officer.

3. Consider confining the media representatives to one location. While this is not always possible, it is less disruptive if they can be kept out of the search area. One technique often used with success is to "close" the search area to them, but arrange regular trips for the media, as a group, to the search area.

4. Another useful technique is to have media representatives designate a "pool" reporter or reporting team that will represent the interests of all. This is particularly useful in situations such as arranging for a "media" over flight of the area with pooled video feeds, or when talking with relatives to avoid overwhelming them.

5. Brief all searchers as to location of the media and who the Public Information Officer is. Make it clear that incident policy demands that ONLY the Public Information Officer or the IC is authorized to make formal statements to the media.

6. Establish good access to your Public Information Officer and ensure that he or she stays fully informed so that he or she retains credibility.

7. Do not forget to disseminate information to those parts of your own organization that normally dispense information (for example, switchboards, dispatchers, higher authorities.) People often first turn to traditional sources before the media.

8. Although the complexity of the incident may require you to have several people answering questions, make sure they are all reading off "the same sheet of music". Again, a single Public Information Officer must ensure this.

9. Assure that the news media has equal access to all information. Media representatives can wait for an aspect of the story as long as no one else is getting it ahead of time. Do not allow a previously established good working relationship with a reporter to evolve into one in which you appear to favor that reporter over others. Because of different deadlines for different media, rotating the schedule of news conferences and news releases will help overcome the appearance of favoritism. Set specific times for updating information. By sticking to predictable times, the updates become worthwhile to the interested media.

Crafting messages for the media:
— Remember the needs and concerns of the reporter and of the larger audience.
— Speak from personal experience.
— Be honest and direct.
— Include a carefully considered example.
— Provide one strong statistic.
— Do not use jargon.

Getting Ready to Face the Music

Plan to take advantage of the opportunities! Remember, you are the expert, and media people are human. Talk to them.

As the IC, you should plan to attend at least one media conference each

day. This gives them the opportunity to "get it from the horse's mouth". Get prepared. Be ready to provide expert opinion to a non-expert and to provide it in the easiest possible way for him or her to understand it. Anticipate the questions you are likely to get. If it will help, then set up a "mock interview" to practice answers.

Whenever possible, plan to deal with reporters individually rather than in groups. You will be better able to control the substance of what you say, and you will be more likely to leave the reporter with a sense that he or she must be fair with you. Reporters in groups tend to play to each other, often at the expense of the source they are interviewing.

Think of the public's interest in your story — that's usually the way a reporter looks at it.

Plan to give frequent reference and credit to all the organizations involved in the incident. Volunteer organizations, especially, thrive on recognition.

Protect your credibility. Do not join forces with an organization that is capable of tarnishing your image through its own poor performance. If you are forced to appear jointly with them before the media and public, then make sure the media knows what information and actions your organization is and is not responsible for.

Talking to Reporters: A Glossary

Off the record: Material that may not be published or broadcast, period. Do not go off the record casually or with anyone you do not have good reason to trust. In many cases, this category is illusory. Never say what you don't want broadcast or published!

Not for attribution: Information that may be published, but without revealing the identity of the source. Always specify whether that applies to your organization as well as to you. Be sure of the attribution the reporter will use — "an official at the scene," or "a spokesperson from the county sheriff's office," before you open your mouth. However, this practice should be discouraged as it gives the impression that by not stepping up and providing the source that there is "something to hide."

Background: Usually means not for attribution, but do not take that for granted. Discuss it with the reporter.

Deep background: Usually means off the record. Again, make sure.

Just between us: Along with other ambiguous statements or phrases, this means little to reporters. Do not use them.

Check it with me before you use it: Means just what it says. Specify whether the restriction applies to quotations as well as facts. When the reporter checks back, you have the right to correct errors and misunderstandings, but not to withdraw statements you now regret saying.

Read it to me before you use it: Gives you no right even to correct errors. All you get is advance warning of what the reporter will use.

No: Means that you have decided not to answer a reporter's question. Used judiciously, this is a lifesaver.

The Interview — General Considerations

1. Establish ground rules. Establish that these will be scrupulously followed and enforced.

2. Assure that there is a commonly understood definition of terms, based on the media glossary above.

3. Be yourself! Do not attempt to change your voice or sound

differently. Do not play-act or try to be someone else.

4. Prepare written notes, and do not be afraid to refer to them during the interview. Sometimes the brief interlude during which you are checking your notes helps you and others to relax.

5. Start any statement with a direct and calmly expressed sentence about what is happening or what is expected to happen. Immediately follow that with a description of what authorities have done in response.

6. Whatever you think is most important is what you should say first. That is what is most likely to be quoted.

7. Your attitude should be open, friendly, and helpful.

8. Be clear and to the point. Do not "beat around the bush".

9. Use "plain talk." How would you explain it to your nephew?

10. Avoid jargon. Using technical terms such as military or policy idioms, confuses the public or leads them to think you are hiding something.

11. Watch out for emotional "buzz words." The use of ethnic labels, an inappropriate term, or disparaging characterizations of groups or individuals involved can create mini-crises of their own.

12. Do not panic. Admit problems if they exist, but point out your positive efforts to correct them.

13. Avoid exaggeration. Stick to the facts. Do not risk giving the reporter the impression that you are trying to manipulate the story or give yourself or your agency a favorable impression.

14. Be candid and honest. If you give a reporter any reason to be suspicious of your integrity, then he or she will find a way to trip you up. However, there is no need or obligation to tell them "everything."

15. Emphasize the positive action authorities are taking to alleviate the situation.

16. Do not talk down to the public through the reporter; they will know it and resent it.

17. Determine three topics about which you want to speak to the media. Lead with one or more of these, return to them in the middle of the interview and close with the most

important one. This gives you three chances (opening, middle and end) during the interview to get your message across and alert the media and the public to its importance.

Answering Questions

Never say, "No comment." To a mass audience "no comment" conveys one of three negative sentiments: "I don't know, "I know but I'm hiding the information," or "Go ask someone else." That someone else could say something a lot worse than what you might be forced to reveal. **In the real world, "no comment" is a direct challenge to a reporter to discover what is being concealed and why**. A story in the media that describes an official as "refusing to comment" does not speak well for that person. **The best response when you do not know the answer to a question is, "I don't know, but I will find out."** Always offer to tell what you or your organization is doing to find out (when that information is appropriate for public release). And, when you find the answer, keep your promise and tell the questioner and all others interested in the answer what you found out. At the next media briefing, close your comments with answers to previously unanswered questions before taking on any new questions.

Use caution in answering questions that call for speculation on your part. The media will push for opinions such as, "Do

you think you will find Johnny alive?" Either a "yes" or a "no" answer to this is speculation. Something like, "We're doing everything we can to find him as soon as possible," may be a more appropriate response. Promise to get facts and then produce them. People understand when you tell them that you "don't play lottery – by taking unnecessary risks" with people's lives.

Answer the questions as briefly as possible without being curt, reticent, or non-communicative. Do not try to be glib or to add a light touch. When you are talking about people's lives or well being, no one is laughing.

At a loss for words? Anyone who has been interviewed has been asked the unanswerable question. It can be in the form of an innuendo, a non sequitur, or an assumption. Or, it might be a question requiring enormous amounts of detailed information or history.
- Do not attempt to answer the question but explain why you cannot answer it — at least for now.
- Do not win a battle at the price of losing a war. In short, do not fight with tenacious reporters. Never get into an adversarial position, regardless of the provocation. You might win the first round but you will lose in the long run.
- Do not make it worse than it is, but do not try to make it appear better than it is. Stick to the facts.

If you cannot control your anger or keep your voice in check during times of stress, then have someone else act as spokesperson for a portion of the media presentation. Then, remain available for answering questions that the spokesperson cannot.

If a question is offensive or distorts the subject or the situation, then say so! Then either ask the reporter to reword it, or rephrase it yourself and answer it. Use caution here, as rephrasing questions can be viewed as attempts to dodge the issues.

Keep calm — do not lose your cool. If you lose your temper, then that will be the story, not the substance of what you said.

Interview Traps to Avoid

- If the reporter's questions put your actions in a negative light, then admit it, and explain the corrective steps that have been taken.

- Do not repeat the reporter's terminology unless you like the words.

- Beware of false assumptions, conclusions, and "facts".
Avoid answering hypothetical questions.

- Listen to the whole question before you respond.

- Be alert to the multiple question: ask for the questioner to repeat the parts for you and/or pick the part you want to answer.

- Beware of the "speed-up" technique in which the reporter shoves the microphone back and forth rapidly between two interviewees.

- Beware of the "stall" technique in which the reporter leaves the mike in your face after your answer, hoping for you to say more. When you are finished, do not be afraid to remain silent, or (when the camera is on) to look the person in the eye, smile, and ask, "Do you have any more questions?"

Watch out for questions that are:
— Leading: the question points to a particular conclusion or opinion, such as, "Don't you agree that this search is taking longer than it should?"
— Loaded: the question contains provocative words or phrasing that could bias your answer, such as, "How do you respond to critics who say that you have bungled this search."
— Double-barreled: there are actually two questions in one, such as, "Are your searchers well

trained and familiar with the area?"

News (Press) Releases

The news release represents the basic technique for getting information to the media. The release should cover the basic information needed to answer the questions who, what, why, when, and where. It should be written in the "pyramid" style: the most important news should appear in the first paragraph, the next most important in the second paragraph, and so forth. This style is useful because news editors generally cut a news release from the bottom up. If only the first paragraph is used, then the critical information will still be included. The news media will use the release in one of two ways. Either they will print or read the news release (or some portion of it) verbatim, or they will write their own story based on the release. In the latter case, they will want more information and no doubt will start asking questions.

A news release issued during a complex mission is a luxury. Often events change the situation too rapidly. Consider issuing fact sheets, with quotes for distribution (from key staff) whenever appropriate. Put a DATE, TIME and SOURCE on all news releases.

News releases should stick to the known facts; often this will mean you can describe the

nature of the incident, but not the aspects still under investigation.

News Conferences

Definition: A News Conference is a prearranged meeting to which all of the news media are invited. Proper preparation for an effective news conference requires detailed planning. The "stage" should be set — adequate seating, lighting, and equipment such as projectors, screens, or TV monitors must be arranged.

It is useful to distribute press kits of written information before, during, or after the news conference. Normally, once the news conference is over, reporters will want to interview the speaker with follow-up questions and should be permitted to do so.

How to Handle Damaging Information

The adage that the best defense is a good offense holds true in dealing with bad news. If information becomes known that is damaging, and is bound to find its way to the media, then the public officials involved should participate in the first release of the story. This will ensure that the news is accurate, even if it is not positive. Otherwise, officials will find themselves in the position of defending their actions in a follow-up story. The defensive posture more often than not suggests a cover-up, especially if the first story included a refusal to comment.

How to Handle Sensitive Information

There are times when some information is of such a sensitive nature that it should not be released to the news media. While officials are under constraints not to disclose certain kinds of information, they should never deliberately misrepresent the facts. Misrepresenting public information is both unethical and illegal. An honest explanation about why sensitive information cannot be discussed is both appropriate and useful in maintaining credibility.

After the Story Comes Out

If the reporter has reported the story fairly and accurately, then it is appropriate to let the reporter know that. After all, words of thanks are as rare for reporters as they are for public officials.

Some reporters may warp your words or take them out of context, or simply report the story inaccurately. If you think you have been mistreated in a story, then tell the reporter as quickly as possible. Remind her or him that you expect accuracy and fairness more than you want attention.

Unless there are gross inaccuracies that are likely to be highly damaging, requesting a retraction or formal correction is not advisable. A retraction rarely gets the same attention as the original story. Often a follow-up story that also clarifies the previous inaccuracies is possible.

> ### There is Risk in Any Public Exposure!

When meeting the media, the best possible attitude is to be able to say, "I'm glad you asked!" and mean it. It is your opportunity to present yourself and your organization to the public. However, there are other occasions when confronted by a hostile media, that the best you can possibly say afterwards is, "I don't think I hurt us."

Distinctions Among the Media

1. Television leans toward action and entertainment. It's an intimate medium.
2. Radio tends to be relatively casual and personal and likes stories about people.
3. Community newspapers want news that directly affects that community.
4. Generally, newspapers translate complex ideas best.

Television

Television is an emotional medium, not an intellectual one. Viewers will often forget the content of your message but remember your style — how you looked, how you behaved, and the quality of your voice. So check your appearance, and then forget it. You cannot change your clothes or your hairline on a moment's notice. Instead, concentrate on the questions you may be asked. If at all possible, be prepared to conduct the on-camera interview without checking your notes.

The way you are perceived on television is frequently quite different from the way you are accepted in person. Remember that while preparing; sit upright at your desk, or in the chair. Stand if that is more comfortable.

Look straight into the camera unless instructed to do otherwise; do not look up for guidance or down to hide. Whatever helps you concentrate on the camera or reporter, do it! Even a slight slip of your eyes left or right will look like you are shifty or distracted.

The camera can make you look flat; it steals your vitality. Remember the "10% Factor" and increase your energy level to compensate, especially if you tend to be a low-key communicator. Even though they are likely to stay on a tight "head shot," use your hands to gesture naturally. It keeps you loose and helps your voice. Be animated, but not artificial. Try to bring a sense of "controlled urgency" to all media interviews.

Print: The Face to Face Interview

The face to face print interview can cause you to relax too much. Seemingly benign chit-chat

can become fodder for big stories. Behave as if the microphones are on and the cameras are running, even as you stroll through the incident base with the reporter. The print reporter needs quotes just as the television reporter needs sound bites. Make your message quotable. Often, print reporters are more open to being educated on an issue, so you might have more time to explain. But do not ramble. Be specific and stay simple. Keep the readership in mind — the reporter is your conduit to that audience.

Support your facts with written material. Depending on the deadline pressure, the reporter may have more time to mull over your situation.

Just because this reporter is turning your words into a printed article does not mean body language is not important. You are communicating, with everything you say, as well as everything you do. The impression you make will influence the story he or she writes. Be animated, enthusiastic, and show your commitment. The way you deliver your message determines how you get quoted.

Radio

Even though the audience cannot see you, behave as if you are "on camera." This will help your voice stay animated and energetic. Listeners are depending on your voice to communicate the meaning of your words.

You must sound as if you are confident and in control.

When a Reporter Calls on the Phone, Be on Your Guard!

Never take the call cold. Find out why he or she is calling, discuss the deadline, and call back. Even if you can buy only five minutes, tell the reporter that you are in a meeting or otherwise engaged. Ask pertinent questions so you can provide a good response. ***Do not fail to call back!***

Assume he or she wants information that can be published or recorded and broadcast. Do not use the speaker phone: it makes you sound like you're in a rain barrel.

Stand up to talk on the telephone. It is really very simple: monotone voices are connected to monotone bodies. When you sit down to talk on the telephone, you tend to ramble on with a monotone voice. When you stand, you speak with more energy and vocal variety. Plus, you are more succinct.

When you cannot see the reporter's face, you do not have nonverbal reinforcement to know if you are getting your message across. Explain complex information in simple language, then ask questions to be sure the reporter understands.

Remember, some reporters are on "fishing expeditions." Listen carefully to the questions and do not offer them news, unless you want them to do a story on it. Again, always assume you are "on the record" and never go off it. You cannot see what the reporter is "doing" with your information.

Dealing with the "Unprofessional" or Unscrupulous Reporter

We often assume a much higher level of professionalism by those who work in the media than is sometimes there. The absolute minimum requirements for a radio announcer, for example, is the ability to read — nothing else. Often in small communities, part-time students who know very little about professionalism of the industry are hired by radio and newspapers. They may, at times, perhaps unknowingly, violate your agreement or quote you out the context, or misquote you — or use unscrupulous methods of getting information. Remember that "Off The Record" really doesn't exist in these situations.

You have a means of recourse in such instances. Discuss the incident with the reporter first and then with the editor. The editor will want to know about such instances. However, if the editor does not agree with you, then you may have no further recourse. You may want to advise the editor that if they want any further information from you, they should not send that reporter.

Look at it From Their Perspective

Problems the news media must deal with:

Information is often unavailable or very difficult to obtain.

"Kill the messenger" syndrome: the media are often blamed for bad news.

Fears that the media distorts the news, leading officials to withhold or sanitize information.

Competition with other local, state, and national media can be fierce.

Conflicting information about what actually happened.

Technical and logistical problems.

Pressure of DEADLINES!

Dealing With the Media: Summary

Far too often, the relationship with the media on an incident becomes an adversarial one. This helps no one. To avoid this, <u>preplan</u> all media aspects. Manage this influence — do not let it control you. Meet and greet. Being able to talk with reporters on a first name basis is easier than regarding them as adversaries. The media can be used to advantage, if a good relationship is established prior to the incident. For example:

• Assistance in obtaining and disseminating information, and getting resources, including helicopters.

• Emergency preparedness education.

• Funding or donations, especially to volunteer groups.

• Public relations.

While much of the previous discussion focused on being protective against intrusive or inaccurate media coverage, it's important to remember that the media is not the enemy. Handled with discretion, the media can be an essential asset in disseminating information which can assist in locating lost or missing persons. The media also serves an essential role in a democratic society, keeping the public informed during the course of a newsworthy incident and on the conduct of taxpayer funded agencies.

Managing the Subject's Relatives

- Do not ignore them. Take the initiative and contact them. At the incident base, locate them in a comfortable place, preferably somewhere away from the center of activity.

- Assign one person to assist them and to provide them with regular feedback on the progress of the search. This should be someone who has real sensitivity to this type of situation and, if possible, someone who has had training in dealing with grief reactions.

- Keep them constantly informed about what is being done. Do not make them come to you for information.

- Maintain an atmosphere of encouragement, but do not build up false hopes.

- Help them feel useful. In some cases, people close to the subject are going to want to or even insist on being "involved." They feel that they must "contribute" to the effort. This is their way of dealing with stress and uncertainty and possibly guilt. While it is unwise to send a relative out with a search team, often there are some tasks around the incident base with which he or she could assist. It is important to gently but firmly keep family members from interfering with SAR operations or endangering themselves. In any case, it makes sense to have someone knowledgeable available for confirming the identification of clues, and assisting with the investigation activities.

- Locate unstable relatives or associates somewhere away from the incident base. **Idle comments by searchers or accidentally overheard radio messages can cause negative reactions.**

- Determine if the relatives or associates want to be contacted by the media. If not, then provide privacy for them, especially in cases where the subject is found dead or in very poor condition.

- Brief all searchers on the situation with relatives or associates, particularly the locations and identification of those in the search area or incident base. Emphasize the need to avoid idle comments.

- Consider having specialists in dealing with grief reactions present or on call to assist the family, if needed.

- Consider tying colored flagging or other identifier on the arm of relatives. This way you and your staff will be able to locate them when you have additional questions or want confirmation on the relevance of a clue. It also alerts others to "watch their words" in the presence of the missing subject's relatives.

Dealing with Grief

The following are some suggestions for dealing with members of the subject's family who are on the scene of a search incident.

1. Help make them comfortable. Water, juice, blankets, etc., are tangible expressions of concern and greatly appreciated. Also, be alert for shock or other physical reactions, as they may need assistance dealing with a

more intimate version of critical incident stress.

2. Support the venting of feelings and, if necessary, help channel them within realistic and controllable limits. Avoid aggressive confrontation with irrational beliefs by the family. They may need those beliefs as protection against the shock of the loss or traumatic injury.

3. In cases of serious injury or death of the subject, to help avoid additional stress at the scene, it may be advisable to influence the family to leave the area if the subject is to be brought to the incident base. ALWAYS have the deceased covered with something clean and professional looking, as these are the remains of somebody's loved one.

4. Advise the family that the subject has been located and where he or she ultimately will be taken. Wait until after the family leaves to evacuate the subject, thus avoiding a stressful situation for both the search personnel and the family. Alternatively, evacuate the subject by way of another location and then inform the family where he or she has been taken.

5. Encourage continued professional or paraprofessional help. If the family is willing to get support but appears immobilized by events, then make the contact for them. Friends, clergy, or others close to the family can be helpful at this time and can serve in a liaison role.

Managing Political Influences

Two situations that could occur that trigger unusual political interest:

1. A politician or VIP (or member of their family) is the lost subject
2. Media publicity or family contacts generate interest by political entities.

Generally, intensification of political influence is not likely to occur until a search progresses past the initial operational period and becomes more complex and receives greater publicity. The principles for managing contacts with political entities are the same for either situation listed previously. In most cases, agency policies will dictate how to deal with political contacts, but the following general guidelines have proven useful.

- Assign one person as the liaison with the entity's contact person.

- Seize the initiative and keep them informed. Call them before they call you.

- Put them in the position of telling you when they think you are giving them more than they need. Many of the principles for dealing with the media are applicable in dealing with political entities as well.

- Recognize that everything becomes a bit more "touchy" when politics are involved. However, if you are managing an incident effectively, then there should be little need for changes when political interest arises. This type of influence simply heightens the need for doing really well those things that "show," such as media briefings, investigation and background checks, searcher briefings, and documentation.

Be aware that this may be one of the few opportunities for political people to see how well your organization functions during searches. The experience may have far-reaching impacts on funding, recruiting and inter-agency relations.

In Dealing with Relatives, Media, or Political Influences, Remember:

HONESTY REDUCES RUMORS
and
TACT REDUCES PROBLEMS

Parapsychological Influences

Although unlikely to be much of an influence during the first operational period, a search generating substantial publicity almost always will bring out these types of people, such as psychics, clairvoyants, and astrologers.

Generally, when a search effort extends unsuccessfully over a number of days, friends, relatives, and even some searchers can begin to clutch at straws. If these types of influences are available, then there is sometimes a tendency to place some emphasis on their use. In fact, some of these people will actively seek out family members to "advise" them. Be forewarned that many psychics are quite practiced at dealing with skeptics who profess an "open-minded" view of things. They are typically quite skilled at describing their visions (from dreams, or by handling an object belonging to the missing subject) in a vivid manner that lends a distinct and "compelling" aspect to their report. And no one is nearly as creative as a psychic whose prediction has apparently been proven "wrong."

Realize also that the use of psychics can be detrimental to the morale of searchers. Psychics lend a circus atmosphere to an incident, and will be quite popular with the press. Generally, their use lends an air of desperation to the search.

Regardless of your view of psychics, they must be effectively managed, or they can quickly become a source of irritation or stress, diverting your efforts away from the task of finding the lost subject. To ignore or publicly belittle them only to have their information subsequently proved "accurate" can result in adverse public reaction.

While psychics may provide some comfort to the family of the missing subject, psychic inputs have generally improved results by only one or two percent greater than mere chance. Focus on all of those things that improve the overall chance of success.

Suggestions for Handling Parapsychological Influences

- Try to prevent them from talking to family members alone.

- Do not get placed in the position of being the avenue of contact between them and either the family or the media.

- Do not let them into the field without being escorted by a qualified incident management team member.

- Do not let these influences become a drain on your efforts to achieve your incident objectives.

- If you are sympathetic to their use, then do not wait until an incident happens before testing their capabilities. Treat them like any resource: evaluate them between incidents and include them in your preplan accordingly.

- Pre-brief relatives that some psychics will attempt to get money from them for their services, only if family members not involve incident staff. Because of the emotional strain, family members are more susceptible under these conditions to paying for services which cannot be validated. If the family does want to involve a psychic, tell them that the medium's involvement should be "part of the plan" and include incident staff.

Summary

Four types of external influences were described: the <u>media</u>, <u>relatives and friends</u> of the missing subject, <u>political entities</u> interested in the search, and <u>persons claiming parapsychological powers</u>. With respect to the media, it was explained that newspapers, radio stations, and television newscasters all have different audiences, deadlines, and needs. We described the three distinct phases that news coverage will take during an extended incident, including <u>early concern</u>, <u>accusation</u>, and the <u>real story behind the news</u>. It was pointed out that communication is only partly verbal, and we suggested ways of controlling the nonverbal components of one's message.

General principles for media management were proposed, including the suggestion of appointing an <u>Public Information Officer</u> to control all media communications. A <u>glossary</u> of terms was provided, and some suggestions on how to answer media questions were proposed, including the avoidance of <u>interview "traps</u>."

With respect to dealing with the subject's friends and family, we described the importance of <u>keeping them informed</u> of search activities and progress. It was suggested that a <u>specific location</u> should be assigned to family members who insist on remaining on scene, but that they should not be permitted to join search teams in the field.

Personnel who deal with the family should provide an <u>atmosphere of encouragement</u> without creating false hopes, and should be sensitive to their feelings and possible <u>grief reactions</u> that may ensue before the subject is actually found.

Political influences may arise either when a politician or VIP (or member of the person's family) is the missing subject, or when media publicity or family contact generates interest by politicians. Similar to dealing with the media, dealing with political influences requires <u>tact, sincerity, and initiative</u>. Provide them with information before they can ask for it, and never express resentment over their involvement.

Parapsychological influences, such as psychics and astrologers, commonly volunteer their services when there is much publicity over an ongoing incident, or sometimes when contacted directly by family members. Psychics, though usually well-meaning individuals with genuine concern for the subject, can sometimes be disruptive to incident management and demoralizing to search personnel. Methods of managing their influence were described, including <u>controlling their contact with family members</u>, and <u>limiting their access to the search area</u>. Search managers who are sympathetic with the use of psychics should consider treating them as any potential search resource and including them in their preplans accordingly.

Questions for Discussion:

1. How would you handle an unscrupulous reporter who has been caught trying to sneak onto a search team?

2. What would you say to the distraught father of a missing child who insists on going into the field to search?

3. What additional external influences, besides the one discussed in this chapter, must sometimes be managed? Discuss possible methods for managing external influences.

CHAPTER 24

SEARCH MANAGEMENT TECHNOLOGY

For the search planner, the question is not whether to employ technology, but rather which technology to adopt, and to which management tasks to apply it. Technology of one sort or another adorns the shirt pockets, belts, and planning kits of the most "low-tech" search manager, and even a technophobe of a planner will nevertheless rely on such technological wonders as the magnetic compass, the ballpoint pen, and the calculator. In this chapter we will focus on **the adoption of electronic technology in the management of the lost person incident**. Specifically, we will discuss developments in computer hardware and software, as well as the application of satellite navigation systems to search management.

CHAPTER OBJECTIVES:

When you finish studying this chapter, you should be able to:

1. Describe how SAR managers may benefit from employing the appropriate technology effectively.
2. Identify the manner in which computers can assist in search management.
3. Describe the application of Global Positioning Systems in SAR.

Computers in SAR

In 1975, impressed by the U.S. Coast Guard's use of large, mainframe computers in the ocean search for lost ships and downed aircraft, William Syrotuck proposed that computers could similarly be used in land searches lost or missing persons.[5] Generally, he suggested that **computers could be used as an aid in search planning**, particularly with respect to setting priorities as to where to look for the subject, as well as how best to employ search resources, and to keep track of shifting probabilities as the search proceeds.

The use of computers in SAR has come a long way since Syrotuck's original vision Today, portable devices allow planners to prioritize the search area in terms of probabilities of area (POA), shift POA based on POD results from the field, consult lost person behavior profiles, print forms and run optimal resource allocation scenarios.

---

[5] William Syrotuck (1975), *An Introduction to Land Search Probabilities and Calculations.* NY: Arner Publications.

The portability of computers makes it possible to employ several or more computers in various locations throughout the search base, such as tracking support resources by the Logistics Section, or for "number crunching" the shifting POA in the Planning Section. What is more, all computers on scene, despite their location, can be set up to communicate with each other via a local area network (LAN) or some other system for linking computers spatially dispersed. In addition, computers can be connected to **modems** that can send and receive **packet radio data** to and from locations away from the scene.

While many kinds of software may be employed, there are two types of programs that are especially important to search organizers: **I. Data Management** programs, and **II. Tactical Decision-making Aids (TDA's)**.

I. Data Management. There are numerous search management tasks that involve the management of data, involving both the **recording** and **retrieval** of information. An incomplete list of these tasks includes:

> **Tracking search resource status:** . For example, who is "in the woods", who is on the scene and waiting to be deployed, who is coming (and when), and who has gone home. A popular resource status tool is the T-card

system, which does not rely on technology.

Updating the situational status (SITSTAT). For example, what areas have been searched (and how well), what clues have been found, and what progress has been made toward finding the subject. The Plans Section may use a variety of maps for this purpose, including some sort of "status map" on which search progress is recorded.

Obtaining relevant lost person statistics for the search. For example, how far have similar types of subjects traveled in the past, how long can they be expected to survive, and how thoroughly will you have to search in order to find them?

Locating supplies and equipment. For example, where do you get food, kitchen supplies, portable toilets, toilet paper, batteries, generators, tents, cots, and everything else you will need to support searchers?

Obtaining maps of the search area. Computer technology now allows for direct printing of maps from local software or by Internet download.

Recording critical data on completion of the search for future reference. Some examples include:

— Lost person behavior.

— Updated map information.

— Financial expenditures.

Geographical Information Systems (GIS)

GIS refers to database-type software in which the "data" (for example, supplies, equipment, people) are **spatially referenced** with respect to geographical position, that is, "where is it, exactly?" A very primitive GIS might merely have longitude and latitude coordinates encoded with the data, but a more useful system for SAR is to have the data referenced to **computerized maps** that are structured according to **themes** or **layers** (for example, buildings, roads, trails, waterways, vegetation), and that may be independently accessed. For example, the search planner can instruct the GIS software to display only the trails (without buildings or other map features), or only the roads, or only the waterways — or any combination of these. More importantly, the location of resources can be quickly identified with respect to map features. For example, the Logistics Section can have the map display only roads and SAR vehicles, or buildings, roads, kitchen facilities, staging areas, and first aid stations. Similarly, the Planning Section can choose to display only trails, vegetation, waterways, grid searchers, hasty teams, and safety hazards. Note though, that the proliferation of powerful laptop computers has allowed access to adequate computer mapping systems in the field without the need for a full blown GIS application. These locally installed mapping applications provide the ability to print detailed maps to give to individual search teams.

> **A major advantage of employing Geographical Information Systems is <u>data visualization</u>. The search manager can not only retrieve critical information quickly, such as the nature of resources at his or her disposal, but also can instantly grasp the spatial location of resources with respect to geographical position.**

Advantages of GIS and mapping programs:

- Promotes efficiency in incident management.
- Reduces time required to make critical decisions.
- Reduces errors in resource deployment.
- Facilitates briefing of management personnel.
- Provides a comprehensive record of the incident for future reference.

II. Tactical Decision-making Aids (TDAs)

As indicated earlier, computer software is available to aid the Planning Section in making decisions regarding the allocation of search resources. Examples include:

Shifting the probability of area (POA) after segments have been searched. This involves "crunching the numbers" according to the Bayesian formula (see Chapter 16).

Calculating cumulative probabilities of detection (POD) for segments that have been searched more than once (see Chapter 15).

Estimating the number of searchers required for a grid search, in order to obtain a desired Coverage in a segment of specified size in a specified period of time (see the planning formulas in Chapter 15).

Conducting "What If?" analyses in order to obtain optimal use of available search resources.

Caveats on Using Computers in Search Management

The quality of information provided by the computer is totally dependent on the quality of data it receives, subject to the "GIGO" rule: **"Garbage In, Garbage Out."**

Computers cannot compensate for poorly trained or inexperienced search managers. They are merely a management aid, not a replacement for systematic thinking. Search

planners must ultimately rely on their own judgment, regardless of the information provided by the computer. Finally, computers need electricity, whether stored in batteries or direct from outlets. Besides power needs, their use requires adequate clean dry spaces for setting up the computers, printers and peripherals.

CASIE: Computer Aided Search Information Exchange

An example of the application of computers to SAR is **CASIE** (Computer Aided Search Information Exchange), originally developed in the 1980's for DOS-based computers by John Bownds, Mike Ebersole and David Lovelock (its principal programmer). A very user-friendly version called Win C.A.S.I.E. III, which operates under Microsoft's Windows XP operating system, was released in the Fall of 2006. Win C.A.S.I.E. III is a search planner's toolbox that includes the following functions:

• Shifting POA according to the Bayesian formula.
• Keeping track of cumulative probabilities of detection (POD).
• Performing "What If?" analyses on alternative decisions.
• Factoring in the influence of clue information to POA.
• Assisting with consensus assignment of POA to segments.
• Facilitating the splitting or addition of

segments.

- Providing summaries of lost person behavior categories.
- Keeping a complete record (an audit trail) of planning decisions and actions.
- Converting Coverage to POD and POD to Coverage.
- Using the grid search planning formulas.
- Printing search management forms.
- Resource allocation advice.

Win C.A.S.I.E. III (WC3) is free and can be downloaded from http://wcasie.com/.

OTHER EQUIPMENT

Laser Rangefinders

Laser rangefinders are handy tools for measuring the distances that an object can be detected for use in developing surrogates for sweep width. Basic rangefinders cost about as much as a good pair of binoculars.

Camera Phones

Cell phones are now commonly equipped with internal cameras for snapshots or real-time video transmission. This type of technology greatly enhances the rapid processing of clues. Searchers can take a picture of a clue and transmit the picture to the command post for evaluation without having to leave the field. Wireless phones also provide a needed backup, and sometimes a

replacement, for more cumbersome two-way radios of limited range.

Global Positioning System (GPS)

GPS allows for quick and relatively accurate identification of one's geographical position anywhere in the world. The system is driven by a series of navigation satellites circling the earth at approximately 11,000 miles altitude (see Figure 24.1). The **GPS receiver**, which may be as small as a pocket calculator, listens to the microwave transmissions emitted from these **NAVSTAR** satellites and uses the information it receives to triangulate its position in 3-dimensional space, providing geographical coordinates as well as altitude.

Figure 24.1

GPS Satellites in Orbit

Garmin Corp. schematic of GPS satellites in orbit around the Earth.

These coordinates are constantly updated, or displayed in **real time** as the receiver is moved. Consequently the GPS receiver is a valuable **navigational** as well as **positional** tool for SAR purposes

In addition to providing coordinate information, there are other features of most GPS receivers that enhance their utility for SAR:

Recording of numerous **waypoints** (specific geographical positions), such as the location of clues or other important spots. The unit can provide compass bearings (including appropriate declination, if desired) between any two waypoints.

Besides individual waypoints, GPS units also hold entire tracks in memory. These tracks can provide a fairly accurate record of the actual path it has traveled with a searcher. For example, the handler of a bloodhoubd, who may have been too preoccupied to pay careful attention to his or her location, can refer to the unit's track log to reconstruct the route taken. With many units, this information can be downloaded and saved to a computer hard drive.

The user can describe a specific path or **route**, that is, a series of waypoints, and have the receiver signal audibly whenever he or she deviates from the route.

As discussed later, many GPS receivers can be interfaced with computers.

Factors Limiting the Effectiveness of GPS

Selective Availability (SA): When the U.S. Department of Defense first introduced GPS, the agency degraded non-secure civilian signals, up to a random error margin of 100m, to prevent their use for military purposes by hostile forces. Beginning in the year 2000, SA was gradually turned off as the U.S. military devised a scheme for jamming GPS reception near sensitive military facilities. However, unlike the Earth's magnetic field, which is always "on" for orienting compasses, the U.S. Government has the option, albeit an unlikely one, to selectively degrade or turn off the GPS signal in times of national emergencies.

Obstruction or distortion of signals from forest canopy or ravines (which may cause temporary losses of signals), or reflection of signals from cliffs, buildings, or hillsides (which may introduce additional error). Receivers vary widely in their ability to "hold onto" a signal that is being disrupted or obscured.

Expense. Although prices of GPS receivers have been dropping considerably, they are not cheap and low end models are still about ten times the price of a durable orienteering compass. Add the price of peripherals (antennas, chargers, batteries, carrying cases), software for downloading and mapping GPS data on computers, plus special modems for users who want to connect their GPS units to portable radios, and the price increases significantly.

Temporal Variations. GPS signal strength can vary through the day because the satellites are not geo-synchronous but are in constant orbital motion at about 7,000 mph. A strong signal from four or more satellites is required for an accurate three dimensional fix that includes altitude. As the satellites constantly reorient themselves relative to the receiving GPS unit, the signal strength, and with it accuracy, are subject to change.

Dead Batteries. GPS units are electronic devices that require charged batteries. Backlit displays reduce battery life. Besides bringing back-up batteries into the field, GPS users should always have a map and compass to fall back on when batteries go dead at the wrong time.

Interfacing GPS with Computers

Many GPS receivers have a serial connection or a **USB port,** which can be used to transfer data to and from a computer. The transfer usually requires software that can read the GPS data and do something useful with it, such as plotting waypoints and tracks onto a computerized map. A collection of waypoints, combined with times that the receiver was at each location, can provide an accurate record of the actual path traveled by the search team at the time of debriefing. Such records are important to the search planner concerned about probability of detection estimates and possible gaps in coverage.

Real-time Monitoring of GPS Data

For search management purposes, the most efficient use of GPS data involves tracking it in **real time**, that is, at the moment the coordinate data is calculated by the receiver, rather than waiting until the receiver returns to the search base. This is also known as an Automatic Position Reporting System (APRS). Such real time data, especially when fed into a GIS database, would become a powerful method of resource tracking.

One, very unrealistic, method of accomplishing this is to call the search team on the radio every few minutes and ask them for their GPS reading. Obviously, few searchers or search managers have the time for such interruptions. Current technology allows automation of the process of real-time monitoring by interfacing the receiver with a portable radio. The radio, according to a preset schedule, will periodically transmit the GPS data in **packet** format (electronically compressed data transmitted in short bursts of packages). The data can be relayed to the search base without any involvement of the searcher carrying the GPS receiver. And because the packet data is fed directly to the computer (see Figure 24.2), there is little or no involvement by radio operators at the search base. Figure 24.2 provides a simplified diagram of how GPS positional data can be transmitted from searchers in the field to search managers in the command post.

Figure 24.2

Signal Processing from NAVSTAR Satellites

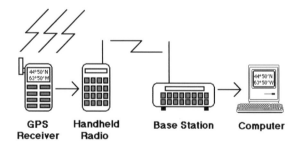

GPS Receiver — Handheld Radio — Base Station — Computer

The receiver is "married" to the portable radio by way of telecommunications hardware and software, as is the base radio and the computer. The computer can simply display the team's location on the monitor, or enter the input into a database of positions

recorded during the search. In addition to providing a quick overview of the positions of all search teams, the database could provide estimates of probability of detection, assist with record keeping, and even be interfaced with Geographical Information Systems software. (Adapted from D. Bower and K. Hill, "GPS Navigation in Land Search," Response Magazine, 1992.)

Summary

There are several advantages to employing SAR technology to search management:

It facilitates **better and quicker decisions** by search managers, through enhancing data visualization, keeping accurate and up-do-date records, performing complex mathematical computations, and comparing alternative courses of action.

It makes possible an important objective of the ICS: **fully integrated communications**. With the interlinking of computers, radios, and GPS receivers, search managers can theoretically access or obtain any information they need in order to conduct a successful search.

Questions for Discussion:

1. What additional technologies have been successfully applied to SAR missions?

2. What are some hazards of becoming dependent on SAR technology, and what can searchers do to prevent them?

3. What can search teams do when they lack the financial resources to purchase technology, such as computers or GPS receivers, for deployment during SAR incidents?

4. Given the availability of SAR technology (for example, through donations), how can search teams lacking the appropriate technological expertise improve their ability to employ the technology effectively?

CHAPTER 25

POST-INCIDENT CONSIDERATIONS

One of the major responsibilities of an IC is to provide for an effective follow-up of the entire search incident. The most critical post-incident consideration is the **After Action Review**. Other considerations include preparation of final documentation and reports, processing claims, replacing equipment, sending letters of appreciation, reestablishing relationships with the media and organizational representatives, and any other appropriate or agency-required actions.

CHAPTER OBJECTIVES:

When you finish studying this chapter, you should be able to:

1. Define an After Action Review
2. Describe what actions are appropriate once an incident is over.

The After Action Review

An After Action Review is an analytical process for identifying the lessons learned from an incident. It occurs soon after the incident is over and demobilization is complete, preferably within a few days.

A review and analysis is NOT:

x - A public session intended to lay blame on those who have made mistakes.

x - A finger-pointing session.

x - An opportunity for adversaries to embarrass each other.

Incident Review and Analysis Objectives

A complete after action review of the incident, from start to finish, should be conducted to:

- Determine why and how the search occurred.

- Determine how it could have been prevented.

- Provide a historical record of the incident and the actions taken.

- Review all operating procedures.

- Provide a vehicle for accountability for actions in the future.

- Create a means to increase effectiveness and productivity on future incidents.

- Determine what could be added to or improved in training.

Elements of the After Action Review

The review should be a gathering of key incident personnel immediately after the search has ended. It should include written comments on the search, suggesting corrections and improvements. It should analyze the corrections recommended:

- Decide which corrections should be accepted.
- Make appropriate changes to the preplan.
- Make changes in facility arrangements, if necessary.

After Action Review Considerations

Compile all necessary information and statistics related to the incident. Consider the search planning maps, logs, lost person questionnaire, debriefing summaries, and other documents. Select a review format and organize your presentation, considering:

— Where will the review be held?
— Who should attend?
— Should it function as a Board of Inquiry?
— Consider using maps, slides, photos, and other audiovisual aids.

After Action Review Suggestions

- Prepare a chronological listing or sequence of time and events.
- Assess the positive and the negative on a step-by-step chronological basis.
- Provide a mission report for everyone at the review.
- Submit an initial report to review members, and have them read it and identify questions. Prepare a list of these questions in advance.
- Record the review proceedings.
- Examine the search plan.
— Was the preplanning effective?
— Were the objectives appropriate?
— Was the organization effective?
— Did the strategy/tactics execution and procedure work?
— Did you have the right equipment and resources?
— Were there any special problem areas?
— Were communications a problem?
— Was the incident operation efficient?
— Were the Standard Operating Procedures (SOP) listed in the Preplan effective and complete? P

Review the investigation. Was it adequate? Was there any criminal activity involved? If so, then remember, all clues become evidence.

Controlling the Oral Review - Avoiding Irrelevant Distractions

- The speaker sets the tone by saying what went right.
- Limit number of people commenting.
- Limit time allotted to speakers.
- Control the person who did not understand the incident but likes the sound of his own voice.
- Control the person who sees only the negative side of things.

Review Follow-Up

- Revise your preplan as appropriate.
- Have follow-up meetings with organizations, units, or agencies where improvements are needed.
- Share information, at least in summary, with all of the teams and agencies which participated in the incident.

Post-Incident Tasks

Final paperwork:

Mission Report — include all information on the decision-making process as well as the results.

Media Release — be sure to credit all the units involved.

Letters of Appreciation.

Claims. Types of claims include:
— injury.
— property loss or damage.
— expendable supplies.
— transportation costs.
— "out-of-pocket" expenses.

Note: Often all of these considerations are overlooked. As the IC, your job is not over until the paperwork is finished.

Replace equipment. Immediately replace or service any used or damaged equipment so that you are ready for the next incident.

Review. It should be a requirement that a review is conducted as soon as possible after the incident.

Follow-up tasks. Determine what needs to be accomplished and assign jobs with a definite completion date.

Update the lost person database. For the benefit of future incidents, record significant information such as category, distance traveled, and methods of finding the subject (see "Suggested Items for a Lost Person Behavior Database," at Figure 11.1).

Summary

The IC's job is not over until the incident is thoroughly reviewed and the paperwork is completed, including whatever revisions to the preplan may be appropriate. It is important that the incident be thoroughly reviewed so that problems can be identified and fixed. The review should consist of key incident personnel and occur soon after the search has ended. All aspects of the search plan, as well as all tactical decisions made during the search, should be subjects for analysis. Additional post-incident tasks include completing the necessary paperwork (mission report, media release, letters of appreciation, and claims), replacing equipment and supplies, and updating the lost person behavior database.

Question for Discussion:

What additional tasks, besides those discussed in this chapter, must be accomplished once an incident is over (consider planning, operations, logistics, and finance)?

CHAPTER 26

THE AGENCY ADMINISTRATOR

The Agency Administrator is responsible for ensuring that **all incident finance and administrative activities are conducted in a consistent and legal manner**, applying the principles of effective incident business management. How to do that is the focus of this final chapter.

CHAPTER OBJECTIVES:

When you finish studying this chapter, you should be able to:

1. Define the role of an Agency Administrator as related to the ICS.
2. Describe the three major responsibilities of an Agency Administrator for an incident.
3. Understand the Agency Administrator's needs for adequate incident fiscal and administrative procedures.

Role of the Agency Administrator

The Agency Administrator (AA) is the administrator, chief executive officer, or designee of the agency, corporation or political subdivision that has responsibility for the incident. The Agency Administrator establishes policy, direction and delegates authority, in writing, to the IC.

Normally, the AA is not at the scene of the incident, but must have the ability to communicate and meet with the IC if necessary. At some incidents, the agency having jurisdiction may not have available a person who is qualified to perform the role of a search and rescue incident commander. In that case, the senior person from the organization with jurisdiction will have better success by performing as the AA and enlisting an experienced incident commander from another agency.

Agency Administrator Concerns

There are at least three major issues which concern AAs relative to their responsibilities and roles at incidents.

1. "What are the implications of an incident to the organization and to me?"

Any incident can have a mix of political, economic, social, environmental, and cost implications with potential serious long term effects. Also, increasingly more incidents are multi-agency and/or multi-jurisdictional.

2. "How do I maintain control when incidents occur?"

As the AA, you establish written policy and provide guidelines on priorities, objectives, and constraints to a qualified IC.

3. "Where do I fit into the incident management process?"

ICS has a hierarchy of command. Once you have clearly articulated the policy you wish followed, and delegated certain authorities, the IC who reports to you will have the necessary authority and guidance to manage the incident.

Agency Administrator Responsibilities

Three of the most important responsibilities of an AA are to:

1. Articulate agency/jurisdiction policy.

In order for the IC to develop the incident objectives and determine the appropriate strategy, the IC must be well informed and clear on agency policy and, most importantly, on the AA's interpretation of that policy.

2. Evaluate effectiveness and correct deficiencies.

As the AA, you are responsible for evaluating the effectiveness of the IC. The following will help you to monitor the effectiveness of the IC:

> #### The IC should:
> - Understand agency policy and direction.
> - Be proactive.
> - Provide clear objectives based on

agency direction.
- Have a good match between objectives and strategies.
- Staff the organization.
- Monitor span of control and adapt to incident size as necessary
- Work within cost constraints.
- Integrate other agency personnel in appropriate locations in the organization.
- Consider long term impacts:
  — environmental
  — fiscal
  — political
- Re-delegate authority to Command and General Staffs.
- Identify problem areas and work to solve them.

3. Support a multi-agency approach.

As more incidents take on a multi-agency aspect, planning for a multi-agency approach to incident management becomes increasingly important. The AA must recognize this and plan for it prior to the incident. This will create a more effective emergency management organization.

Ways to Promote Multi-Agency Involvement

> Planning conferences and agreements (memoranda of understanding and of agreement). It has been shown that when agencies meet and plan for joint operations the results are far more

effective than makeshift arrangements made at the time of an emergency.

Involvement of other personnel. By bringing other agency personnel into the ICS organization as deputies, agency representatives, or supervisors, a stronger and more balanced response organization may be formed.

Promoting the use of Unified Command. The Unified Command structure, as described in Chapter 4, ensures that all agencies with responsibility at the incident are part of the incident organization at the highest level

Joint training. Joint courses and training exercises serve useful purposes. They bring people together on an interagency basis prior to an emergency. Establishing familiarity with names and faces is done in advance of the incident.

Incident evaluations. After all major incidents, some form of evaluation should take place. Whenever possible, this should be done in an interagency environment.

Incident Finance and Administration

As a manager, an AA is ultimately responsible for authorizing and accounting for potentially large sums of money expended in a very short

time frame when your agency is impacted by a search incident.

Who Does What?

Figure 26.1 depicts the typical roles and responsibilities for incident management.

Figure 26.1

Who Does What?

The What	The Who
Agency Policy, Direction & Support	Agency Administrator
Incident Objectives	Incident Commander
Strategies to achieve Objectives	Incident Commander
Tactical Direction	Operations & Planning Section Chiefs
Monitoring Incident Finances	Finance & Admin. Section Chief

Preplanning Key Activities

Preplanning and training will help to ensure readiness in performing key activities. For the finance and administrative portion of incident management, the following initiatives are recommended:

Finance & Admin Preplanning Activities

1. Have trained personnel on your staff.

2. Have preplanning agreements in place.

3. Develop a Supply Plan that provides telephone numbers and contacts for local vendors who can supply equipment, food, fuel and other services which might be utilized to support a search.

Administrative Responsibilities

The incident management organization should be responsible for the following kinds of finance and administrative activities:

- Recording of time for incident personnel and equipment.
- Providing daily cost data for the incident.
- Administering all vendor contracts, blanket purchase orders and rental agreements.
- Processing all claims and compensation for injury related to the incident.

Documentation. The F&A staff should provide a complete financial summary to the AA at the end of the incident.

Conclusion

As the AA, you should expect — and demand — that all incident finance and administrative activities are conducted in a consistent and legal manner, applying the principles of effective incident business management.

Glossary & SAR Acronyms

SAR GLOSSARY

Achievement-Oriented Leadership

A leadership style in which the leader sets challenging goals and attempts to motivate subordinates through his or her charismatic personality.

Active Listening

Occurs when a listener provides feedback to a speaker regarding the extent to which a message has been understood.

After Action Review

A non-critical analytical process, conducted after the conclusion of an incident, for constructively identifying the lessons learned from the incident for the purpose of improving the quality of response to future incidents.

Agency Administrator

An executive officer or designee of the agency that has the ultimate responsibility for the incident. Normally, it is the person to whom the Incident Commander reports.

Agency Representative

Representative of an agency involved in an incident who reports to the Incident Commander or Liaison Officer.

Air Scent Dog

A search dog that attempts to find a lost subject by locating the cone of airborne scent that is emitted by the person.

Archival Data

Information from past search incidents which is collected and collated for future search planning.

Attraction

A search tactic involving attempts to signal the subject and get him or her to travel toward searchers.

Bayes Theorem

A mathematical formula for systematically revising the probability of a prior hypothesis, given the nature of new evidence, or search effort.

Binary Search Method   Broadly, any technique that can limit the search area by conclusively determining where the subject has not been.

Bogus Search   A search for a subject who is not in the area, or not missing. Also referred to profanely as a "bastard" search.

Briefing   The process of providing searchers with the information they need to adequately perform their task.

Camp   A temporary location within the area of the incident (though not at the base) which is equipped and staffed to provide support to incident personnel, including sleeping, food, water, and/or sanitary services.

CASIE   Computer-Aided Search Information Exchange. A popular computer program used for various search management activities such as creating an initial consensus, shifting POA, resource allocation advice and documenting actions taken.

Clue   A message or signal that serves to reduce uncertainty with respect to the subject's location.

Clue Awareness   Ability to perceive clues left by the subject (e.g., tracks and other sign), rather than just the subject himself.

Clue Finder   A search resource that is capable of detecting clues rather than just subjects, such as human trackers and hasty teams.

Command Post   The location on the incident base where the primary command functions are performed.

Command Staff   Those officers who contribute to the command function and report directly to the Incident Commander, including the Safety Officer, Liaison Officer, Information Officer, and Technical Specialists (if appointed).

Communications Unit

The part of the Logistics Section that coordinates radio communications and assigns frequencies.

Compensation/Claims Unit

The part of the Finance/Administration Section that processes compensation-for-injury and claims.

Conditional Probability

The likelihood that some event "A" will occur, given the occurrence of another event "B." Mathematically described by $P(A|B)$ as the "probability of A, given B."

Confinement

Taking steps to ensure that the subject does not travel out of the search area. Also referred to as "containment."

Consensus Method

A method of estimating the initial POA for the segments in the search area, by averaging the POAs for two or more search planners.

Cost Unit

The part of the Finance/Administration Section that provides cost analysis data for the incident, such as estimating costs of resource use.

Coverage

The ratio of two areas: search effort (track length times width) divided by total area searched. When the total area is searched at a width of 1 ESW, the Coverage = 1.

Crew Leader

In ICS, the person who is in charge of a single search resource in the field; the team leader or section leader.

Critical Incident Stress

A stress reaction experienced by emergency responders during the incident that may have long term, debilitating psychological and physiological effects upon them.

Critical Separation

A technique in which searchers first determine the distance from which a representative clue or subject type can just barely be detected, then use twice that distance for spacing between searchers (1 CS) in an actual search. Coverage at

1 ESW can be expected to vary between 0.5 and 0.7 CS based on the expertise of the searchers and prevailing conditions.

Cumulative Probability of Detection	The computed probability of detection that results when a segment has been searched more than once.
Debriefing	The process of obtaining information from search resources returning from the field.
Delegation of Authority	Allocating some level of decision-making authority to subordinates.
Demobilization	The process of systematically closing down the incident and sending resources home safely.
Demobilization Unit	That part of the Planning Section that is responsible for developing the Demobilization Plan.
Despondent	A type of missing person who is severely depressed or suicidal.
Direct (Active) Searching	Active search techniques that depend upon the searchers seeking the subject.
Direction Sampling	A type of lost person behavior in which the subject travels short distances in different directions away from an identifiable "base."
Directive Leadership	A leadership style in which the leader tells people exactly what is expected of them and provides guidance while they are performing the task.
Documentation Unit	That part of the Planning Section that collects and maintains documentation that is generated by other units.
Eco-Region	A geographical area with relatively uniform ecological characteristics across the designated region.

Effective Sweep Width (ESW)   An experimentally derived distance where, for a particular set of randomly placed objects of the same size and type along either side of a uniform sensor track, the number of detections equals the number of non-detections.

Efficient Tactic   A relatively fast but systematic search of high probability areas using techniques that result in sufficient POD values, but which are lower than PODs derived from slower yet more thorough tactics.

Emergency Locator Transmitter (ELT)   A small radio transmitter, required equipment on virtually all large and small passenger aircraft, which activates in the event of a crash. ELT's transmit at one of three frequencies: 121.5 MHz, 243 MHz and 406 MHz. ELT's operating at a 406 MHz signal can be coded with the owner's or aircraft's identification and can be configured to transmit the aircraft's last known position. Starting in the year 2009, only the 406 MHz ELT will have satellite-based monitoring of its signal.

Facilities Unit   The part of the Logistics Section that establishes, maintains, and demobilizes all facilities used in support of the incident.

Finance Section Chief   Head of the Finance/Administration Section; responsible for managing financial services, such as budgetary considerations and claims.

Food Unit   The part of the Logistics Section that determines food and water requirements, plans menus, and orders, prepares, and serves food to incident personnel.

General Staff   In ICS, the Incident Commander and the Section Chiefs (Planning, Operations, Logistics, and Finance/Administration).

Global Positioning System	A system of navigation satellites that permit — with the appropriate GPS receiver — the determination of one's position, within a few meters, on the face of the globe.
Grid Search	An attempt to find the subject (or clues) by lining up three or more searchers and having them proceed in a parallel fashion through their assigned search area. Also referred to as a "sweep," "line," or "creeping line" search.
Ground Support Unit	The part of the Logistics Section that maintains and repairs tactical vehicles and equipment, and provides transportation services.
Hasty Search	An initial response aimed at quickly searching high probability areas, trails, and likely spots by highly trained SAR resources. May also be referred to as "Reflex Tasking."
Helibase	The main location with the incident area for parking, loading, fueling, and maintaining helicopters.
Helispot	A temporary location in the incident area where helicopters can safely land and take off.
Human Trackers	Searchers who attempt to follow the visible signs left by the lost person; sometimes called "man-trackers" or "visual trackers."
Incident Action Plan (IAP)	In ICS, the plan for finding the lost person, including the incident objectives and other planning documents.
Incident Base	The area where all primary incident services and support activities are located.
Incident Commander	The person who is in charge of all on-scene incident activities.
Incident Command System	A widely applied management system for handling any type of emergency incident or public event.

Incident Objectives	Part of the Incident Action Plan, a document outlining search objectives for the current operational period.
Indirect (Passive) Searching	Passive search techniques like trail blocks and track traps that depend upon the subject coming to the searchers.
Information	Any message or signal that may reduce uncertainty when analyzed and turned into knowledge.
Information Officer	The officer in the Command Staff who serves as the initial contact person for the media and other persons seeking information about the incident.
Integrated Communications	All incident communications are coordinated in such a fashion that the Incident Commander has constant access to relayed information, and can speak to any person involved in the incident.
Inter-Quartile Range	The range of the middle 50% of points in a dataset between the 25th and 75th percentiles, unaffected by outliers or other extreme values.
Liaison Officer	The officer in the Command Staff who serves as the initial contact person for external agencies providing assistance.
Likely Spot	Features or areas that may offer some attraction to the lost person.
Limited, Continuing Search	An alternative to merely terminating a search, it involves maintaining some form of limited search activity following demobilization, such as conducting training sessions in the area.
Logistics Section	In ICS, the Section that is responsible for supporting the incident, such as providing transportation, communication, services, and supplies.

Logistics Section Chief	Head of the Logistics Section; responsible for providing all support needs to the incident.
Long Range Patrol	A crew of searchers that functions remotely and independently of the search base.
Lost Person	A known individual in an unknown location, whose safety may be threatened by conditions related to the environment or other factors.
Lost Person Incident	An organized search for a person who has been reported missing to a jurisdictional authority.
Management	The organization of individual efforts toward a common goal.
Management by Objectives	Management guided by written objectives which are time-referenced, attainable, measurable, and accountable.
Median Distance Traveled	The middle distance that subjects of a specific type have traveled from the IPP to the point where they were found; half of all distances traveled lie at or above the median and half lie at or below the median
Medical Plan	The plan for treating and evacuating injured searchers.
Medical Unit	The part of the Logistics Section that treats injuries to incident personnel.
Micro-Management	Inappropriately performing activities that are the responsibility of subordinates in the organization.
Modular Organization	Sections within the ICS structure are designed to grow in a systematic and orderly fashion as the incident becomes larger.
National Incident Management System	NIMS: A system that provides a consistent nationwide approach for Federal, State, local, and tribal governments; the private-sector; and nongovernmental organizations to work effectively and efficiently together to prepare for, respond to,

and recover from domestic incidents, regardless of cause, size, or complexity.

National Track Analysis Program	NTAP: Commonly pronounced "N-Tap." A radar-based data processing program, originally designed to assist in Search and Rescue missions, aimed at locating missing or suspected downed aircraft. NTAP information can be obtained from the AFRCC, if available, using data from the last Air Route Traffic Control Center (ARTCC) which recorded the final track of the missing aircraft on radar.
Northumberland Rain Dance	Nickname for the procedure to determine Critical Separation based on the locale in the UK where it originated.
Operational Period	The period of time for which there is a separate overhead team and Incident Action Plan; normally 12 hours.
Operations Section Chief	Head of the Operations Section; responsible for deploying tactical resources and implementing strategic objectives; aka "Ops Chief."
Organizational Chart	The component of the Incident Action Plan that graphically depicts the management structure for a particular operational period.
Overall Probability Of Success (OPOS)	The sum of all of the calculated POS values (from POA x POD) prior to any expansion of the initial search area.
Packet Radio Data	Electronically compressed data transmitted in short bursts of packages or "sentences."
Participative Leadership	A leadership style in which the leader consults with subordinates and carefully considers their input before making decisions.
Planning Data	That information that the Planning Sections requires in order to plan a strategy for finding the lost person, including maps,

weather forecasts, the subject's trip plans, circumstances of loss, and relevant lost person behavior data.

Planning Section Chief   Head of the Planning Section; responsible for gathering information relevant to the incident, tracking the status of search resources, tracking search progress, and formulating strategies for finding the lost person; aka "Plans Chief."

Preplan   A document which provides incident managers with information, instructions, resource lists, checklists, standard operating procedures, and technical data that will be used during a search incident.

Proactive   Taking steps to prevent or ameliorate a problem before it has a chance to occur.

Probability Density   The POA of a specific area or segment, divided by the size of the area. High pDen segments will normally receive higher priority.

Probability Of Area (POA)   The likelihood or probability that the subject is located in a specific area; expressed as a percentage (50%) or decimal number (0.50).

Probability Of Detection (POD)   The likelihood or probability of finding clues (assuming that clues are available to be found), given the nature of the search and the type of resource employed; expressed as a percentage (50%) or a decimal number (0.50).

Probability Of Success (POS)   The probability of finding the subject in a specific place or area, given the type of search tactic employed. Derived from the formula POS = (POA x POD).

Probability Theory   A branch of mathematics used for estimating the likelihood of uncertain random events.

Probability Zone   Based on recorded distances traveled by categories of lost persons, probability zones are statistically derived ranges where some percentage of lost subjects have been found in the past or can be expected to be found in the future.

Procurement Unit

The part of the Finance/Administration Section that administers all financial matters pertaining to vendor contracts with respect to rentals and supplies.

Region

In relation to a search area, a Region is generally a large sub-section of a search area supposed to have roughly uniform probability (POA) of containing the subject. Regions are typically too large to be searched by a single team and can be divided into manageable segments for purposes of searching.

Resource List

A list of search or logistical resources that can be employed during an incident; part of the preplan.

Resources Unit

That part of the Planning Section that tracks the status of search resources.

Rough Terrain Responders

SAR personnel with skills and equipment to work in mountains and other rugged terrain; also referred to as "steep terrain" or "high angle" responders.

Safety Officer

The officer in the Command Staff who assesses hazards and develops measures for assuring safety during the incident.

Scenario Analysis

An attempt to prioritize the segments in the search area when more than one scenario explaining why the subject is lost may be present, or when there is conflicting information about the lost person's PLS or direction of travel.

Scent Article

An article of clothing or other material with which a trailing dog can determine the subject's unique scent.

Scent Discriminating

Regarding trailing dogs, ability to discriminate the unique scent of a particular person from all other scents.

Searching Data

That information that searchers require in order to search for the lost subject, such as the subject's name, description, clothing, footwear, and items carried.

Search Strategy

A plan or objective for finding the subject.

Search Tactics

Methods of searching; implementation of a strategy.

Sector Ladder

A method for creating an initial consensus, shifting POA or revising search priorities without performing Bayesian mathematical calculations.

Segmenting the Area

Parceling the search area up into manageable sections or segments with clearly defined boundaries

Shifting Probability of Area (Shifting POA)

Updating or recalculating the POA for segments, following the search of one or more segments; changing the Probabilities Of Area after segments have been searched, usually by applying the Bayesian formula.

Sign-Cutting

A search strategy that involves sending human trackers to look for disturbances or "sign" (like footprints, broken branches, etc.) to find evidence of the subject's passage. Sign-cutters may often be deployed in a direction that is perpendicular to the subject's assumed direction of travel, in an effort to cross and intercept evidence of the subject's track.

Situation Unit

That part of the Planning Section that tracks the status of the search incident, including whatever progress has been made to find the lost subject.

Situational Leadership

Knowing what type of leadership is required for a given situation, and being able to respond accordingly.

Span of Control

Refers to the number of people that a manager can effectively supervise; in SAR, the upper limit is estimated to be about seven, and the optimal span is considered to be 5 to 1.

Spontaneous Volunteer

A person not belonging to a participating agency or SAR team who appears at an incident and volunteers assistance.

Staging Area

A temporary location during an incident where personnel and equipment are kept while awaiting tactical assignments on short notice.

Statistical Search Areas

Areas based on a parameter from historical distance traveled data, compiled from searches for similar subject types. Using the 75th percentile, the median (50th percentile) or other percentile or statistically derived distance traveled, as the radius for determining the circular search area, would be examples of calculating one of many possible statistical search areas.

Stress Defusing

A short meeting (30 to 60 minutes) held shortly after an incident, conducted by qualified peer counselors, directed at those people who are assumed to be experiencing stress from the incident.

Strike Team

A number of resources of the same type, functioning together under a single leader.

String Line

String that is automatically dispensed from a container as the searcher moves in a straight line; used to place a clearly defined segment edge or boundary, with the option of attaching signs addressed to the lost person (sometimes called a "hip chain").

Subject Finder

A search resource that is limited largely to searching for subjects rather than clues, such as fixed-wing aircraft or untrained searchers.

Subjective Search Area   The area that is defined after a consideration of limiting factors, such as natural boundaries, and other geographical features, such as travel aids or likely spots.

Supply Unit   The part of the Logistics Section that orders, receives, stores, and processes all incident-related supplies.

Supportive Leadership   A leadership style in which the leader treats subordinates as equals in a friendly manner, with most communications aimed at maintaining morale and group cohesiveness, rather than being task-oriented.

Task Force   In ICS, a combination of single resources of various types (e.g., hasty teams, dog teams, human trackers) which can be assembled for a specific task.

Terrain Analysis   An attempt by a search planner to determine how the terrain may have affected the lost person's behavior, such as mazes, confusion factors, boundaries, and travel aids.

Theoretical Search Area   The area that is defined by the distance that a subject or subjects could theoretically have traveled in the time elapsed since they became missing.

Thorough Tactic   A slow, systematic search, using highly thorough techniques such as grid searching, which typically yields a high POD.

Time Unit   The part of the Finance/Administration Section that ensures that time recording documents are prepared in accord with agency requirement.

Track Trap   An area where tracks would be easily made and clearly visible to searchers, such as a river bank or a sandy area. Alternatively, a track trap can be man-made by raking or brushing smooth an area which is rechecked periodically for new tracks.

Trail Running

A type of lost person behavior in which the subject hurries down a trail or other travel aid in an effort to find some familiar location. The longer they run the trail, the more reluctant they become to reverse direction.

Trailing Dog

A search dog that attempts to follow the exact route the lost subject traveled, by finding the subject's unique scent contained in skin particles or bacterial by-products that have been discarded by the subject.

Travel Aids

Natural or artificial pathways that facilitate travel by the lost person, such as roads, trails, switchbacks, power lines, railroad tracks, or drainages.

Unified Command

In ICS, agencies involved in a multi-jurisdictional incident participate in the command and control of the incident.

Unity of Command

A management principle that states that no individual in the organization should have more than one director, supervisor or boss.

View Enhancement

A type of lost person behavior in which the subject tries to improve his or her view by climbing a tree or hill.

Vulnerability Assessment

Based on previous searches, in what areas are people most likely to become lost, what kinds of problems have been encountered, and what kinds of tactics and strategies have been effective.

Walkaway

A type of missing person with some mental or cognitive deficiency, who has wandered away from a care facility.

SAR ACRONYMS

AFRCC	Air Force Rescue Coordination Center
AMDR	Average Maximum Detection Range
ARTCC	Air Route Traffic Control Center
ASPCA	American Society for the Prevention of Cruelty to Animals
CAP	Civil Air Patrol (U. S.)
CASARA	Canadian Air Search and Rescue Association
CASIE	Computer-Aided Search Information Exchange
CIS	Critical Incident Stress
CISD	Critical Incident Stress Debriefing
CP	Command Post
CS	Critical Separation
EDF	Exponential Detection Function
ELT	Emergency Locator Transmitter
EMS	Emergency Medical Service
EMT	Emergency Medical Technician
ESAR	Explorer Search and Rescue
ESW	Effective Sweep Width
FAA	Federal Aviation Administration
FEMA	Federal Emergency Management Agency (U. S.)
GIS	Geographical Information System
GPS	Global Positioning System
IAP	Incident Action Plan
IC	Incident Commander
ICS	Incident Command System
IPP	Initial Planning Point
LKP	Last Known Position
LRP	Long Range Patrol
MBO	Management by Objectives
MBWA	Management By Walking Around
MOA	Memorandum of Agreement
MOU	Memorandum of Understanding
MRA	Mountain Rescue Association
NASAR	National Association for Search and Rescue
NCMEC	National Center for Missing and Exploited Children

NIMS	National Incident Management System
NSS	National SAR Secretariat (Canada)
NTAP	National Track Analysis Program
pDen	Probability Density
PLB	Personal Locator Beacon
PLS	Place Last Seen
POA	Probability of Area
POC	Probability of Containment (term in maritime searches for POA)
POD	Probability of Detection
POD$_{cum}$	Cumulative Probability of Detection
POS	Probability of Success
PSAR	Preventive Search and Rescue
ROW	Rest of the World (outside of the search area)
SA	Selective Availability (of GPS signals)
SAR	Search And Rescue
SOP	Standard Operating Procedure

Photo Credits

Richard J. Toman, unless otherwise noted.

p.12, Dennis Holman

p.42, Rensselaer County Search & Rescue, NY

p.54, Civil Air Patrol

p.209, Massachusetts State Police

p. 229, Chad Council, FEMA TF-1

p.246, Massachusetts State Police

p.278, John Tranghese

p.303 & p.307, courtesy of Garmin Corp.

In Memoriam:

Cover, center position,

Trooper Dennis Eugin, MSP

Index

50th Percentile 167, 172

75% Plus................................ 161, 162, 163, 164

75th Percentile 159, 160, 161, 164, 167, 172

Abduction 128, 129

Active Listening.................................... 123, 124

After Action Review............................ 308, 309

Agency Administrator 15, 26, 255, 312, 313

Agency Representative 41, 266

Air operations.. 98

Air scent dogs.. 55

Aircraft. 50, 53, 70, 76, 150, 203, 205, 206, 228

Allocating Resources 188, 189

AMDR 216, 219, 222

Analytical evidence 109

Andy Warburton 4, 7, 12, 24

Attraction 141, 150, 191, 198, 199, 208

Average Maximum Detection Range 216

Behavior While Lost.................................... 136

Binary search.....................................72, 191

Bogus Search 146

Briefing.....................35, 49, 99, 103, 219, 249

Camera Phones.. 303

Camps 30, 266, 269

CASIE................. 177, 179, 180, 181, 232, 302

Categories of Lost Persons.................. 138, 166

Circumstances of Loss 81, 114

CIS................... 273, 274, 275, 276, 277, 278

Clue Finders...70, 203

Clue Information 111

Clue Management 67

Clue Orientation.. 67

Clues 5, 8, 10, 28, 36, 58, 59, 61, 66, 67, 68, 69,
    70, 71, 73, 74, 77, 79, 80, 81, 82, 85, 90, 91,
    92, 96, 103, 105, 107, 108, 112, 113, 114,
    115, 116, 131, 134, 136, 138, 139, 141, 144,
    147, 149, 152, 153, 158, 161, 167, 168, 169,
    170, 173, 176, 181, 188, 191, 195, 196, 197,
    200, 202, 203, 204, 205, 206, 208, 209, 219,
    229, 235, 236, 250, 256, 258, 259, 262, 272,
    274, 293, 300, 303, 304, 309

Clues, Recording...71

Clue-Seeking 73

Command..... 13, 16, 17, 22, 23, 24, 25, 26, 28,
    30, 32, 33, 34, 39, 41, 55, 63, 69, 192, 193,
    195, 266, 267, 272, 275, 276, 313, 314

Communicating.. 281

Computers 62, 299, 302, 305

Confinement....47, 85, 134, 140, 144, 146, 150,
    191, 194, 198, 201, 202, 208

Consensus...... 47, 178, 179, 180, 181, 183, 257

Consensus POA... 179

Coverage 178, 206, 210, 212, 213, 214, 215,
    216, 217, 218, 219, 221, 222, 224, 225, 226,
    228, 229, 231, 280, 302, 303

Critical Incident Stress 50, 273

Critical Separation 215, 216, 217, 222, 228

CS 216, 219, 222

Damaging Information 288

Data management...................................... 300

Debriefing.. 103

Delegation.. 15, 16

Demobilization 36, 50, 250, 260, 261

Detectability 80, 113

Detection Resources 70

Direct Tactics................................198, 208

Direction sampling...................................... 138

Distance traveled 80, 167

Documentary evidence 108, 109

Documentation.36, 39, 50, 247, 248, 252, 262,
    315

Effective Sweep Width 212, 213, 215, 216,
    228

Efficiency... 221

ESW......212, 213, 215, 216, 217, 222, 228, 231

Evidence 58, 107

Exponential Detection Function....... 210, 214,
    217, 225, 228

Facilities 26, 30, 38, 266, 269

Family members, interviewing 116

Finance/Administration 27, 30, 32, 38

Fixed-wing aircraft 54

Geographical Information System 301, 306

Global Positioning System 197, 299, 303

Grid Search Planning.................................. 222

Grid searchers 59

Grief 293

Gut Feelings 169

Hasty 5, 37, 39, 59, 63, 64

Hasty search 5, 37, 39, 59, 63, 64, 75, 90,
    142, 163

Hasty Searching 204

Hasty teams 62

Helibases 30, 266, 269

Helicopters 53, 54, 191, 227

Helispots 30, 266, 270

Historical Data 169

Homicide 128

ICS Forms 99, 249

ICS Organizational Chart 39

ICS Training 41

Incident Base 30, 266, 268, 269, 272

Incident Facilities 265

Incident Objectives.33, 35, 47, 95, 97, 99, 103, 194, 249

Indirect Tactics 198, 208

Information Gathering 105

Information Management 94

Initial Consensus 179, 181, 182, 183

Initial Contact 75

Initial Information 77

Initial Planning Data 79

Initial Planning Point 80, 113, 152, 153, 193

Initial Response 191, 195

Initiating a Search 76

Interrogation 110

Interview 110, 111, 197, 284, 287, 290

Interview Traps 287

Interviewing 107, 110, 119, 120, 126

Interviewing Pitfalls 126

Investigation 33, 90, 91, 105, 106, 107, 110, 148, 194, 204

IPP.47, 113, 150, 152, 153, 154, 155, 158, 159, 160, 161, 162, 164, 165, 172, 174

K9 POD 224, 226

Last Known Position 39, 80, 90, 113, 152, 153, 157, 193

Leadership 18

Likely Spots 168

Limited, Continuing Search 258

Limiting the Search Area 72

LKP 39, 56, 57, 58, 71, 80, 85, 90, 97, 100, 113, 152, 153, 157, 184, 193, 194, 201, 204, 205, 251

Logistics ... 20, 27, 28, 30, 32, 36, 37, 42, 46, 62, 99, 101, 195, 265, 268, 269, 270, 272, 300, 301

Long Range Patrol Camp 271

Look-outs 202

Lost person 2, 3, 4, 5, 7, 12, 14, 15, 16, 17, 19, 22, 23, 24, 25, 28, 29, 34, 35, 39, 41, 46, 48, 49, 52, 53, 55, 56, 61, 63, 64, 66, 67, 70, 75, 76, 77, 79, 83, 85, 87, 88, 90, 92, 95, 100, 103, 105, 107, 108, 128, 130, 131, 132, 133, 134, 135, 136, 137, 138, 142, 143, 146, 148, 149, 151, 152, 157, 160, 163, 164, 165, 168, 170, 174, 175, 179, 186, 188, 193, 194, 198, 200, 201, 208, 209, 230, 231, 261, 265, 273, 274, 275, 278, 280, 299, 300, 303, 309, 310, 311

Lost person incident, ICS type 32

Lost Person Behavior ... 47, 132, 133, 135, 147, 150, 310

LRRP 271, 272

Management by objectives ... 13, 14, 19, 22, 24, 25, 26, 30, 41, 48, 49, 50, 53, 61, 62

Management concepts 13, 14, 19, 22, 24, 25, 26, 30, 41, 48, 49, 50, 53, 61, 62

Managers 19, 20, 21, 22, 101, 225, 226, 269, 270

Managing an emergency 13

Mattson Consensus 178, 179, 180, 181, 182, 183

Mean 161, 162, 163, 170

Media ... 279, 280, 282, 283, 289, 292, 294, 295, 310

Median .. 156, 159, 160, 163, 164, 166, 167, 170

Micro-management 16

Modular ICS 27, 34, 40

Multiple-Subject Searches 146

Natural Barriers 168

NCMEC 129, 130, 148

News Conferences 288

News release 288

Note-Taking 118

Operations 27, 29, 30, 32, 36, 37, 39, 48, 62, 63, 69, 96, 97, 99, 101, 102, 103, 104, 188, 190, 191, 202, 208, 212, 219, 222, 250, 267, 268, 269, 270

Operations Research 212

OPOS 47, 92, 93

Organizing Resources 189

Overall Probability of Success 92, 93

Parapsychological Influnces 295, 296

Peter Principle 21

Physical Clues 169

Physical evidence 108

Place Last Seen 39, 80, 90, 113, 153
Planning...20, 27, 30, 31, 32, 33, 34, 35, 36, 38,
 39, 43, 45, 47, 48, 62, 63, 69, 85, 88, 90, 95,
 96, 98, 99, 100, 101, 102, 103, 104, 107,
 109, 114, 119, 130, 132, 133, 167, 180, 183,
 184, 185, 196, 211, 218, 219, 221, 222, 250,
 251, 252, 262, 266, 267, 277, 300, 301, 313
Planning Clock 101
Planning Data 85, 90
PLS.... 39, 46, 56, 57, 58, 66, 80, 83, 85, 87, 88,
 90, 97, 100, 103, 113, 114, 133, 134, 140,
 145, 148, 149, 152, 153, 193, 194, 201, 202,
 251, 257
POA.... 91, 92, 93, 94, 100, 164, 175, 177, 178,
 179, 180, 183, 184, 185, 186, 189, 211, 230,
 231, 232, 233, 234, 236, 237, 299, 300, 302
POD........ 57, 91, 92, 93, 94, 97, 100, 178, 183,
 189, 199, 206, 210, 211, 212, 213, 214, 215,
 216, 217, 218, 219, 220, 221, 222, 224, 226,
 227, 228, 229, 231, 232, 233, 234, 236, 237,
 254, 262, 299, 302, 303
Political entities, managing.......................... 294
Political influence.......................... 33, 294, 297
Poor media relations............................... 5
POS.............................. 45, 91, 92, 93, 94, 211
Post-Incident Tasks 310
Preplan.....43, 44, 45, 47, 48, 51, 163, 196, 248,
 271, 309
Preplanning...............44, 51, 119, 204, 314, 315
Press 50, 288
Preventative SAR 148
Preventing CIS 276
Probability Density 100, 164
Probability of Area........... 92, 93, 183, 196, 230
Probability of Detection . 92, 93, 210, 228, 233
Probability of Success............................92, 211
Probability Theory 91
Psychics.................5, 10, 279, 295, 296, 297
Purposeful Wandering...............................217
Quantification.................................... 94
Radio 8, 28, 49, 50, 62, 103, 197, 250, 280,
 289, 290
Reasoning...170
Recording Clues 71
Reporter Calls 291
Resource lists 45, 50
Resource Priority.. 191
Resource Status 31, 103, 250, 252

Safety Guidelines 270
SAR Resources.....................................53, 206
Scaling Down 258
Scenario Analysis 180, 183-4
Scent Articles.......................................85
Scientific POD 212
Search Area... 47, 152, 154, 160, 167, 175, 182,
 200, 201
Search Area Problems.................................. 167
Search coverage.....................91, 109, 183, 254
Search coverage, not recorded...................... 4
Search Initiation Guide............................... 191
Search Tactics... 188
Search Urgency 77, 189
Searching Data 79, 90
Sector Ladder 181, 182, 183, 235, 236, 237
Segment Boundaries.................................... 175
Segmenting 175, 177
Sensitive Information................................... 289
Shifting POA.......................232, 234, 235, 302
Shifting the POA, what happens................. 231
Sign Cutting..73, 205
Single resource 31
Situation unit 252
Situational leadership 18
Size of Segments.. 176
SMART Objectives 95
Sound Sweep 199
Staged Incident 128
Staging Area, characteristics....................... 267
Staging Areas...........................30, 266, 267, 268
Standard Deviation.................................161, 162
Statistical data....... 140, 141, 142, 143, 144, 145
Statistical Search Areas 157
Stress...273, 275
Strike Team 31
String Lines.. 202
Subject Condition 89
Subject Finders..............................70, 203
Survivability 80, 113
Survivors 255
Suspending................................ 254, 255, 259
Tactical Decision-making Aids.................... 301
Task Force 31
Television...280, 289
Terminology..................................26
Terrain Analysis 71
Terrain Features... 168

Testimonial Evidence.......................................109
Theoretical Search Area 154, 155, 167
Thoroughness...221
Track Identification 71
Track Traps..202
Trackers.. 70, 194, 206
Trailing dogs 56
Travel aids 80, 137

Unified Command............... 22, 28-29, 266, 314
Unity Of Command 17, 22
Unprofessional Reporter 291
Verbal Cues 180, 181
View enhancement....................................... 138
Warburton 4, 7, 12, 24
Work/Rest Guidelines....................................261

Bibliography and Suggested Readings

Anderson, P. (1989). "Why Customize ICS?" *Response, 7 (6),* 21.

Anderson, P. (1995). "Saving Lives Via Satellite." *RESCUE, 8 (6),* 84 - 85.

Bassett, C. (1993). "The Use of Infrared Technology to Assist Search and Rescue Operations." *Proceedings of the Annual Conference of the National Association for Search and Rescue,* 91 - 105.

Blake, B., Baynes, R., Dougher, H., & Bownds, J. (1983). *Applying Shifting Probabilities of Area (POA) in Open System Searching: A New Concept in Search Management.* Unpublished manuscript. [Reprinted in *Managing the Search Function* (1987). Fairfax, VA: National Association for Search and Rescue.]

Blakely, R. D. (1992). "Briefing Families in a Search and Rescue Operation." *Emergency Preparedness Digest, 19 (4),* 15 - 18.

Bower, D. C., & Hill, K. A. (1992). "GPS Navigation in Land Search." *Response, 11 (2),* 18 - 23.

Bownds, J., Ebersole, M., Lovelock, D., & O'Connor, D. (1991). "Reexamining the Search Management Function" (I). *Response, 10 (1),* 12 - 15 ff.

Bownds, J., Ebersole, M., Lovelock, D., & O'Connor, D. (1991). "Reexamining the Search Management Function" (II). *Response, 10 (2),* 16 - 19.

Bownds, J., Ebersole, M., Lovelock, D., & O'Connor, D. (1991). "Reexamining the Search Management Function" (III). *Response, 10 (3),* 12 - 15

Bownds, J., Ebersole, M., Lovelock, D., & O'Connor, D. (1991). "Reexamining the Search Management Function" (IV). *Response, 11 (3),* 10 - 14.

Bownds, J., Harlan, A., Lovelock, D., & McHugh, C. (1989). "Mountain Searches: Effectiveness of Helicopters." *Proceedings of the 18th Annual Conference of the National Association for Search and Rescue.* Fairfax, VA: NASAR.

Bownds, J., Lovelock, D., McHugh, C., & Wright, L. (1981). *Desert Searches: Effectiveness of Helicopters.* Pima County Sheriff's Department, Tucson, AZ.

Collins, S. (1993). "The Role of Peer Support Groups and Peer Counselors." *Response, 12 (2),* 10 - 12.

Colwell, M. (1993). "New Concepts for Grid Searching." *Response, 12 (2),* 18 - 27.

Cornell, E. H., & Heth, C. D. (1996). "Distance Traveled During Urban and Suburban Walks Led by 3- to 12-Year-Olds." *Response, 15 (1),* 6 - 9.

Cowan, R. (1990). "The UTM Map Coordinate System." *Response, 9 (4),* 22 - 26.

Downs, M. A., & Dolan, M. A. (1995). "SARDAT: A Search Database." *Response, 14 (1)*, 22 - 27.

Dougher, H. (1988). "A Good Tool Made Better." *Response, 7 (8)*, 14 - 19.

Dougher, H. (1992). "Integrating External Influences." *Response, 11 (3)*, 26 - 27.

Farabee, C. R. Jr. (1981). *Contemporary Psychic Use by Police in America.* Unpublished master's thesis, California State University, Fresno.

Frost J. R. (1999). "Principles of Search Theory." Souza & Company, Ltd.

Goodman, R. (1989). "The Real Truth About POA/POD." In *Probability of Detection (POD) Research, and Other Concepts for Search Management.* Olympia, WA: Emergency Response Institute.

Goodman, R. (undated). "Using Formal Search Theory In A Land Search Environment." Downloaded June 2006 from the International SAR Alliance on-line library at www.isaralliance.com.

Gordon, T. J., & Tobias, J. T. (1979, May). "Managing the Psychic in Criminal Investigations." *The Police Chief*, 58 - 59.

Graham, H. (1994). "Probability of Detection for Search Dogs, or How Long is Your Shadow?" *Response, 13 (1)*, 9 - 12.

Graham, T. (1995). "Casualties" [SAR poetry]. *Coal City Review #9.*

Groebner, D., Shannon P., et al. (2005). Business Statistics: *A Decision-Making Approach* (6th Edition). Upper Saddle River, NJ. Pearson Education , Inc.

Henning, K. (1997). "Managing Your Volunteers." *RESCUE, 10 (1)*, 60 ff.

Hill, K. A. (1991). "Predicting the Behavior of Lost Persons." *Proceedings of the Annual Conference of the National Association for Search and Rescue, Winston-Salem, NC.*

Hill, K. A. (1992). "Analyzing Lost Person Scenarios." *Response, 11 (1)*, 23 - 27.

Hill, K. A. (1992). "Spatial Competence of Elderly Hunters." *Environment and Behavior, 24 (6)*, 779 - 794.

Hill, K. A. (1993). "Preventing Stress in Wilderness SAR." *Response, 12 (3)*, 6 - 9.

Hill, K. A. (1995). "How Many Clues Do You Need? Applying Information Theory to Land Search." *Response, 14 (3)*, 6 - 8.

Hill, K. A. (1996). "Telecommunications in SAR," *RESCUE, 9,* 57.

Hill, K. A. (1996). *Distances Traveled and Probability Zones for Lost Persons in Nova Scotia.* Unpublished data.

Jones, A. S. G. (1989). "Leadership in Search and Rescue." In *Probability of Detection (POD) Research, and Other Concepts for Search Management.* Olympia, WA: Emergency Response Institute.

Kearney, J. (1978). *TRACKING: A Blueprint for Learning How* (6th Printing 1996). El Cajon, CA. Pathways Press.

Kelley, D. (1973). *Mountain Search for the Lost Victim.* Lompoc, CA: Search and Rescue Magazine.

Kelley, D. (1976, August). "The $250,000 Message, or How to Use Information Theory to Find Lost Persons." *Search and Rescue Magazine.* [Reprinted in Winter, 1990]

Koenig, M. (1987). "Wilderness Search Strategy for Dog Handlers." *Response, 6 (2),* 28 - 35.

Koester, R. J., & Stooksbury, D. E. (1992). "Lost Alzheimer's Subjects — Profiles and Statistics." *Response, 11 (4),* 20 - 26.

Kreitner, R. (1989). *Management* (4th Ed.). Boston: Houghton Mifflin.

LaValla, P., Stoffel, R., & Jones, A. S. G. (1995). *Search is an Emergency (4th Ed.).* Olympia, WA: Emergency Response Institute.

Lawson, N. (1986). "Some Suggestions for Keeping Out of Trouble." *Response, 5 (5),* 28 -29.

Marshall, E. (1980). "Police Science and Psychics." *Science, 210,* 994- 995.

Marshall, L. (1994). "Communications 2000: Taking the Search out of Search and Rescue." *RESCUE, 7 (5),* 44 - 48.

Millen, T. C., Gilmore, M. C., & Seitz, M. A. (1995). "Long Range Patrol Land Search Tactics," *Proceedings of the Annual Conference of the National Association for Search and Rescue,* 163 - 179.

Mitchell, B. L. (1983). *NASAR Data Collection Committee Report.* Fairfax, VA: NASAR.

Mitchell, J. T. (1986). "Critical Incident Stress Management." *Response, 5 (6),* 24 - 25.

Mitchell, J. T. (1988). "Managing Stress in Emergency Operations." *Response, 7 (5),* 26 - 28.

Mitchell, J. T., & Bray, G. (1990). *Emergency Services Stress.* Englewood Cliffs, NJ: Prentice-Hall.

Mitchell, J. T., & Everly, G. S. Jr. (1993). *Critical Incident Stress Debriefing: (CISD).* Ellicott City, MD: Chevron.

Moore, J. (1996). "Cultural Clues: Information for Public Safety Interviewers." *Response, 15 (1),* 12 - 20.

Oklahoma State University. (1983). *Incident Command System.* Stillwater, OK: Fire Protection Publications.

Perkins, D. (1989). "Critical Separation." In *Probability of Detection (POD) Research, and Other Concepts for Search Management.* Olympia, WA: Emergency Response Institute.

Perkins, D., & Roberts, P. (1994). *The Sector Ladder.* Northumberland National Park, UK: Authors.

Perkins, D., & Roberts, P. (1995). "Who is in Charge of Your Search Plan?" *Response, 14 (3),* 18 - 22.

Perkins, D., & Roberts, P. (2005). *A New Look At The Sector Ladder.* Northumberland National Park, UK: Authors.

Pierce, B. (1986). "'All Risk' Emergency Management." *Response, 5 (5),* 18 -20.

Ray, S. (1994). "Public Pressure — Can Your Incident Management Team Take It?" *Response, 13 (2),* 6 - 7.

Reiser, M., Ludwig, L., Saxe, S., & Wagner, C. (1979). "An Evaluation of the Use of Psychics in the Investigation of Major Crimes." *Journal of Police Science and Administration, 7 (1),* 18 - 25.

Setnicka, T. J. (1980). *Wilderness Search and Rescue.* Boston: Appalachian Mountain Club.

Shea, G. (1988). "Formula for the Field." *Response, 7 (3),* 21 - 24.

Shiers, K., & Kimber, S. (1987, April). "The Search for Andy Warburton." *Cities,* 14 - 22.

Stoffel, R. C., & LaValla, P. H. (1988). *Personnel Safety in Helicopter Operations: Helirescue Manual.* Olympia, WA: Emergency Response Institute.

Stone, L. D. (1989). *Theory of Optimal Search.* Arlington, VA. Military Applications Section, Operations Research Society of America.

Syrotuck, W. G. (1974). *Some Grid Search Techniques for Locating Lost Individuals in Wilderness Areas.* Westmoreland, NY: Arner Publications.

Syrotuck, W. G. (1975) *An Introduction to Land Search Probabilities and Calculations."* Westmoreland, NY: Arner Publications.

Taylor, A. & Cooper, D. C (1992). *Fundamentals of Mantracking: The Step-by-Step Method* (2nd Ed.). Olympia, WA: Emergency Response Institute.

Twardy, Charles (2006) Personal conversation with Daniel O'Connor during "Detection In the Berkshires" SAR workshop and sweep width experiment June 2006.

Turner J. C. (1996). "Uniform Random Search." SM230 – Spring 1996. U.S. Naval Academy.

Syrotuck, W. G. (1977). *Analysis of Lost Person Behavior: An Aid to Search Planning.* Westmoreland, NY: Arner Publications

Vines, T. (1988). "And Now, for a Roundup of Outstanding Bastard Searches." *Response, 7 (5)*, 8.

Vines, T. (1989). "Sifting for Clues: Paths Cross in the Desert." *RESCUE, 2 (3)*, 28 - 35.

Vines, T. (1990). "Tough Englishman Survives Extended Yosemite Incident." *Response, 9 (2)*, 12 - 13.

Wartes, J. (1974). *An Experimental Analysis of Grid Sweep Searching.* Sunnyvale, CA: Explorer Search and Rescue.

Wartes, J. (1980). "New Concepts in Sweep Searching: The Evidence Favoring Non-Thorough Methods." *Proceedings of the Annual Meeting of the National Association for Search and Rescue, Seattle.*

Wartes, J. (1983). *Probability Density as an Aid to Search Planning.* Unpublished manuscript.

Washburn, A. R. (2002). *Search And Detection* (4th Ed.) Linthicum, MD. Institute for Operations Research and the Management Sciences.

West, P. D. (1992). "Developing a Search and Rescue Information System." *Response, 11 (4)*, 10 - 13.

Young, C. & Wehbring J. (2007). *Urban Search – Managing Missing Person Searches in the Urban Environment.* Charlottesville, VA: dbS Productions. Pre-publication excerpt on investigation and interviewing.

Appendix A: Map of the Andy Warburton Search Area

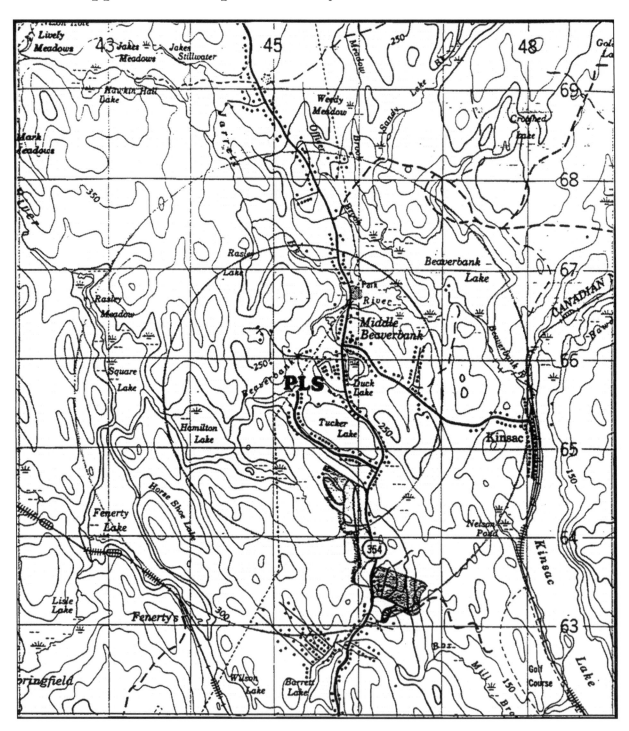

Map of the area for the Andy Warburton search (Chapter 2), with the area between the two circles representing the middle 50% zone from 1.6 km to 2.73 km based on Nova Scotia data from eight cases of distance traveled for children between the ages of 7-12 years old. For the same category with fifteen cases, the middle 50% zone (between the 25th and 75th percentiles) would extend from 0.8 km to 2.50 km. The map uses a UTM projection with grid lines 1 kilometer (.62 miles) apart.

Appendix B: The K9 Resource for SAR – A Compilation

The K9 Resource for Search and Rescue
Compiled by Valerie Mokides, Physician,
SARTECH II, NASAR K9 SARTECH III

Making the Most Out of Your K9 Resource

"An advantage to using a dog team is the speed at which an area can be cleared."[1]

When deploying a K9 team, the IC's goal is to obtain 'optimal K9 effort'. That is, to set up the K9 team in the most advantageous position to most effectively clear the area (or find the subject) in the minimal amount of time. Like any other search and rescue resource, the level of success that can be achieved by the K9 team is directly proportional to the correct usage of this resource. Misunderstanding and misuse of this resource may result in delaying success of the mission, or may cause the resource to be out of service.

Most agencies agree that the K9 resource should be dispatched using the buddy system. For safety reasons, there should be two humans on the team, the handler and a pre-trained K9 support person. This pre-trained person should be qualified not only in K9 support, but also in communication, navigation, first aid, sign cutting and other SAR skills. Furthermore, K9's should be trained to accept a second human and not be distracted by them.

Understanding scent detection
"Scent is produced when molecules from an object are dispersed into the air and register a sensory reaction in the brain" [1a]
"Understanding how scent work is accomplished helps us set the right conditions for the scent source to be found. A dog's sense of smell is said to be a thousand times more sensitive than that of humans. In fact, a

dog has more than 220 million olfactory receptors in its nose, while humans have only 5 million." [2] This enormous capacity is accomplished through extensive sensory receptors in the dog's nose and a vomeronasal organ called Jacobson's organ. This coupled with the K9's larger brain area dedicated to smell, is the reason the K9 has an enhanced olfactory sense.

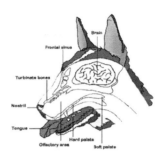

The Dog's Sense of Smell [3]

The Scent Theory
"Humans constantly shed dead skin cells, known as rafts, which are discarded at a rate of approximately 40,000 per minute." [4]

The scent theory states that these composites of particulate matter from our subject (skin rafts), oils, organic compounds, molecules and bacteria, combined with any scent released from crushed vegetation or disturbed soil, and are carried in the air by wind and thermal currents, and become dispersed in a cone pattern. It is the cone patterns that the K9 will be sensitive to and follow.

4 ARDA (scent cone)

Scent Behaviors
"Different wind, weather, heat and terrain have major impact on the dispersion of scent. The way scent travels and its availability will depend on the following elements: weather, terrain, age of the scent trail and source, the condition of the scent source, the air flow, wind, vegetation, concealment of the source, and the time of day."[5]

Besides the major influence of scent dispersion, mainly the wind, there are other factors that determine how much scent is available and where the scent travels.

By understanding the way the scent travels, the handler and search manager will have an extra tool to adapt their strategy to the existing conditions and increasing the Probability of Success.

Thermals

Chimney Effect: During the day, warm air rises upslope from drainages. Linda Warshaw

Linda Warshaw

As the sun warms the earth there is an upward flow of warm air (thermals) and thus the dispersion of scent has an upward movement from the source. To most effectively make use of this thermal pattern, a K9 team may start a morning search at the top of the mountain or hill and work downward.

The reverse happens as the air cools, night falls, and scent dispersion proceeds downward from the source. Scent will often behave like water taking the path of least resistance.

Cooling air can carry the scent down a drainage gully or any other terrain feature that would channel it. To make effective use of the night air flow pattern, during the evening the search manager should have K9 teams start in the valleys, edges of streams, lakes, gullies and other low lying areas and work uphill.

Obstacles

Joseph T McNichols

When scent is carried over land features that drop suddenly, there can be a dead space area in the drop. Drawing by Joseph T. McNichol.

Joseph T McNichols

Terrain features such as tree lines, rock walls, and plowed fields influence where scent travels. These obstacles can cause scent to eddy, swirl around trees, move behind, up or over a wall, or leak scent into a clearing, or create dead spaces where no scent has been carried. The scent from a subject located in the dead spaces can be trapped or blocked by a passing breeze. Another combination that can cause dead space is a depression and a strong breeze over the depression.

Looping

4 ARDA

Looping sometimes occurs in still wind conditions. If there is a cool layer of air above with a warm air beneath, the scent will rise, be carried for a few hundred feet (or more) and may dropped back down. When scent loops, it can loop several times leaving many pools of scent near the ground with no connecting trail to the subject. The dog will make signal alerts but will be unable to find the source. To guide the dog you must note the pattern of alerts and guide the dog in the direction you feel the scent is coming from based on the weather and the wind.

ADAPTING FOR SUCCESS
A poor searching condition doesn't necessarily mean poor results. To increase probability of success, adaptations are vital.

In low wind conditions, grid widths that the air scenting K9 team uses can be decreased. With variable winds, an area can be worked by a double grid pattern at two angles. Areas in which dogs alert or otherwise show interest can be searched more thoroughly and a second K9 can be used to re-search the area.

Scent that was dried by a hot day may be "revived" as the evening becomes cool and the humidity rises. As availability of the scent is increased by humidity as bacterial growth enhances the action of decay on the skin raft. Working the environment efficiently would

require activating a second K9 team in the evening.

A torrential down pour may wash scent away creating a big disadvantage for one K9 search type, but not for another. Search managers should not rely on only a single K9's results in a high POA area. If the search manager is not sure about the reported POD – they should send a second or third K9 team into the area to verify. The best time to work the K9's are generally early mornings and evenings.

"Search managers must be cautious about putting K9 teams in too close together unless the K9 teams have trained previously to work together." [3]

"Search managers should recognize that K9's are a live resource, needing breaks and have their own 'nose time.' *Nose Time* is the actual time a canine, while on a directed search pattern, can continue to 'sniff' for a particular odor and be able to recognize that odor at an acceptable level of reliability." [3a]

Search managers should determine the skill level of the dog and the handler, and to what standards they have trained. The effectiveness of dog teams as SAR tools is directly related to the degree of training of the dog and the knowledge and skill of the SAR dog handler.

An experienced handler will get the dog in the most advantageous place in the given sector using a strategy that covers the whole area. The experienced K9 learns to range persistently to find the source of the scent as the handler adjusts the techniques to adapt to the existing conditions.

Know the K9 specialty kinds that are available fit the requirements for the job.

Kinds of K9s
The most common specialty kinds are Air Scenting and Trailing/Tracking dogs.

Air Search/Air scenting K9's

The K9's job is to use its sense of smell to detect the subject (or a clue leading to the subject), alert its handler that it has found the subject, and bring the handler to the subject.

These dogs work off leash along grid search patterns that are predetermined by the handler, in conjunction with search planners, to be the most advantageous for the find.

The dog follows the hand signals from the handler, directing it to go left, right, up that rock, into that cranny, under that bush, or to any other place that a person could be hidden. Once the dog enters/finds the human scent cone it leaves the planned search grid and follows the scent until it is lost or until finding the subject. If the subject is found, the K9 will then return to the handler, give a recognizable alert and lead the handler back to the subject. Air scenting dogs are *usually* non-discriminating and do not need a specific scent article. That is, air scenting K9s will indicate on the presence any human scent and are trained that *all human scent is good scent*. [3] Common usages for air scent search dogs would be to assist in a search for an overdue hiker, a lost hunter, or a child missing from a campground.

Air Scent K9 Advantages:
1- Doesn't need a scent article (but if one is available advise the handler).
2-Can search large areas efficiently.
3- Are easily integrated into the search (can be assigned to segments of an area).
4-They can work off lead, and can search thick, difficult areas more easily than humans (and complain less).
5- Can work at night.
6-Can work an area even after searchers have been through it.
7-Can often find hidden and buried subjects.

Air Scent K9 Disadvantages:
1-Are less effective in the middle of the day, due to lower humidity or high thermal convection.
2-Are less effective in steep, cliffy areas with narrow restricted canyons where wind is restricted and terrain is difficult.
3-Other workers in the area may need to be cleared from a search segment and adjacent upwind segments for effective separation from other human sources.

Trailing/Tracking Dogs

These dogs are worked off of a long lead (leash) and are trained to look for one specific person. They are scent discriminating, focusing on the individual scent belonging to the missing subject, and usually start at the point where the subject was last seen (PLS) or was known to have been (LKP). Trailing/Tracking dogs are trained to follow the trail from the PLS or LKP to the victim. [3]

Tracking dogs are trained to locate each footprint as in man tracking. Trailing dogs combine tracking with the air scent of the subject near the ground.

Trailing/Tracking K9 Advantages:
1-Can be an excellent resource for finding the subject quickly.
2- Since they are scent discriminating, the segment doesn't have to be cleared of other searchers.
3-Functions independently without requiring re-tasking.
4- Can indicate direction of travel (a helicopter can search ahead of the dog).
Trailing/Tracking K9 Disadvantages:
1-Needs a properly attained, uncontaminated scent article or source.
2- Requires a specific place on which to begin.
3-Maybe less effective if the trail scent has faded over time, or if the trail was stomped on.

4-May not be as effective in hot dry environments.
5-Difficult to provide a measurable POD when subject is not found.

Other K9 Specialties

a) Urban Disaster Dog

This discipline trains dog and handler to navigate with safety in confined areas, and rubble piles, take directional commands and look for human scent in collapsed structures. [3]

Disaster teams are called out to assist finding trapped victims in urban disaster situations such as; earthquakes, building bombings, hurricanes or anywhere there is a collapsed structure and humans are suspected inside.

b) Avalanche Dog

The goal in this discipline is for theK9 team to quickly locate victims that have been buried by an avalanche. Quick response, thorough searching and safety are all important elements. The dog is trained to locate any human scent and alert the handler where the scent is strongest. The dog will attempt to put their nose to the strongest pool of scent and may dig to get to it. If the scent weakens they will back out and cast around looking for the strongest pool again. The sense of urgency during this kind of search cannot be underestimated. Survival statistics tell us that 90% of the victims are alive after 15 min. 30% after 35 min and the level drops quickly after that. [3]

c) Water Search Dog

These dogs are trained to identify the presence of, and help locate drowned victims in bodies of water. They may work from a shore line, pier, or from a boat. The dogs are able to work by detecting the by-products of decomposition as they start to rise slowly to the surface of the water. The search manager needs to have information about the currents and underground water movement to successfully direct divers for body recovery. Water search dogs can be used to find drowned victims in a lake, bay, stream, etc. [3]

d) Cadaver (HRD) Dog

Cadaver dogs are now properly called Human Remains Detection (HRD) dogs. This discipline borrows from area search in that a dog is given an assignment area in which they are to determine if a body is present in it. These K9's search the given area and focus on finding human remains or human cadaver material. HRD dogs can be used to locate human remains in a suspected suicide, buried body or parts, forensics, after a fire, at homicide scenes or on archeological digs to locate historical graves. [3]

Keys to successfully using the K9 search team as a resource
1 - Use plenty of search dogs early in the search and place them strategically.
2 - Know each of your K9 resources – their strengths and weaknesses.
3 - Know how many dogs are available and their specific disciplines.
4 - Use them early morning and late day (or night) as their prime working times for wilderness searches.
5 - Collect the scent source properly.

Estimating Coverage with a K9 Team Please see Chapter 15 of NASAR's MLPI manual for a discussion of estimating search effectiveness for an air scent K9 team upon debriefing.

Proper Collection of the Scent Source

The single most important factor in achieving success in your scent discriminating K9 teams is having a good scent article.

Finding the correct scent source

A good scent article contains the scent of the subject you are looking for and only that subject. A bad scent article is an article that doesn't have the scent of the person you are looking for or has been contaminated with one or more other scents.

They way you collect the scent source is as important as the scent source itself, and is crucial to success. Note that since scent sources can become evidence, a proper technique of chain of custody must be followed.

It is crucial that teams are educated in advance on how to preserve the crime scene and how to properly collect the scent source.

"A crime scene involves any area of response that the commission of a crime took place in or any area that may contain evidence of the commission of the crime." [6]

Do not allow an entire team go into an area and look for scent sources. Choose one or two of the K9 handlers to work together in search of scent source. The presence of many persons near the scent source is more likely to create cross contamination.

1 - Get permission before entering any area to collect a scent source.

2 - Have a family member, who knows the victim and their belongings, available nearby, but not in, the room from which scent sources are being collected.

3 - Put on clean latex gloves before going into an area to collect scent. Gloves will help the collector from accidentally contaminating the scent source or leaving finger prints. Remember the area is a potential crime scene.

4 - Initially check the collection area for any hazards and retreat if concerned.

5 - Move around as little as possible (try not to destroy any evidence).

6 - Take a mental picture of the room and ask questions.

Your job is to find domestic articles that were unique to the victim and only touched by the victim. Some examples: undergarments (but not underwear), hats, scarves, wallets, bed sheets, glasses, and hairbrushes (things that were next to the subject's skin for any period of time).

7 - When the domestic articles are found, take a food-quality, new plastic bag or a new brown paper bag (avoid any plastic garbage bags, scented bags or used bags). Turn the bag inside out over your hand making sure that the bag fits over your hand like a glove, so that only the inside of the bag touches the scent article. You can alternately use a clean tool to pick up the article and put it inside your bag. Use one article per bag.

8 - If there are no domestic articles, you may need to create a self-made scent article. A self-made article is from scent wiped off an area that you know was unique to the subject.

If the subject was the only user of a computer – use the keyboard. Other options include wiping scent from dresser handles, a car steering wheel, or stick shift. Let the police know what you intend to do so you do not inadvertently wipe off needed finger prints.

9 - Take a 4x4 sterile gauze, open it enough to expose the pad and wipe only the chosen area and nothing else. Drop the gauze into the collection bag.

10 - Seal and label the bag exactly as you would for chain of custody.
>   Subject's name.
>   Date and time collected.
>   Source and How collected.
>   Collector's name.
>   Signatures of Collector & Users.
>   When and Where used and under what circumstances.

11 - Place the scent articles in a safe and secure place, preferably under lock and key.

Endnotes:
1. Hatch Graham Probability of detection for search dogs
1a. Cadaver dog Handbook, Rebmann, David and Sorg
2.http://www.sonomasar.org/trainings/k9.php
3. The Dog's Sense of Smell UNP-0066, July 2005, Julio E. Correa, *Extension Animal Scientist,* Associate Professor, Food and Animal Sciences, Alabama A&M University
3a. Understanding Nose Time, Jonni Joyce
4. Training your K9 Hero ARDA Wiley publishing, Inc2002
5. Scenting on the wind Susan Bulanda
6. "Crime scene preservation and field note taking" – Jonni Joyce, quoted in [1].

ANIMAL POISON CONTROL CENTER
A note on any suspected animal poisoning: If you believe that a SAR animal has been exposed to, or ingested a potentially hazardous substance, the ASPCA maintains a 24-hour poison hotline at (888) 426-4435. Consultation may be fee based.

Appendix C: SAR Debriefing Form

SEARCH AND RESCUE DEBRIEFING FORM

INCIDENT NAME: _____

DATE:	TEAM #	ASSIGNMENT #	OP. PERIOD

STATE RESOURCE TYPE AND TACTICS UTILIZED:

STATE EXPLICIT COVERAGE OF THE AREA SEARCHED:

STATE CLUES LOCATED, EVENTS, HAZARDS AND IDENTIFY ALL ON AN ATTACHED MAP:

COMMUNICATIONS ISSUES:

RECOMMENDATION FOR FUTURE EFFORT:

SEGMENT SPLITTING

IDENTIFY AREAS THAT WERE NOT THOROUGHLY SEARCHED OR SEARCHED WITH DIFFERENT POD'S THAT NEED TO BE SPLIT.

THE PLANS SECTION WILL ASSIGN A NUMBER TO THE SPLIT SEGMENTS. AS THE TACTICAL TEAM LEADER YOU MUST ACCURATELY DEPICT BOUDARIES.

ARE YOU SPLITTING YOUR SEGMENT? _____

HAVE YOU IDENTIFIED SEGMENT BOUNDARIES TO THE PLANS SECTION? _____

HAVE YOU DRAWN YOUR COVERAGE ON AN ATTACHED MAP? _____

STATE ESTIMATED COVERAGE OR POD FOR EACH SEGMENT SEARCHED DURING THE ASSIGNMENT. BE SURE TO IDENTIFY THE SEGMENT BY NUMBER.

SEGMENT NUMBER	LIVE RESPONSIVE	NON-RESPONSIVE	CLANDESTINE GRAVE SITE	FOOTPRINT	_____	_____

SIGNED TEAM LEADER: _____ **DATE:** _____

Made in the USA
Middletown, DE
22 September 2015